Sliding Mask

Exam Tips:

1. Read each question carefully before looking at the possible answers.

2. After formulating an answer, determine which of the choices most nearly corresponds with that answer. It should completely answer the question.

3. Answer each question according to the latest regulations and procedures. You will receive credit if the regulations or procedures have changed. Computerized exams may be updated as regulations and procedures change.

4. There is only one answer that is correct and complete. The other answers are either incomplete or are derived from popular misconceptions.

5. If you do not know the answer to a question, try not to spend too much time on it. Continue with those you can answer. Then, return to the unanswered or difficult questions.

6. Unanswered questions will be counted as incorrect.

7. On calculator problems, select the answer nearest your solution. If you have solved it correctly, your answer will be closer to the correct answer than the other choices.

JEPPESEN®

COMMERCIAL PILOT

FAA airman knowledge

TEST GUIDE

- Questions, Answers, Explanations, References
- New FAA Learning Statement Codes
- Keyed with GFD Instrument/Commercial Textbook
- Organized by Topic, Includes Full-Color Charts
- Perforated and 3-Hole Punched Pages
- Includes FAA Airplane Questions
- Online Updates Available on www.jeppesen.com

ISBN-13: 978-0-88487-541-3
ISBN-10: 0-88487-541-5

Jeppesen
55 Inverness Drive East
Englewood, CO 80112-5498
Web Site: www.jeppesen.com
Email: Captain@jeppesen.com
Copyright © Jeppesen
All Rights Reserved. Published 1993, 1994, 1996,
1997, 1998, 1999, 2000, 2001, 2002, 2004, 2005,
2006, 2007, 2008, 2011
Printed in the United States of America

Preface

Thank you for purchasing this *Commercial Pilot FAA Airman Knowledge Test Guide*. This Test Guide will help you understand the answers to the test questions so you can take the FAA computer test with confidence. Included are the correct answers and explanations, along with study references. Explanations of why the other choices are wrong have been included where appropriate. Questions are organized by topic, with explanations conveniently located adjacent to each question. The three-hole punched, perforated pages provide flexibility so you can select and remove specific pages for effective study. Full-color charts identical to those on the FAA test are included, plus our unique sliding mask for self-testing. Please note that this Test Guide is intended to be a supplement to your instructor-led flight and ground training, not a stand alone learning tool.

THE JEPPESEN TRAINING PHILOSOPHY

Flight training in the developing years of aviation was characterized by the separation of academics from flight training in the aircraft. For years, ground and flight training were not integrated. There were lots of books on different subjects, written by different authors, which produced a general lack of continuity in training material. The introduction of **Jeppesen's Training Products** changed all this. Our proven, professionally integrated training materials include extensive research on teaching theory and principles of how people learn best and most efficiently. Effective instruction includes determining objectives and completion standards. We employ an important principle of learning a complex skill using a step-by-step sequence known as the **building block principle**. Another important aspect of training is the principle of **meaningful repetition**, whereby each necessary concept or skill is presented several times throughout the instructional program. Jeppesen training materials incorporate these principles in our syllabi, textbooks, videos, computer-based training (CBT), exercises, exams, and this Test Guide. When these elements are combined with an instructor's class discussion and the skills learned in the simulator and airplane, you have an ideal integrated training system, with all materials coordinated.

Observation and research show that people tend to retain 10% of what they read, 20% of what they hear, 30% of what they see, and 50% of what they both hear and see together. These retention figures can be increased to as high as 90% by including active learning methods. Videos and textbooks are generally considered passive learning materials. Exercises, stage exams, student/instructor discussions, CBT, and practice in a simulator and airplane are considered to be active learning methods. Levels of learning include rote, understanding, application, and correlation. One of the major drawbacks with test preparation courses that concentrate only on passing the test is that they focus on rote learning, the lowest level of learning. Students benefit from Jeppesen's professional approach through standardized instruction, a documented training record, increased learning and increased passing rates. Our materials are challenging and motivating, while maximizing knowledge and skill retention. Nearly 3 million pilots have learned to fly using our materials, which include:

TEXTBOOKS — Our training textbooks contain the answers to many of the questions you may have as you begin your training program. They are based on the **study/review** concept of learning. This means detailed material is presented in an uncomplicated way, then important points are summarized through the use of bold type and color. The best results can be obtained when the textbook is studied as an integral part of the coordinated materials. The textbook is the central component for academic study and is cross-referenced to video presentations.

VIDEOS — These motivating, high-quality ground school DVDs are professionally produced with actual inflight video and animated graphics. They allow you to review and reinforce essential concepts presented in the textbook.

SUPPORT COMPONENTS — Supplementary items include a training syllabus, stage and end-of-course exams, CBT, FAR/AIM Manual, FARs Explained, airmen knowledge test and practical test study guides, test preparation software and videos, question banks and computer testing supplements, an aviation weather book, student record folder, computer, plotter, and logbook. Jeppesen's training products are the most comprehensive pilot training materials available. In conjunction with your instructor, they help you prepare for the FAA exam and practical test; and, more importantly, they help you become a more proficient and safe pilot.

You can purchase our products and services through your Jeppesen dealer. For product, service, or sales information call 1-800-621-JEPP, 303-799-9090, or FAX 303-328-4153. If you have comments, questions, or need explanations about any component of our GFD Training System, we are prepared to offer assistance at any time. Contact us directly at **TrainingServices@Jeppesen.com**.

If your dealer does not have a Jeppesen catalog, please request one and we will promptly send it to you. Just call the above telephone number, or write:

Jeppesen
55 Inverness Drive East,
Englewood, CO 80112-5498

Please direct inquiries from Europe, Africa, and the Middle East to:

Jeppesen & Co., GmbH
Frankfurter Strasse 233
63263 Neu-Isenburg, Germany
Tel: +49-6102-5070
Fax: +49-6102-507-999

UPDATES OF FAA QUESTIONS — You can obtain free updates for the FAA questions in this Test Guide by visiting Jeppesen's web site. These updates are generally valid within one year of book publication; if you are using an older Test Guide, the web site may not update all questions that have changed since the book was printed.

To find Test Prep Updates, go to **www.jeppesen.com/testprep**.

LATEST INFORMATION REGARDING AIRMAN KNOWLEDGE TESTS

The FAA continues to be concerned that many students are memorizing the position of the correct answers on the FAA knowledge tests. Because of this, they regularly change the order of the answer choices to most questions in their knowledge test databases. This means that if you learn the answer to a question based on the letter of the correct answer or its position below the question, you will likely answer the question incorrectly. Because the FAA changes the sequence of the answer choices on a regular basis, it is impossible for test preparation courses to match the answer sequence as it appears on the test.

In addition, the FAA now publishes only selected questions from their database, limiting the number of questions available to the public. Therefore, you might see questions on your knowledge test that are worded differently than those in this guide. This Jeppesen question bank contains the questions published on the FAA web site plus additional questions that should help you pass your airmen knowledge test. If are able to answer the questions in this guide, then you can reasonably expect to have the required knowledge to pass the FAA Knowledge Test.

Jeppesen has never encouraged its students to memorize answers to FAA questions. We provide comprehensive, no-nonsense study material that teaches you what you need to know to answer the test questions correctly. Our test prep materials always tell you why the correct answer is correct and, if it is not obvious, why the other answers are incorrect. We want you to know the material, not memorize it.

When answering each FAA question, carefully read and evaluate each answer choice and choose the correct answer based on what you know from your study, not from that answer's position.

TABLE OF CONTENTS

Introduction

The Commercial Pilot FAA Airmen Knowledge Test Guide is designed to help you prepare for the Commercial Pilot Computer Test. It covers FAA exam material that applies to airplanes, including pertinent Federal Aviation Regulations (FARs). Questions and answers pertaining to rotorcraft, gliders, balloons, powered-lift, and airships have been omitted.

We recommend that you use this Test Guide in conjunction with the Guided Flight Discovery (GFD) Pilot Training System. The Test Guide is organized like the Instrument/Commercial Pilot Textbook, with fifteen chapters and distinctive sections within each chapter. Questions are covered in the Test Guide in the same sequence as the material in the textbook. References to applicable chapter and section in the textbook are included along with the answers. A separate chapter (Chapter 15) in the Test Guide is devoted to FAR questions and answers.

Within the chapters, each section contains a brief introduction. FAA test questions appear in the left column and answers and explanations are in the right column. Below is an example of a typical reference for a question.

[1]	[2]	[3]	[4]	[5]	[6]
4-59	**PLT101**	**4-59**	**Answer C**	**GFDICM 4-47**	**AIM**
(FAA Question)			(Explanation of FAA Question)		

[1] Jeppesen designated test guide question number. The first number is the chapter where the question is located in the Test Guide. In most cases, this corresponds to the chapter in the GFD textbook. The second number is the question number within the chapter. This number may or may not be in sequential order. In this example, the question is in chapter 4 of the Test Guide and it is the 59th question.

[2] The FAA learning statement code. For the learning statement associated with this code, refer to Appendix A.

[3] The Jeppesen test guide number is repeated in the right hand column above the explanation.

[4] Correct answer to the question, in this case answer C is correct.

[5] The location where the question is covered in the GFD textbook. In this case, the question is covered on page 4-47 in the GFD Private Pilot Textbook.

[6] Abbreviation for the FAA or other authoritative source document. In this case, the reference is the Aeronautical Information Manual (AIM). Abbreviations used in the Test Guide are as follows:

AC — Advisory Circulars
A/FD — Airport/Facility Directory
AIM — Aeronautical Information Manual
AW — Aviation Weather, AC 00-6A
AWS — Aviation Weather Services, AC 00-45
FAR — Federal Aviation Regulation
AFH — Airplane Flying Handbook, FAA-H-8083-3A
IAP — Instrument Approach Procedure
IFH — Instrument Flying Handbook, FAA-H-8083-15
GFDICM — Guided Flight Discovery Instrument/Commercial Textbook

GFDPPM — Guided Flight Discovery Private Pilot Textbook
NAVWEPS — Aerodynamics for Naval Aviators
PHB — Pilot's Handbook of Aeronautical Knowledge, FAA-H-8083-25
WBH — Aircraft Weight and Balance Handbook, FAA-H-8083-1
TERPS — U.S. Standard for Terminal Instrument Procedures

Below the reference line is the FAA question in the left column and the explanation in the right column. The explanation includes the correct answer followed by an explanation of why the answer is correct and why the other answers are wrong. In some cases, the incorrect answers are not explained. Examples include instances where the answers are calculated, or when the explanation of the correct answer obviously eliminates the wrong answers.

The answers in this Test Guide are based on official reference documents and, in our judgement, are the best choices of the available answers. Some questions which were valid when the FAA test was developed may no longer be appropriate due to ongoing changes in regulations or official operating procedures. However, with the computer test format, timely updating and validation of questions is anticipated. Therefore, when taking the FAA test, it is important to answer the questions according to the latest regulations or official operating procedures.

Two appendices from the FAA test materials are included in the back of the Test Guide. These are Appendix A, Subject Matter Knowledge Codes and Appendix B, which consists of legend information from FAA charts and the Airport/Facility Directory (A/FD). You will need to refer to this legend to answer some questions concerning A/FD information.

Figures in the Test Guide are the same as those that are used in the FAA Computerized Testing Supplement. These figures, which are referred to in many of the questions, are placed throughout the Test Guide as close as practical to the applicable questions. In addition, pages in this Test Guide are three-hole punched and perforated to allow you to easily remove any figure for reference while answering a specific question.

HOW TO PREPARE FOR THE FAA TEST

It is important to realize that to become a safe, competent pilot, you need more than just the academic knowledge required to pass a test. For a comprehensive ground training program, we recommend a structured ground school with a qualified flight or ground instructor. An organized course of instruction will help you complete the course in a timely manner, and you will be able to have your questions answered. The additional instruction will be beneficial in your flight training.

Regardless of whether or not you are in a structured ground training program, you will find this Test Guide is an excellent training aid to help you prepare for the FAA computerized test. The Test Guide contains all of the airplane questions as they are presented in the FAA computerized test format. By reviewing the questions and studying the Guided Flight Discovery Pilot Training materials, you should be well equipped to take the test.

You will also benefit more from your study if you test yourself as you proceed through the Test Guide. Cover the answers in the right-hand column, read each question, and choose what you consider the best answer. A sliding mask is provided for this purpose. Move the sliding mask down and read the answer and explanation for that question. You may want to mark the questions you miss for further study and review prior to taking the exam.

The sooner you take the exam after you complete your study, the better. This way, the information will be fresh in your mind, and you will be more confident when you actually take the FAA test.

WHO CAN TAKE THE TEST

When you are ready to take the FAA computerized test, you must present evidence that you have completed the appropriate ground instruction or a home study course. This proof may be in the form of a graduation certificate from a pilot training course, a written statement, or a logbook entry by a certified ground or flight instructor. Although you are encouraged to obtain ground instruction, a home study course may be used. If you cannot provide one of the above documents, you may present evidence of a completed home study course to an FAA aviation safety inspector for approval.

You also must provide evidence of a permanent mailing address, appropriate identification, and proof of your age. The identification must include a current photograph, your signature, and your residential address, if different from your mailing address. You may present this information in more than one form of identification, such as a driver's license, government identification card, passport, alien residency (green) card, or a military identification card.

GENERAL INFORMATION — FAA COMPUTER TESTS

Detailed information on FAA computer testing is contained in FAA Order 8080.6B, Conduct of Airmen Knowledge Tests. This FAA order provides guidance for Flight Standards District Offices (FSDOs) and personnel associated with organizations that are participating in, or are seeking to participate in, the FAA Computer-Assisted Airmen Knowledge Testing Program. You also may refer to FAA Order 8700.1, General Aviation Operations Inspector's Handbook, for guidance on computer testing by 14 CFR Parts 141 and 142 pilot schools that hold examining authority.

As an applicant, you don't need all of the details contained in FAA Orders, but you will be interested in some of the general information about computer testing facilities. A **Computer Testing Designee (CTD)** is an organization authorized by the FAA to administer FAA airmen knowledge tests via the computer medium. A **Computer Testing Manager (CTM)** is a person selected by the CTD to serve as manager of its national computer testing program. A **Testing Center Supervisor (TCS)** is a person selected by the CTM, with FAA approval, to administer FAA airmen knowledge tests at approved testing centers. The TCS is responsible for the operation of the testing center. A **Special Test Administrator (STA)** is a person selected by a CTD to administer FAA airmen knowledge tests in unique situations and remote or isolated areas. A test proctor is a properly trained and qualified person, appointed by a TCS, authorized to administer FAA airmen knowledge tests.

CTDs are selected by the FAA's Airmen Testing Standards Branch. Those selected may include companies, schools, universities, or other organizations that meet specific requirements. For example, they must clearly demonstrate competence in computer technology, centralized database management, national communications network operation and maintenance, national facilities management, software maintenance and support, and technical training and customer support. They must provide computer-assisted testing, test administration, and data transfer service on a national scale. This means they must maintain a minimum of 20 operational testing centers geographically dispersed throughout the United States. In addition, CTDs must offer operational hours that are convenient to the public. An acceptable plan for test security is also required.

TEST MATERIALS, REFERENCE MATERIALS, AND AIDS

You are allowed to use aids, reference materials, and test materials within specified guidelines, provided the actual test questions or answers are not revealed. All models of aviation-oriented computers, regardless of manufacturer, may be used, including hand-held computers designed expressly for aviation use, and also small electronic calculators that perform arithmetic functions. Simple programmable memories, which allow addition to, subtraction from, or retrieval of one number from the memory, are acceptable. Simple functions such as square root or percent keys are also acceptable.

In addition, you may use any reference materials provided with the test. You will find that these reference materials are the same as those in your Test Guide. They include a printed Computerized Testing Supplement with the legend data and the applicable figures. You also may use scales, straight-edges, protractors, plotters, navigation computers, log sheets, and, as already mentioned, electronic or mechanical calculators that are directly related to the test. Permanently inscribed manufacturer's instructions on the front and back of these aids, such as, formulas, conversions, regulations, signals, weather data, holding pattern diagrams, frequencies, weight and balance formulas, and ATC procedures, are permissible.

WHAT TO EXPECT ON A COMPUTER TEST

Computer testing centers are required to have an acceptable method for the "on-line" registration of test applicants during normal business hours. They must provide a dual method, for example, keyboard, touch screen, or mouse, for answering questions. Features that must be provided also include an introductory lesson to familiarize you with computer testing procedures, the ability to return to a test question previously answered (for the purpose of review or answer changes), and a suitable display of multiple-choice and other question types on the computer screen in one frame. Other required features include a display of the time remaining for the completion of the test, a "HELP" function which permits you to review test questions and optional responses, and provisions for your test score on an Airman Computer Test Report.

x

On computer tests, the selection of questions is done for you, and you will answer the questions that appear on the screen. You will be given a specific amount of time to complete the test, which is based on past experience with others who have taken the exam. If you are prepared, you should have plenty of time to complete the test. After you begin the test, the screen will show you the time remaining for completion. When taking the test, keep the following points in mind

1. Answer each question in accordance with the latest regulations and procedures. If the regulation or procedure has recently changed, you will receive credit for the affected question. However, these questions will normally be deleted or updated on the FAA computerized exams.
2. Read each question carefully before looking at the possible answers. You should clearly understand the problem before attempting to solve it.
3. After formulating an answer, determine which of the alternatives most nearly corresponds with that answer. The answer chosen should completely resolve the problem.
4. From the answers given, it may appear that there is more than one possible answer; however, there is only one answer that is correct and complete. The other answers are either incomplete or are derived from popular misconceptions.
5. Make sure you select an answer for each question. Questions left unanswered will be counted as incorrect.
6. If a certain question is difficult for you, it is best to proceed to other questions. After you answer the less difficult questions, return to those which were unanswered. The computer-aided test format helps you identify unanswered questions, as well as those questions you wish to review.
7. When solving a calculator problem, select the answer nearest your solution. The problem has been checked with various types of calculators; therefore, if you have solved it correctly, your answer will be closer to the correct answer than the other choices.
8. Generally, the test results will be available almost immediately. Your score will be recorded on an Airman Knowledge Test Report form. [Figure 1]

U.S. DEPARTMENT OF TRANSPORTATION
Federal Aviation Administration
Airman Knowledge Test Report

NAME: Jeffrey Scott   APPLICANT ID: 123456789

EXAM: Private Pilot-Airplane   EXAM ID: 90121120070468013

EXAM DATE: 12/11/2007   EXAM SITE: ABS80102

SCORE: 75%   GRADE: PASS   TAKE: 1

Below are learning statement codes which represent learning statements for incorrectly answered questions. For code descriptions, refer to the Learning Statement Reference Guide for Airman Knowledge Testing on the Internet: **www.faa.gov/education_research/testing/airmen/media/LearningStatementReferenceGuide.pdf** .

A single code may represent more than one incorrect response.

PLT012 PLT023 PLT090 PLT091 PLT141 PLT161 PLT173 PLT263 PLT366 PLT369 PLT420 PLT446 PLT447 PLT514

DO NOT LOSE THIS REPORT
(emboss here)

(Place red stamp above here)

EXPIRATION DATE: 12/31/2009

- -

Authorized instructor's statement. (If applicable)

On_____(date) I gave the above named applicant _____ hours of additional instruction in each subject area shown to be deficient and consider the applicant competent to pass the test.

Last _____ Initial _____ Cert. No. _____ Type _____
(Print clearly)

Signature _____

FRAUDULENT ALTERATION OF THIS FORM BY ANY PERSON IS A BASIS FOR SUSPENSION OR REVOCATION OF ANY CERTIFICATES OR RATINGS HELD BY THAT PERSON.

ISSUED BY: Computer Assisted Testing Service, CATS (01/06)
FEDERAL AVIATION ADMINISTRATION

Figure 1. This sample Airman Knowledge Test Report shows the applicants test results. Take 1 indicates this is the first time the applicant has taken the test. Learning statement codes for incorrect answers are included in the report, and an additional instruction section is included in the last part.

The Airman Knowledge Test Report includes learning statement codes for incorrect answers. To determine the knowledge area in which a particular question was incorrectly answered, compare the learning statement codes on this report to those in Appendix A.

Computer testing designees must provide a way for applicants, who challenge the validity of test questions, to enter comments into the computer. The test proctor should advise you, if you have complaints about test scores, or specific test questions, to write directly to the appropriate FAA office. In addition to comments, you will be asked to respond to a critique form which may vary at different computer testing centers. The TCS must provide a method for you to respond to critique questions projected on the computer screen. [Figure 2]

---

1. Did the test administration personnel give you an adequate briefing on testing procedures?

2. Was the "sign-on" accomplished efficiently?

3. Did you have any difficulty reading the computer presentation of test questions?

4. Was the test supplementary material (charts, graphs, tables, etc.) presented in a usable manner?

5. Did you have any difficulty using the "return to previous question for review" procedure?

6. Was the testing room noise level distracting?

7. Did you have adequate work space?

8. Did you have adequate lighting?

9. What is your overall evaluation of the computer testing experience?

    a.   Unsatisfactory.
    b.   Poor.
    c.   Satisfactory.
    d.   Highly Satisfactory.
    e.   Outstanding.

Figure 2. Critique forms used at different computer testing centers may vary. This sample form contains typical questions.

RETESTING AFTER FAILURE

The applicant shall surrender the previous test report to the test proctor prior to retesting. The original test report shall be destroyed by the test proctor after administering the retest. The latest test taken will reflect the official score.

As stated in 14 CFR section 61.49, an applicant may apply for retesting after receiving additional training and an endorsement from an authorized instructor who has determined the applicant has been found competent to pass the test.

WHERE TO TAKE THE FAA TEST

Almost all testing is now administered via computer at FAA-designated test centers. As indicated, these CTDs are located throughout the U.S. You can expect to pay a fee and the cost varies at different locations. The following is a listing of the approved computer testing designees at the time of publication of this Test Guide. You may want to check with your local FSDO for changes.

Computer Assisted Testing Service (CATS) 1-800-947-4228 Outside U.S. (650) 259-8550
PSI/LaserGrade Computer Testing 1-800-211-2754 Outside U.S. (360) 896-9111

BUILDING PROFESSIONAL EXPERIENCE

This textbook chapter introduces some of the training requirements and the opportunities for pilots with instrument ratings and commercial certificates. It presents highlights of aviation history as well.

Each chapter and section in the Commercial Pilot Airmen Knowledge Study Guide directly corresponds to the same chapter and section in Jeppesen's Instrument/Commercial Manual, part of the Guided Flight Discovery Pilot Training System. The manual explores in depth each topic presented in this guide, and covers many areas not tested in the computer exam. This additional information is vital to your commercial pilot preparation, and we strongly encourage you to study the manual, in addition to this guide.

Although certain textbook chapters cover material not directly tested in the knowledge test, those chapters are referenced in this study guide and comments provided that may be useful in preparing for the oral portion of your practical test.

SECTION A - INSTRUMENT/COMMERCIAL TRAINING AND OPPORTUNITIES

COMMERCIAL PILOT CERTIFICATE

For you to be eligible for a commercial pilot certificate, you must be at least 18 years of age, hold a private pilot certificate, be able to read, write, speak, and understand the English language, and meet specific training and flight time requirements described in the FARs, as well as pass a knowledge and practical test. Under Part 141, you must hold an instrument rating or be concurrently enrolled in an instrument rating course.

COMMERCIAL PILOT PRIVILEGES

- Although you need at least a third-class medical certificate to be eligible for a commercial pilot certificate, you must have a second-class medical certificate to exercise commercial pilot privileges.
- As part of the commercial pilot training requirements, you must receive 10 hours of flight training in a complex airplane (an airplane with retractable landing gear, flaps, and a controllable pitch propeller)
- A high performance airplane is defined as an airplane having an engine of more than 200 horsepower.
- FAR Parts 119, 121, 125, and 135 govern operations ranging from scheduled air carriers to on-demand charters.
- Under FAR Part 91, you may not engage in common carriage which involves holding out, or advertising your services, to furnish transportation for any member of the public.
- Student instruction, certain nonstop sightseeing flights within limited areas, crop dusting, banner towing, aerial photography or survey, fire fighting, and some types of corporate flights are examples of operations which are not governed by FAR Parts 121, 125, and 135.

REQUIREMENTS FOR COMMERCIAL PILOT CERTIFICATION

The addition of a multi-engine rating to your private or commercial certificate does not require a minimum number of ground or flight instruction hours under FAR Part 61. Under FAR Part 141, a multi-engine rating course must include the ground and flight instruction hours in accordance with the applicable Part 141 appendices.

SECTION B - ADVANCED HUMAN FACTORS CONCEPTS

From your previous training and pilot experience, you know that flying requires a continuous series of decisions. If you are at your best, you should be able to plan effectively and safely handle most situations that occur during a flight.

AERONAUTICAL DECISION MAKING

- Aeronautical decision making is a systematic approach to the mental process used by aircraft pilots to consistently determine the best course of action in response to a given set of circumstances.
- Approximately 75% of all aviation accidents are attributed to human factors-related causes. Studies have identified five hazardous attitudes which can interfere with a pilot's ability to make sound decisions and exercise authority properly.

PILOT-IN-COMMAND RESPONSIBILITY

As pilot in command, you are the final authority in the airplane you are flying. When only one pilot is in the cockpit, the PIC is obvious, but when two pilots are present, each pilot's responsibilities must be defined before the flight. Within the cockpit, one person is pilot in command, and the other serves to assist the PIC.

RESOURCE USE

- Resource use is an important part of human factors training. Cockpit resources increase as you fly more complex aircraft with advanced systems. If you are not thoroughly familiar with the equipment in your aircraft or you rely on it so much that you become complacent, flight safety is compromised.
- The focus of crew resource management (CRM) programs is the effective use of all available resources: human resources, hardware, and information. CRM training helps flight crews understand the limitations of human performance, especially under stressful situations, and makes them aware of the importance of crew coordination to combat error.

COMMUNICATION

When flying with another pilot, it is important to use standard terminology and verify that your meaning is understood. A breakdown in communication can cause friction and frustration, detracting from important tasks, or lead to a hazardous situation where one pilot believes the other is controlling the airplane, but in reality, neither pilot has control.

WORKLOAD MANAGEMENT

Effective workload management directly impacts safety by ensuring that you are prepared for the busiest segments of the flight through proper use of down time. Organizing charts in the order of use, setting radio frequencies, and writing down expected altitudes and route clearances will help you visualize and mentally prepare for what comes next.

SITUATIONAL AWARENESS

Controlled flight into terrain (CFIT) occurs when an aircraft is flown into terrain or water with no prior awareness on the part of the crew that the crash is imminent.

AVIATION PHYSIOLOGY

The study of aviation physiology is an important part of human factors training. How you feel, physically, has a direct impact on how well you fly.

DISORIENTATION

- When there is a conflict between the information relayed by your central vision and your peripheral vision, you may suffer from spatial disorientation. When subjected to the various forces of flight, the vestibular system can send misleading signals to the brain resulting in vestibular disorientation.
- A pilot is more subject to spatial disorientation if body signals are used to interpret flight attitude. The sensations which lead to spatial disorientation during instrument flight conditions must be suppressed and complete reliance placed on the indications of the flight instruments.

MOTION SICKNESS

Nausea, sweating, dizziness, and vomiting are some of the symptoms of motion sickness. To overcome motion sickness without outside visual references, you should focus on the instrument panel, since it is your only source of accurate position information.

HYPOXIA

- Hypoxia occurs when the tissues in the body do not receive enough oxygen. It can be caused by an insufficient supply of oxygen, inadequate transportation of oxygen, or the inability of the body tissues to use oxygen. Hypoxic hypoxia occurs when there are not enough molecules of oxygen available at sufficient pressure to pass between the membranes in your respiratory system.
- If you are planning a flight with a cruise altitude over 12,500 feet MSL, you should review FAR Part 91 for the requirements regarding supplemental oxygen. Prior to operating a pressurized aircraft with a service ceiling or maximum operating altitude higher than 25,000 feet MSL, you must complete high-altitude training.
- Hypemic hypoxia occurs when your blood is not able to carry a sufficient amount of oxygen to your body's cells. Since it attaches itself to the hemoglobin about 200 times more easily than does oxygen, carbon monoxide (CO) prevents the hemoglobin from carrying sufficient oxygen. Even without considering the dangers of incapacitating the flight crew, carbon monoxide poisoning can be fatal. Frequent inspections should be made of aircraft exhaust manifold-type heating systems to minimize the possibility of exhaust gases leaking into the cockpit.
- Hypoxia is particularly dangerous during flights with one pilot because symptoms of hypoxia may be difficult to recognize before the pilot's reactions are affected.
- Stagnant hypoxia is an oxygen deficiency in the body due to the poor circulation of the blood. It can result from pulling excessive positive Gs. The inability of the cells to effectively use oxygen is defined as histotoxic hypoxia. This can be caused by alcohol and other drugs such as narcotics and poisons

HYPERVENTILATION

Hyperventilation is a physiological disorder that develops when too much carbon dioxide (CO_2) has been eliminated from the body, usually caused by breathing too rapidly or too deeply. To overcome the symptoms of hyperventilation, you should slow your breathing rate. Some of the symptoms include dizziness, tingling of hands and feet, muscle spasms, coolness, feelings of suffocation, drowsiness, weakness or numbness, rapid heart rate, apprehension and mental confusion, and finally, loss of consciousness.

DECOMPRESSION SICKNESS

Decompression sickness (DCS) is a painful condition that can occur if flying too soon after diving. It is very important that you allow enough time for the body to rid itself of excess nitrogen absorbed during diving.

FITNESS FOR FLIGHT

- Stress is the body's reaction to the physical and psychological demands placed upon it, and it can adversely affect your ability to fly safely. When you are fatigued, you are more prone to error in the cockpit. Getting adequate rest and improving your overall fitness will help you perform at your best.
- Preflight use of the I'm Safe Checklist will help ensure you are fit for flight. Consider illness and medication that might affect your safety as a pilot. Factors such as rest, a good breakfast, and issues at work can interfere with

your concentration level in the airplane. If you have any reservations about your ability to make the flight, save the trip for another time.

- Judgment and decision-making abilities can be adversely affected by even small amounts of alcohol.

VISION

- Effective traffic scanning is accomplished by allowing time for the eyes to focus at 10 degree increments across the sky.
- The best night vision is achieved by allowing the rods of the eyes to adapt to the night environment, which usually takes 30 minutes in the dark.

1-1   PLT097

Frequent inspections should be made of aircraft exhaust manifold-type heating systems to minimize the possibility of

A–exhaust gases leaking into the cockpit.
B–a power loss due to back pressure in the exhaust system.
C–a cold-running engine due to the heat withdrawn by the heater.

1-1. Answer A. GFDICM 1B, AC 91-59
FAA studies show that approximately 50% of exhaust system failures occurred in the exhaust gas-to-air heat exchanger, resulting in carbon monoxide gas entering the cabin through the aircraft heater. Because of this, the owner/operator should make frequent inspections on the exhaust system.

1-2   PLT332

As hyperventilation progresses, a pilot can experience

A–decreased breathing rate and depth.
B–heightened awareness and feeling of well-being.
C–symptoms of suffocation and drowsiness.

1-2. Answer C. GFDICM 1B, PHB
Some of the symptoms of hyperventilation include dizziness, tingling of hands and feet, muscle spasms, coolness, suffocation, drowsiness, weakness or numbness, rapid heart rate, apprehension and mental confusion, and finally, loss of consciousness.

1-3   PLT099

To scan properly for traffic, a pilot should

A–use a series of short, regularly spaced eye movements that bring successive areas of the sky into the central visual field.
B–slowly sweep the field of vision from one side to the other at intervals.
C–concentrate on any peripheral movement detected.

1-3. Answer A. GFDICM 1B, AIM
Effective traffic scanning must be accomplished by using a series of short, regularly spaced eye movements that bring successive areas of the sky into the central, or foveal, area of vision. A series of 10-degree movements while pausing in between each for approximately 1 second is most effective.

1-4   PLT332

Which is a common symptom of hyperventilation?

A–Drowsiness.
B–Decreased breathing rate.
C–A sense of well-being.

1-4. Answer A. GFDICM 1B, PHB
Some of the symptoms of hyperventilation include dizziness, tingling of hands and feet, muscle spasms, coolness, suffocation, drowsiness, weakness or numbness, rapid heart rate, apprehension and mental confusion, and finally, loss of consciousness.

1-5   PLT332

Which would most likely result in hyperventilation?

A–Insufficient oxygen.
B–Excessive carbon monoxide.
C–Insufficient carbon dioxide.

1-5. Answer C. GFDICM 1B, PHB
Hyperventilation is caused by a breathing rate that is too rapid and too deep. This process forces too much carbon dioxide from your body and creates a chemical imbalance in the blood.

1-6   PLT096

Hypoxia is the result of which of these conditions?

A–Excessive oxygen in the bloodstream.
B–Insufficient oxygen reaching the brain.
C–Excessive carbon dioxide in the bloodstream.

1-6. Answer B. GFDICM 1B, PHB
Hypoxia occurs when the tissues in your body do not receive enough oxygen. It is considered to be the most lethal factor of all physiological causes of accidents.

1-7   PLT332

To overcome the symptoms of hyperventilation, a pilot should

A–swallow or yawn.
B–slow the breathing rate.
C–increase the breathing rate.

1-7. Answer B. GFDICM 1B, AIM
Hyperventilation is caused by a breathing rate that is too rapid and too deep. Restoring the proper carbon dioxide level in the body is the treatment for hyperventilation. Breathing normally is the best prevention and the best cure.

1-8   PLT503

Which is true regarding the presence of alcohol within the human body?

A–A small amount of alcohol increases vision acuity.
B–An increase in altitude decreases the adverse effect of alcohol.
C–Judgment and decision-making abilities can be adversely affected by even small amounts of alcohol.

1-8. Answer C. GFDICM 1B, PHB, FAR 91-17
Under the influence of alcohol, you experience a dulling of the senses, a decrease in good judgment, and a reduced sense of responsibility.

1-9   PLT330

Hypoxia susceptibility due to inhalation of carbon monoxide increases as

A–humidity decreases.
B–altitude increases.
C–oxygen demand increases.

1-9. Answer B. GFDICM 1B, PHB
As altitude increases, air pressure decreases and the body has difficulty getting enough oxygen. Add carbon monoxide, which further deprives the body of oxygen, and the situation can become critical.

1-10   PLT334

To best overcome the effects of spatial disorientation, a pilot should

A– rely on body sensations.
B– increase the breathing rate.
C– rely on aircraft instrument indications.

1-10. Answer C. GFDICM 1B, PHB

To avoid overcome spatial disorientation, you must learn to disregard false body sensations and rely on the flight instruments. The flight instruments are the only unbiased indicators of what the airplane is really doing. FORCE YOURSELF to believe them no matter what things "feel" like.

PRINCIPLES OF INSTRUMENT FLIGHT

CHAPTER 2

SECTION A - FLIGHT INSTRUMENT SYSTEMS

The major portion of this section is for instrument rating applicants. An instrument rating is required to exercise most commercial airplane pilot privileges. Although the FAA will not test you on instrument knowledge for the commercial test, you may wish to review some of the instrument basics.

HEADING INDICATOR

You must align the heading indicator with the magnetic compass before flight and recheck it periodically during flight.

TURN INDICATOR

- Turn indicators allow you to establish and maintain standard-rate turns of three degrees per second, or in the case of certain high performance aircraft, half-standard-rate turns. At three degrees per second, a 360° turn will be completed in two minutes.
- Both turn coordinators and turn-and-slip indicators indicate rate of turn, but because of the improved design of the turn coordinator, this instrument also indicates rate of roll as you enter a turn.
- One advantage of an electric turn coordinator is that it serves as a backup in case of vacuum system failure.
- During a constant-bank level turn, an increase in airspeed results in a decreased rate of turn, and an increased turn radius.

MAGNETIC COMPASS

Magnetic deviation is error due to magnetic interference with metal components in the aircraft, as well as magnetic fields from aircraft electrical equipment. It varies for different headings of the same aircraft.

PITOT-STATIC INSTRUMENTS

- The pitot-static instruments are the airspeed indicator, altimeter, and vertical speed indicator. Blockages in either the pitot or static systems affect the airspeed indicator, while the remaining instruments are affected only by static system blockage.
- The altimeter and pitot-static system, as well as the transponder, must have been inspected within the preceding 24 calendar months before flying.
- Standard temperature and pressure at sea level are 15°C (59°F) and 29.92 inches of Hg. (1013.2 Mb.). Pressure altitude is indicated on the altimeter when 29.92 is set in the altimeter setting window.

AIRSPEED INDICATOR

- Calibrated airspeed (CAS) is indicated airspeed corrected for installation and instrument errors. Equivalent airspeed (EAS) is calibrated airspeed corrected for compressibility. True airspeed (TAS) is the actual speed your airplane moves through undisturbed air. Mach is the ratio of the aircraft's true airspeed to the speed of sound at the temperature and altitude in which the aircraft is flying.
- V_{S1} is defined as stalling speed or minimum steady flight speed in a specified configuration.

- You should use the same indicated airspeed at higher elevation airports that you use at lower elevations for takeoff, approach, and landing at higher elevation airports, even though the corresponding groundspeeds are faster.
- If, while maintaining a constant indicated altitude, you are able to maintain constant power as outside air temperature increases, true airspeed will increase.
- Design maneuvering speed, V_A, is one important value not shown by the color coding of an airspeed indicator. During operations in turbulence, you should slow the airplane below this speed. Other values can be identified by the color coding on the indicator, like the red line denoting V_{NE}, never-exceed speed.
- V speeds are defined in Part 1 of the FARs. V_F indicates design flap speed. V_X is the best angle of climb speed while, V_Y is the best rate of climb speed. V_{NO} is the maximum structural cruising speed.

ALTIMETER

- The most common altimeter error is failure to keep it set to the current barometric pressure.
- The altimeter indicates high when the actual pressure is lower than what is set in the window. The altimeter also indicates high when in colder than standard temperature conditions.
- It is your responsibility as pilot in command to make sure that an altimeter system check has been made within the preceding 24 calendar months. You must also make sure that the required instruments for VFR are functioning properly.
- Pressure altitude is displayed on the altimeter when it is set to the standard sea level pressure of 29.92 in. Hg. However, to provide for proper vertical separation of aircraft up to 17,999 feet MSL, all pilots should use the local altimeter setting so that their altimeters approximately indicate true altitude. At or above 18,000 feet MSL, all pilots must set their altimeters to 29.92 in. Hg.

2-1   PLT395
Which is the correct symbol for the stalling speed or the minimum steady flight speed in a specified configuration?

A– V_{SO}.
B– V_S.
C– V_{S1}.

2-1. Answer C. GFDICM 2A, FAR 1.2
V_{S1} is defined as stalling speed or minimum steady flight speed in a specified configuration.

2-2   PLT395
Which is the correct symbol for the stalling speed or the minimum steady flight speed in a specified configuration?

A– V_{SO}.
B– V_S.
C– V_{S1}.

2-2. Answer C. GFDICM 2A, FAR 1.2
V_{S1} is defined as stalling speed or minimum steady flight speed in a specified configuration.

2-3   PLT395
14 CFR part 1 defines V_F as

A– design flap speed.
B– flap operating speed.
C– maximum flap extended speed.

2-3. Answer A. GFDICM 2A, FAR 1.2
V_F is the design flap speed. V_{FE} is the maximum flap extended speed. Flap operating speed is not defined in 14 CFR part 1.

2-4   PLT395
14 CFR part 1 defines V$_{NO}$ as

A– maximum operating speed.
B– maximum structural cruising speed.
C– normal operating speed.

2-4. Answer B. GFDICM 2A, FAR 1.2
According to FAR 1.1, V$_{NO}$ is defined as the maximum structural cruising speed of an aircraft.

2-5   PLT395
14 CFR part 1 defines V$_{NE}$ as

A– maximum nose wheel extend speed.
B– never-exceed speed.
C– maximum landing gear extended speed.

2-5. Answer B. GFDICM 2A, FAR 1.2
According to FAR 1.1, V$_{NE}$ is defined as the never exceed speed of an aircraft.

2-6   PLT395
14 CFR part 1 defines V$_Y$ as

A– speed for best rate of descent.
B– speed for best angle of climb.
C– speed for best rate of climb.

2-6. Answer C. GFDICM 2A, FAR 1.2
According to FAR 1.1, V$_Y$ is defined as the speed for the best rate of climb of an aircraft.

2-7   PLT166
What altimeter setting is required when operating an aircraft at 18,000 feet MSL?

A– Altimeter setting at the departure or destination airport.
B– Current reported altimeter setting of a station along the route.
C– 29.92 inches Hg.

2-7. Answer C. GFDICM 2A, FAR 91.121
Up to 17,999 feet MSL, you must use the current reported altimeter setting of a station along the route within 100 nautical miles. At or above 18,000 feet MSL, your altimeter must be set to 29.92" Hg.

2-8   PLT132
Which airspeed would a pilot be unable to identify by the color coding of an airspeed indicator?

A– The never-exceed speed.
B– The power-off stall speed.
C– The maneuvering speed.

2-8. Answer C. GFDICM 2A, PHB
The maneuvering speed, V$_A$, is the speed at which the airplane will stall before excessive G-forces can build up. However, V$_A$ varies with weight and is, therefore, not depicted on the airspeed indicator.

2-9   PLT215
Which statement is true about magnetic deviation of a compass? Deviation

A– varies over time as the agonic line shifts.
B– varies for different headings of the same aircraft.
C– is the same for all aircraft in the same locality.

2-9. Answer B. GFDICM 2A, PHB
Magnetic deviation is the compass error that is caused by the magnetic fields which are produced by the metal and electrical accessories within the airplane. This error distorts the lines of magnetic force produced by the earth and causes the compass to swing away from the correct heading. The amount of error varies from one heading to the next because the lines of force interact at different angles.

2-10   PLT123
At higher elevation airports the pilot should know that indicated airspeed

A– will be unchanged, but groundspeed will be faster.
B– will be higher, but groundspeed will be unchanged.
C– should be increased to compensate for the thinner air.

2-10. Answer A. GFDPPM 8A, AIM
The airspeed indicator displays the speed of your airplane through the air by comparing ram air pressure with static air pressure. The greater the differential, the greater the indicated airspeed. When an indicated airspeed is specified by the manufacturer for a given situation, such as takeoff or landing, you normally should use that speed, regardless of the elevation. At higher elevations the air is less dense so the aircraft must move through the air faster to get the same pressure differential (indicated airspeed). Thus you will have a greater true airspeed resulting in a greater groundspeed.

2-11   PLT187
What is an operational difference between the turn coordinator and the turn-and-slip indicator? The turn coordinator

A– is always electric; the turn-and-slip indicator is always vacuum-driven.
B– indicates bank angle only; the turn-and-slip indicator indicates rate of turn and coordination.
C– indicates roll rate, rate of turn, and coordination; the turn-and-slip indicator indicates rate of turn and coordination.

2-11. Answer C. GFDICM 2A
The gyros in both the turn coordinator and turn-and-slip indicator are mounted so that they rotate in the vertical plane. The gimbal in the turn coordinator is set at an angle which means precession allows the gyro to sense both rate of roll and rate of turn. The gimbal in the turn-and-slip indicator is horizontal. In this case, precession allows the gyro to sense only rate of turn. Both the turn coordinator and turn-and-slip indicator have inclinometers which indicate coordination of a turn.

2-12   PLT187
What is an advantage of an electric turn coordinator if the airplane has a vacuum system for other gyroscopic instruments?

A– It is a backup in case of vacuum system failure.
B– It is more reliable than the vacuum-driven indicators.
C– It will not tumble as will vacuum-driven turn indicators.

2-12. Answer A. GFDICM 2A
On most light airplanes, the vacuum system supplies power to the attitude and heading indicators, while the electrical system powers the turn coordinator. This configuration provides a backup in case one system fails.

2-13   PLT187

If a standard rate turn is maintained, how long would it take to turn 360°?

A– 1 minute.
B– 2 minutes.
C– 3 minutes.

2-13. Answer B. GFDICM 2A

A standard-rate turn is a turn at a rate of three degrees per second. At this rate, you will complete a 360° turn in two minutes.

2-14   PLT173

What are the standard temperature and pressure values for sea level?

A– 15°C and 29.92 inches Hg.
B– 59°F and 1013.2 inches Hg.
C– 15°C and 29.92 Mb.

2-14. Answer A. GFDPPM 2C

The standard temperature and pressure at sea level are 15°C (59°F) and 29.92 inches of Hg. (1013.2 Mb.) respectively.

2-15   PLT395

Calibrated airspeed is best described as indicated airspeed corrected for

A– installation and instrument error.
B– instrument error.
C– non-standard temperature.

2-15. Answer A. GFDICM 2A

Calibrated Airspeed (CAS) is the airspeed indicator reading corrected for position (or installation), and instrument errors. CAS is equal to TAS at sea level in standard atmosphere.

2-16   PLT395

True airspeed is best described as calibrated airspeed corrected for

A– installation or instrument error.
B– non-standard temperature.
C– altitude and non-standard temperature.

2-16. Answer C. GFDICM 2A

True airspeed is the actual speed the aircraft moves through the airmass. It is what you get when you correct calibrated airspeed for temperature and altitude.

2-17   PLT166

To determine pressure altitude prior to takeoff, the altimeter should be set to

A– the current altimeter setting.
B– 29.92 inches Hg and the altimeter indication noted.
C– the field elevation and the pressure reading in the altimeter setting window noted.

2-17. Answer B. GFDICM 2A

Pressure altitude is indicated on the altimeter when 29.92 is set in the altimeter setting window. You can also determine pressure altitude arithmetically from the current altimeter setting and field elevation.

SECTION B - ATTITUDE INSTRUMENT FLYING

Chapter 2, Section B, reviews the basic technique and concepts of attitude instrument flying, or controlling an aircraft solely through the use of flight instruments. While this was the cornerstone of your instrument training, it is not a major part of the preparation for your commercial airplane certificate

SECTION C - INSTRUMENT NAVIGATION

As a commercial pilot, you will refine your instrument interpretation skills to the point where you can easily visualize your position in relation to ground stations. In addition, you will more likely be flying complex or high performance airplanes with more sophisticated navigation equipment and instrumentation.

VOR NAVIGATION

- There are various types of indicators for VOR navigation, including the basic VOR indicator, the horizontal situation indicator (HSI) and the radio magnetic indicator (RMI).
- Flying a heading that is the reciprocal to the bearing selected on the OBS would result in reverse sensing on a conventional VOR indicator.
- An HSI solves nearly all reverse sensing and other visualization problems associated with a conventional VOR indicator. The HSI display combines the VOR indicator with a heading indicator, so the display is automatically rotated to the correct position for you.
- Each dot on an HSI or conventional VOR course deviation scale is 2° deviation, or 200 feet per nautical mile, when tuned to a VOR. Station passage is indicated by the first positive, complete reversal of the TO/FROM indicator. Unlike a conventional VOR indicator, an HSI gives information about your aircraft heading and its relationship to your intended course.

TIME AND DISTANCE TO A STATION

- You can calculate the time and distance to a station by turning perpendicular to the direct course to the station and measuring the time to move a specific number of degrees to a new radial. [Time to the station] = [Time to move to the new radial x 60] ÷ [Degrees to the new radial]. This formula also works when timing the degrees of change in the magnetic bearing to or from an NDB. EXAMPLE: If it takes 3 minutes to traverse 10 degrees of DME arc, the time to the station is 3 minutes x 60 ÷ 10 = 18 minutes. If your speed is 120 knots (2 n.m. per minute), the distance to the station is 18 x 2 = 36 n.m.
- To determine time to a station using the isosceles triangle method, turn 10° (or any angle) to the side of your course and twist your course selector the same amount in the opposite direction. Time to station is the same as the time it takes for your CDI to center (assuming no wind).

ADF NAVIGATION

- To determine time to a station using the isosceles triangle method with an ADF, simply measure the time it takes for the relative bearing (left or right of the aircraft nose) to double while holding a constant heading.
- The angle between the nose of the aircraft and an NDB is the relative bearing. Magnetic heading (MH) plus relative bearing (RB) equals magnetic bearing to the station (MB).
- Because a radio magnetic indicator (RMI) has a slaved compass card that automatically rotates to the correct heading, it always displays the bearing to a station at the head of the arrow, and the bearing from a station at the tail of the arrow.
- A movable card ADF also directly indicates bearing to a station when its compass card is adjusted to agree with the aircraft's actual heading.
- Most RMIs have two bearing pointer needles, either one of which can be set to point to an NDB or VOR station. The tail of an RMI needle set to a VOR station indicates the radial you are on FROM the station, and the arrowhead indicates the course TO the station.
- Intercepting a bearing to an NDB is easiest if you choose an angle, such as 45°, that is easy to read on the compass card. To establish a 45° intercept, turn so that the bearing to be intercepted appears over the heading indicator reference mark 45° to the left or right of the aircraft nose. Precisely maintain this heading and look for the ADF needle to also point 45° to the left or right of the aircraft's nose.
- When turned parallel to the course to the station, the needle indicates any deviation by pointing left or right toward the course. If you simply home to the station with a crosswind, you will fly a curved path to the station.

- If tracking on course to a station and holding a wind correction, the needle indicates the amount of wind correction, but in the opposite direction. If correcting 10° left, the needle points 10° right of the nose. When homing to a station in high wind conditions, the result is a curved flight path until a direct headwind is reached.
- When on the desired track outbound with the proper drift correction established, the ADF pointer will be deflected to the windward side of the tail position.

RADIO NAVIGATION OPERATIONAL CONSIDERATIONS

- At altitudes between 14,500 and 18,000 feet MSL, an (H) Class VORTAC has a usable signal range of 100 nautical miles. Therefore, for direct routes off established airways at these altitudes, the facilities should be no farther apart than 200 nautical miles.
- A VOR receiver check is required within 30 days prior to an IFR flight. Written documentation of this check is required.
- When checking your VOR using a VOT, the CDI should be centered and the OBS should indicate that the aircraft is on the 360° radial, ±4°.
- When using a VOR ground checkpoint, the CDI must center within ±4°. The allowable error using an airborne checkpoint is ±6°. When you conduct a dual system check, the difference between VOR systems should not exceed 4°.
- VOR and DME facilities transmit their identifiers on a time sharing basis, with the VOR transmitting several identifiers for each one from the DME. If, when tuning to a VORTAC, you receive a single coded identification approximately once every 30 seconds, it means the DME component is operative and the VOR component is inoperative. The reverse is true if you hear the 1,020 Hz VOR signal several times and the 1,350 Hz DME tone is missing over a 30-second interval.
- If a station is not transmitting an identifier, it means the station is undergoing maintenance and is unreliable, even if you are receiving navigation indications from that station.

AREA NAVIGATION

- Area navigation (RNAV) allows you to fly direct to your destination without the need to overfly VORs or other ground facilities. These systems include VOR/DME RNAV, inertial navigation system (INS), LORAN, and the global positioning system (GPS).
- GPS provides a 95% probability of horizontal accuracy within 100 meters (328 feet), and a 99.99% probability of accuracy within 300 meters (984 feet).

2-18   PLT507
What is the maximum bearing error (+ or -) allowed for an operational VOR equipment check when using an FAA-approved ground test signal?

A– 4 degrees
B– 6 degrees
C– 8 degrees

2-18. Answer A. GFDICM 2C, FAR 91.171b
A VOR Test (VOT) facility provides the most accurate VOR check. The maximum allowable bearing error with this test is ± 4°.

2-19   PLT454
When must an operational check on the aircraft VOR equipment be accomplished to operate under IFR? Within the preceding

A– 30 days or 30 hours of flight time.
B– 10 days or 10 hours of flight time.
C– 30 days.

2-19. Answer C. GFDICM 2C, FAR 91.171
There must be a written record of a VOR accuracy check within the previous 30 days, containing the date and place of the check, the error and signature of the person performing the check.

2-20   PLT405

Which data must be recorded in the aircraft logbook or other record by a pilot making a VOR operational check for IFR operations?

A– VOR name or identification, place of operational check, amount of bearing error, and date of check.
B– Date of check, place of operational check, bearing error, and signature.
C– VOR name or identification, amount of bearing error, date of check, and signature.

2-20. Answer B. GFDICM 2C, FAR 91.171
There must be a written record of a VOR accuracy check within the previous 30 days, containing the date and place of the check, the error and signature of the person performing the check.

2-21   PLT014

The ADF is tuned to a radiobeacon. If the magnetic heading is 040° and the relative bearing is 290°, the magnetic bearing to that radiobeacon would be

A– 150°.
B– 285°.
C– 330°.

2-21. Answer C. GFDICM 2C, PHB
With a fixed-card ADF indicator, the magnetic bearing TO the station equals your magnetic heading plus your relative bearing TO the station. If the result is greater than 360°, subtract 360°.

MH + RB = MB
040° + 290° = 330°

2-22   PLT014

If the relative bearing to a nondirectional radiobeacon is 045° and the magnetic heading is 355°, the magnetic bearing to that radiobeacon would be

A– 040°.
B– 065°.
C– 220°.

2-22. Answer A. GFDICM 2C, PHB
With a fixed-card ADF indicator, the magnetic bearing TO the station equals your magnetic heading plus your relative bearing TO the station. If the result is greater than 360°, subtract 360°.

MH + RB = MB
355° + 045° = 400° - 360° = 040°

2-23   PLT014

(Refer to figure 2-1 on page 2-11.)

If the aircraft continues its present heading as shown in instrument group 3, what will be the relative bearing when the aircraft reaches the magnetic bearing of 030° FROM the NDB?

A–030°.
B–060°.
C–240°.

2-23. Answer C. GFDICM 2C, PHB

With a fixed-card ADF indicator, the magnetic bearing TO the station equals your magnetic heading plus your relative bearing TO the station. To figure this relationship, use the standard formula for magnetic bearing TO the station. First, convert the 30° magnetic bearing FROM the NDB to 210°, the magnetic bearing TO the station.

MH + RB = MB (TO)
330° + (unknown) = 030° (TO)
330° + (unknown) = 030° + 180 (FROM)
330° + (unknown) = 210° (FROM)

Next, you solve for relative bearing.

RB = 210° - 330°
RB = -120
RB = -120° + 360°
RB = 240

Note:You must add 360° to convert the relative bearing to a positive value.

Figure 2-1. Magnetic Compass/ADF.

2-24   PLT014
(Refer to figure 2-1 on page 2-11.)
At the position indicated by instrument group 1, what would be the relative bearing if the aircraft were turned to a magnetic heading of 090°?

A– 150°.
B– 190°.
C– 250°.

2-24. Answer C. GFDICM 2C, PHB
With a fixed-card ADF indicator, the magnetic bearing TO the station equals your magnetic heading plus your relative bearing TO the station. If the result is greater than 360°, subtract 360°.

MH + RB = MB
300° + 040° = 340°

When MH is changed from 300° to 090° the MB will not change.

MH + RB = MB
090° + RB = 340°
RB = 340° - 090°
RB = 250°

2-25   PLT014
(Refer to figure 2-1 on page 2-11.)
At the position indicated by instrument group 1, to intercept the 330° magnetic bearing to the NDB at a 30° angle, the aircraft should be turned

A– left to a heading of 270°.
B– right to a heading of 330°.
C– right to a heading of 360°.

2-25. Answer C. GFDICM 2C, PHB
Only two magnetic headings will intercept 330° at a 30° angle, 300° and 360°. In order to intercept the 330° bearing TO the station, a heading of 360° must be flown. A heading of 300° would take you away from the 330° bearing at a 30° angle.

2-26   PLT090
Which situation would result in reverse sensing of a VOR receiver?

A– Flying a heading that is reciprocal to the bearing selected on the OBS.
B– Setting the OBS to a bearing that is 90° from the bearing on which the aircraft is located.
C– Failing to change the OBS from the selected inbound course to the outbound course after passing the station.

2-26. Answer A. GFDICM 8B, PHB
When your course selector is in general agreement with your heading indicator in an off course situation, the CDI will be deflected toward the selected course. However, if you mistakenly set your course selector to the reciprocal of the desired course, your CDI will be deflected away from the course you want to follow. This is known as reverse sensing.

2-27   PLT091
To track outbound on the 180 radial of a VOR station, the recommended procedure is to set the OBS to

A– 360° and make heading corrections toward the CDI needle.
B– 180° and make heading corrections away from the CDI needle.
C– 180° and make heading corrections toward the CDI needle.

2-27. Answer C. GFDICM 2C, PHB
When tracking a VOR radial, it is important that the course selector indicates the approximate heading (allowing for wind correction) of the airplane. When tracking outbound on the 180° radial, you should have a FROM indication with 180° selected. This will result in proper sensing.

2-28   PLT091

To track inbound on the 215 radial of a VOR station, the recommended procedure is to set the OBS to

A– 215° and make heading corrections toward the CDI needle.

B– 215° and make heading corrections away from the CDI needle.

C– 035° and make heading corrections toward the CDI needle.

2-28. Answer C. GFDICM 2C, PHB

When tracking a VOR radial, it is important that the course selector indicates the approximate heading (allowing for wind correction) of the airplane. When tracking inbound on the 215° radial, you should have a TO indication with 035° selected. This will result in proper sensing.

2-29   PLT056

(Refer to figure 2-2 on page 2-14.)

Which illustration indicates that the airplane will intercept the 060 radial at a 60° angle inbound, if the present heading is maintained?

A– 6

B– 4

C– 5

2-29. Answer A. GFDICM 2C, PHB

To intercept the 060° radial inbound at a 60° angle, the HSI course arrow must be pointing at 240° with a TO indication, and the aircraft's heading needs to be either 300° or 180° (240° + 60° = 300°) or (240° - 60° = 180°).

UPPER LUBBER LINE
Indicates magnetic heading
of aircraft.

BEARING POINTER
Indicates magnetic bearing
from aircraft to
navigational aid selected.

COURSE ARROW
Indicates course set
in Course Selector Window.

TO/FROM INDICATOR
Shows whether the course
selected, if intercepted
and flown, will take you
TO or FROM station.

HEADING MARKER
Rotates with the Compass Card.
Can be manually set
with the Heading Set Knob.

COURSE SELECTOR WINDOW
Selected course is read
in this window.

COURSE DEVIATION INDICATOR
Shows position of selected
radial in relation to aircraft.

ROTATING COMPASS CARD
Actuated by Master
Compass System and rotates
as the aircraft turns.

COURSE SET KNOB
Used to select any
desired course.

Figure 2-2. Horizontal Situation Indicator (HSI).

2-30   PLT056
(Refer to figure 2-2 on page 2-14.)
Which statement is true regarding illustration 2, if the present heading is maintained? The airplane will

A– cross the 180 radial at a 45° angle outbound.
B– intercept the 225 radial at a 45° angle.
C– intercept the 360 radial at a 45° angle inbound.

2-30. Answer A. GFDICM 2C, IFH
The bearing indicator shows that the VOR station is approximately 10° right of the aircraft's nose. If the present heading is maintained (225°), you will intercept the 180° radial outbound with a 45° angle (225° - 180° = 45°). (Note: the magnetic heading of the aircraft appears to be closer to 226° than 225°).

2-31   PLT056
(Refer to figure 2-2 on page 2-14.)
Which illustration indicates that the airplane will intercept the 060 radial at a 75° angle outbound, if the present heading is maintained?

A– 4
B– 5
C– 6

2-31. Answer B. GFDICM 2C, IFH
The TO/FROM indicator in illustration 5 shows that once you intercept the 060° radial, a heading of 240° will take you TO the station. Since your indicated heading is 345°, you will intercept the 060° radial outbound at a 75° angle.

2-32   PLT056
(Refer to figure 2-2 on page 2-14.)
Which illustration indicates that the airplane should be turned 150° left to intercept the 360 radial at a 60° angle inbound?

A– 1
B– 2
C– 3

2-32. Answer A. GFDICM 2C, IFH
In order to intercept the 360° radial inbound at a 60° angle, the aircraft must be on a heading of 240° (180° + 60° = 240°) and the course arrow must be pointing at 180° with a TO indication. Illustration 1 is the only illustration that, after completing a 150° turn, would indicate this.

2-33   PLT056
(Refer to figure 2-2 on page 2-14.)
Which is true regarding illustration 4 if the present heading is maintained? The airplane will

A– cross the 060 radial at a 15° angle.
B– intercept the 240 radial at a 30° angle.
C– cross the 180 radial at a 75° angle.

2-33. Answer C. GFDICM 2C
The bearing indicator shows you are on the 095° radial. If you maintain the present heading (255°), you will intercept the 180° radial outbound with a 75° angle (255° - 180° = 75°).

2-34   PLT056

(Refer to figure 2-3 on page 2-16.)

To intercept a magnetic bearing of 240° FROM at a 030° angle (while outbound), the airplane should be turned

A–left 065°.

B–left 125°.

C–right 270°.

2-34. Answer B. GFDICM 2C

The tail of the bearing indicator shows that you are on the 165° bearing (southeast) FROM the station (130° + 35° = 165°).To intercept the 240° bearing (southwest) FROM the station, you must first turn left. The heading required to intercept the 240° bearing FROM can be calculated by adding the intercept angle (030°) to 240°.Your new heading is 270° (30° + 240° = 270°).To determine the number of degrees to turn calculate the difference between your present heading (035°) and your new heading (270°). The answer is 125°.

Figure 2-3. Magnetic Heading/Radio Compass.

2-35   PLT091

(Refer to figure 2-3 on page 2-16.)

If the airplane continues to fly on the heading as shown, what magnetic bearing FROM the station would be intercepted at a 35° angle outbound?

A–035°.

B–070°.

C–215°.

2-35. Answer B. GFDICM 2C

You are currently on the 165° bearing FROM the station (130° + 35° = 165°) heading 035°. Since you are southeast of the station, you can determine the bearing you will intercept by adding the angle of intercept to your heading. The answer is 070° (35° + 35° = 70°).

2-36   PLT091
(Refer to figure 2-4 on page 2-17.)
If the airplane continues to fly on the magnetic heading
as illustrated, what magnetic bearing FROM the station
would be intercepted at a 35° angle?

A– 090°.
B– 270°.
C– 305°.

2-36. Answer C. GFDICM 2C, IFH
You are on the 270° bearing FROM the station (340°
- 70° = 270°) heading 340°. Since you are northwest
of the station, you can determine the bearing you will
intercept by subtracting the intercept angle (35°) from
your heading. The answer is 305° (340° - 35° = 305°).

Figure 2-4. Magnetic Heading/Radio Compass.

2-37   PLT091
(Refer to figure 2-4 on page 2-17.)
If the airplane continues to fly on the magnetic heading
as illustrated, what magnetic bearing FROM the station
would be intercepted at a 30° angle?

A– 090°.
B– 270°.
C– 310°.

2-37. Answer C. GFDICM 2C, IFH
You are on the 270° bearing FROM the station (340°
- 70° = 270°) heading 340°. Since you are northwest
of the station, you can determine the bearing you will
intercept by subtracting the intercept angle (30°) from
your heading. The answer is 310° (340° - 30° = 310°).

2-38   PLT012
The relative bearing on an ADF changes from 265° to 260° in 2 minutes of elapsed time. If the groundspeed is 145 knots, the distance to that station would be

A– 26 NM.
B– 37 NM.
C– 58 NM.

2-38. Answer C. GFDICM 2C, PHB
You can estimate the distance to an NDB by using the formula (TAS x minutes flown) ÷ degrees of bearing change. To solve this problem, you have to assume that your groundspeed is equal to your true airspeed. The answer is 58 n.m. (145 x 2) ÷ 5 = 58.

2-39   PLT012
The ADF indicates a wingtip bearing change of 10° in 2 minutes of elapsed time, and the TAS is 160 knots. What is the distance to the station?

A– 15 NM.
B– 32 NM.
C– 36 NM.

2-39. Answer B. GFDICM 2C, PHB
You can estimate the distance to an NDB by using the formula (TAS x minutes flown) ÷ degrees of bearing change. The answer is 32 n.m. (160 x 2) ÷ 10 = 32.

2-40   PLT012
With a TAS of 115 knots, the relative bearing on an ADF changes from 090° to 095° in 1.5 minutes of elapsed time. The distance to the station would be

A– 12.5 NM.
B– 24.5 NM.
C– 34.5 NM.

2-40. Answer C. GFDICM 2C, PHB
You can estimate the distance to an NDB by using the formula (TAS x minutes flown) ÷ degrees of bearing change. The answer is 34.5 (115 x 1.5) ÷ 5 = 34.5.

2-41   PLT012
GIVEN:

Wingtip bearing change...5°
Time elapsed between bearing change...5 min.
True airspeed...115kts.

The distance to the station is

A– 36 NM.
B– 57.5 NM.
C– 115 NM.

2-41. Answer C. GFDICM 2C, PHB
You can estimate the distance to an NDB by using the formula (TAS x minutes flown) ÷ degrees of bearing change. The answer is 115 n.m. (115 x 5) ÷ 5 = 115.

2-42   PLT014

The ADF is tuned to a nondirectional radiobeacon and the relative bearing changes from 095° to 100° in 1.5 minutes of elapsed time. The time en route to that station would be

A– 18 minutes.
B– 24 minutes.
C– 30 minutes.

2-42. Answer A. GFDICM 2C, PHB

You can calculate the estimated time to an NDB station by using the formula (time in seconds ÷ degrees of bearing change). The answer is 18 minutes (90 ÷ 5 = 18).

2-43   PLT014

The ADF is tuned to a nondirectional radiobeacon and the relative bearing changes from 270° to 265° in 2.5 minutes of elapsed time. The time en route to that beacon would be

A– 9 minutes.
B– 18 minutes.
C– 30 minutes.

2-43. Answer C. GFDICM 2C, PHB

You can calculate the estimated time to an NDB station by using the formula (time in seconds ÷ degrees of bearing change). The answer is 30 minutes (150 ÷ 5 = 30).

2-44   PLT014

The ADF is tuned to a nondirectional radiobeacon and the relative bearing changes from 085° to 090° in 2 minutes of elapsed time. The time en route to the station would be

A– 15 minutes.
B– 18 minutes.
C– 24 minutes.

2-44. Answer C. GFDICM 2C, IFH

You can calculate the estimated time to an NDB station by using the formula (time in seconds ÷ degrees of bearing change). The answer is 24 minutes (120 ÷ 5 = 24).

2-45   PLT014

If the relative bearing changes from 090° to 100° in 2.5 minutes of elapsed time, the time en route to the station would be

A– 12 minutes.
B– 15 minutes.
C– 18 minutes.

2-45. Answer B. GFDICM 2C, IFH

You can calculate the estimated time to an NDB station by using the formula (time in seconds ÷ degrees of bearing change). The answer is 15 minutes (150 ÷ 10 = 15).

2-46   PLT012
The ADF is tuned to a nondirectional radiobeacon and the relative bearing changes from 090° to 100° in 2.5 minutes of elapsed time. If the true airspeed is 90 knots, the distance and time en route to that radiobeacon would be

A– 15 miles and 22.5 minutes.
B– 22.5 miles and 15 minutes.
C– 32 miles and 18 minutes.

2-46. Answer B. GFDICM 2C, IFH
You can estimate the distance to an NDB by using the formula (TAS x minutes flown) ÷ degrees of bearing change. The answer is 22.5 miles (90 × 2.5) ÷ 10 = 22.5.

To determine the time to an NDB station use the formula (time in seconds ÷ degrees of bearing change). The answer is 15 minutes (150 ÷ 10 = 15).

2-47   PLT012
GIVEN:

Wingtip bearing change...10°
Elapsed time between bearing change...4 min
Rate of fuel consumption...11 gal/hr.

Calculate the fuel required to fly to the station.

A– 4.4 gallons.
B– 8.4 gallons.
C– 12 gallons.

2-47. Answer A. GFDICM 2C, IFH
To solve this problem you must first calculate the time to the station. You can do this by using the formula (time in seconds ÷ degrees of bearing change). The estimated time enroute (ETE) is 24 minutes (240 ÷ 10 = 24).

To determine the fuel required, multiply your ETE by the fuel consumption rate (11 gal/hr). The fuel required is 4.4 gallons (0:24:00 × 11 = 4.4).

2-48   PLT012
GIVEN:

Wingtip bearing change...5°;
Elapsed time between bearing change...6 min.
Rate of fuel consumption...12 gal/hr.

The fuel required to fly to the station is

A– 8.2 gallons.
B– 14.4 gallons.
C– 18.7 gallons.

2-48. Answer B. GFDICM 2C, IFH
To solve this problem you must first calculate the time to the station. You can do this by using the formula (time in seconds ÷ degrees of bearing change). The estimated time enroute (ETE) is 72 minutes (360 ÷ 5 = 72).

To determine the fuel required, multiply your ETE by the fuel consumption rate (12 gal/hr). The fuel required is 14.4 gallons (0:72:00 × 12 = 14.4).

2-49   PLT012

GIVEN:

Wingtip bearing change...15°
Elapsed time between bearing change...6 min
Rate of fuel consumption...8.6 gal/hr.

Calculate the approximate fuel required to fly to the station.

A– 3.44 gallons.
B– 6.88 gallons.
C– 17.84 gallons.

2-49. Answer A. GFDICM 2C, IFH

To solve this problem you must first calculate the time to the station. You can do this by using the formula (time in seconds ÷ degrees of bearing change). The estimated time enroute (ETE) is 24 minutes (360 ÷ 15 = 24).

To determine the fuel required, multiply your ETE by the fuel consumption rate (8.6 gal/hr). The fuel required is 3.44 gallons (0:24:00 × 8.6 = 3.44).

2-50   PLT012

GIVEN:

Wingtip bearing change...15°;
Elapsed time between bearing change...7.5 min;
True airspeed...85 kts
Rate of fuel consumption...9.6 gal/hr.

The time, distance, and fuel required to fly to the station is

A– 30 minutes; 42.5 miles; 4.80 gallons.
B– 32 minutes; 48 miles; 5.58 gallons.
C– 48 minutes; 48 miles; 4.58 gallons.

2-50. Answer A. GFDICM 2C, IFH

To solve this problem you must calculate the estimated time enroute (ETE), the distance to the station, and the fuel required.

To determine the ETE to the station use the formula (time in seconds ÷ degrees of bearing change). The answer is 30 minutes (450 ÷ 15 = 30).

You can estimate the distance to the NDB by using the formula (TAS x minutes flown) ÷ degrees of bearing change. The answer is 42.5 miles (85 x 7.5) ÷ 15 = 42.5.

To determine the fuel required, multiply your ETE by the fuel consumption rate (9.6 gal/hr). The answer is 4.80 gallons (0:30:00 x 9.6 = 4.80).

2-51   PLT014

While maintaining a constant heading, a relative bearing of 15° doubles in 6 minutes. The time to the station being used is

A– 3 minutes.
B– 6 minutes.
C– 12 minutes.

2-51. Answer B. GFDICM 2C, IFH

When not on a heading perpendicular to a bearing or radial, the estimated time enroute to the station will equal the time it takes to double the relative bearing. You can tell you are not perpendicular to the station because your relative bearing is less than 90°. The answer is 6 minutes.

2-52   PLT014

While maintaining a constant heading, the ADF needle increases from a relative bearing of 045° to 090° in 5 minutes. The time to the station being used is

A– 5 minutes.
B– 10 minutes.
C– 15 minutes.

2-52. Answer A. GFDICM 2C, IFH

When not on a heading perpendicular to a bearing or radial, the estimated time enroute to the station will equal the time it takes to double the relative bearing. The answer is 5 minutes.

Chapter 2 - Principles of Instrument Flight

2-53   PLT012

While cruising at 135 knots and on a constant heading, the ADF needle decreases from a relative bearing of 315° to 270° in 7 minutes. The approximate time and distance to the station being used is

A– 7 minutes and 16 miles.
B– 14 minutes and 28 miles.
C– 19 minutes and 38 miles.

2-53. Answer A. GFDICM 2C, IFH

When not on a heading perpendicular to a bearing or radial, the estimated time enroute to the station will equal the time it takes to double the relative bearing. A relative bearing of 315° is equivalent to having the station 45° off the nose. When you reach the 270° relative bearing, the station will be 90° off the nose. In essence, you double the relative bearing (45° to 90°) in 7 minutes. The answer is 7 minutes.

You can estimate the distance to the NDB by multiplying the time to the station by the aircraft's speed. The answer is 16 miles (0:07:00 × 135 = 15.75).

2-54   PLT012

While maintaining a constant heading, a relative bearing of 10° doubles in 5 minutes. If the true airspeed is 105 knots, the time and distance to the station being used is approximately.

A– 5 minutes and 8.7 miles.
B– 10 minutes and 17 miles.
C– 15 minutes and 31.2 miles.

2-54. Answer A. GFDICM 2C, IFH

When not on a heading perpendicular to a bearing or radial, the estimated time enroute to the station will equal the time it takes to double the relative bearing. The answer is 5 minutes.

You can estimate the distance to the NDB by multiplying the time to the station by the aircraft's speed. The answer is 8.7 miles (0:05:00 × 105 = 8.7).

2-55   PLT507

When checking the course sensitivity of a VOR receiver, how many degrees should the OBS be rotated to move the CDI from the center to the last dot on either side?

A– 5° to 10°.
B– 10° to 12°.
C– 18° to 20°.

2-55. Answer B. GFDICM 2C, IFH

Course sensitivity may be checked by noting the number of degrees of change in the course selected as you rotate the course selector to move the CDI from the center to the last dot on either side. This should be between 10° and 12°.

2-56   PLT507

An aircraft 60 miles from a VOR station has a CDI indication of one-fifth deflection, this represents a course centerline deviation of approximately.

A– 6 miles.
B– 2 miles.
C– 1 mile.

2-56. Answer B. GFDICM 2C, IFH

In addition to telling you the number of degrees off course you are, the course deviation dots may also be used to estimate your lateral distance TO or FROM a selected radial. To make this computation, multiply your distance from the VOR by 200 feet per dot of deflection and divide by 6,076 (feet per n.m.). Each dot equals about a one-fifth deflection. The answer is 2 miles (60 x 200 = 12,000 ÷ 6,076 = 1.97).

2-57   PLT001

(Refer to figure 2-5 on page 2-24.)
Using instrument group 3, if the aircraft makes a 180°
turn to the left and continues straight ahead, it will
intercept which radial?

A– 135 radial.
B– 270 radial.
C– 360 radial.

2-57. Answer A. GFDICM 2C, IFH

Prior to making the turn, the RMI indicates you are
on a heading of 300° and the tail of the VOR needle
indicates that you are on the 135° radial. After making
a 180° turn, you will be heading 120° which will
reintercept the 135° radial outbound.

Figure 2-5. Radio Magnetic Indicator (RMI).

2-58   PLT001
(Refer to figure 2-5 on page 2-24.)
Which instrument shows the aircraft in a position where a 180° turn would result in the aircraft intercepting the 150 radial at a 30° angle?

A– 2.
B– 3.
C– 4.

2-58. Answer C. GFDICM 2C, IFH
To intercept the 150° radial at a 30° angle after making the turn, you would have to fly on a heading of 180° or 120°. The only illustrations that would indicate either of these headings are illustrations 3 and 4. After the turn, illustration 4 would indicate you are heading south (180°) towards the 150° radial.

2-59   PLT001
(Refer to figure 2-5 on page 2-24.)
Which instrument shows the aircraft in a position where a straight course after a 90° left turn would result in intercepting the 180 radial?

A– 2.
B– 3.
C– 4.

2-59. Answer B. GFDICM 2C, IFH
After a 90° left turn, illustration 3 would indicate that you are southeast of the station (135° radial) heading 210° towards the 180° radial.

2-60   PLT091
(Refer to figure 2-5 on page 2-24.)
Which instrument shows the aircraft to be northwest of the VORTAC?

A– 1.
B– 2.
C– 3.

2-60. Answer B. GFDICM 2C, IFH
You can identify the radial you are on by looking at the tail of VOR bearing indicator. Illustration 2 indicates that you are on the 310° radial (northwest).

2-61   PLT091
(Refer to figure 2-5 on page 2-24.)
Which instrument(s) show(s) that the aircraft is getting further from the selected VORTAC?

A– 4.
B– 1 and 4.
C– 2 and 3.

2-61. Answer A. GFDICM 2C, IFH
The head of the VOR indicator always points directly to the VOR station. In these examples, illustration 4 is the only indicator that shows you are heading away from the station.

2-62   PLT012
While maintaining a magnetic heading of 270° and a true airspeed of 120 knots, the 360 radial of a VOR is crossed at 1237 and the 350 radial is crossed at 1244. The approximate time and distance to this station are

A– 42 minutes and 84 NM.
B– 42 minutes and 91 NM.
C– 44 minutes and 96 NM.

2-62. Answer A. GFDICM 2C, IFH
To solve this problem you must calculate the estimated time enroute (ETE), the distance to the station.

To determine the ETE to the station use the formula (time in seconds ÷ degrees of bearing change). The answer is 42 minutes (420 ÷ 10 = 42).

You can estimate the distance to the VOR by using the formula (TAS × minutes flown) ÷ degrees of bearing change. The answer is 84 n.m. (0:42:00 × 120 = 84).

2-63   PLT014
(Refer to figure 2-6 on page 2-26.)
If the time flown between aircraft positions 2 and 3 is
13 minutes, what is the estimated time to the station?

A– 13 minutes.
B– 17 minutes.
C– 26 minutes.

2-63. Answer A. GFDICM 2C, IFH
When not on a heading perpendicular to a bearing or
radial, the time to the station equals the time required
to double the relative bearing. Figure 21 shows aircraft
2 has a relative bearing of 10°. Prior to turning inbound,
aircraft 3 would have a relative bearing of 20°. The
estimated time to the station is 13 minutes.

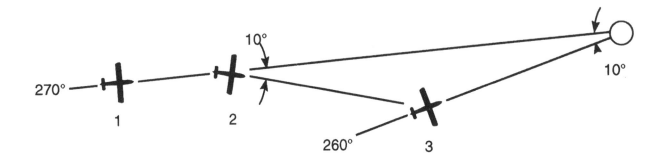

Figure 2-6. Isosceles Triangle.

2-64   PLT014
(Refer to figure 2-7 on page 2-26.)
If the time flown between aircraft positions 2 and 3 is 8
minutes, what is the estimated time to the station?

A– 8 minutes.
B– 16 minutes.
C– 48 minutes.

2-64. Answer A. GFDICM 2C, IFH
When not on a heading perpendicular to a bearing or
radial, the time to the station equals the time required
to double the relative bearing. The relative bearing to
the station for aircraft 2 is 5°. The relative bearing of
aircraft 3 prior to turning is 10°. The estimated time to
the station is 8 minutes.

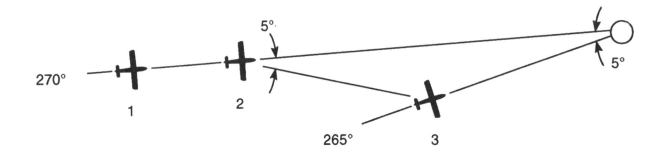

Figure 2-7. Isosceles Triangle.

2-65   PLT014

(Refer to figure 2-8 on page 2-27.)
If the time flown between aircraft positions 2 and 3 is 13 minutes, what is the estimated time to the station?

A– 7.8 minutes.
B– 13 minutes.
C– 26 minutes.

2-65. Answer B. GFDICM 2C, IFH
When not on a heading perpendicular to a bearing or radial, the time to the station equals the time required to double the relative bearing. The relative bearing to the station for aircraft 2 is 20°. The relative bearing of aircraft 3 prior to turning is 40°. The estimated time to the station is 13 minutes.

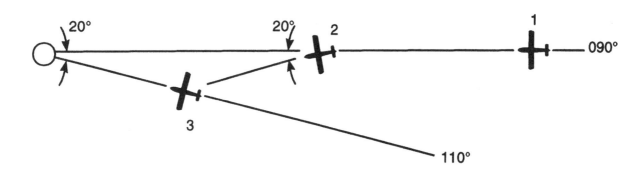

Figure 2-8. Isosceles Triangle.

2-66   PLT014

(Refer to figure 2-9 on page 2-27.)
If the time flown between aircraft positions 2 and 3 is 15 minutes, what is the estimated time to the station?

A– 15 minutes.
B– 30 minutes.
C– 60 minutes.

2-66. Answer A. GFDICM 2C, IFH
When not on a heading perpendicular to a bearing or radial, the time to the station equals the time required to double the relative bearing. The relative bearing to the station for aircraft 2 is 15°. The relative bearing of aircraft 3 prior to turning is 30°. The estimated time to the station is 15 minutes.

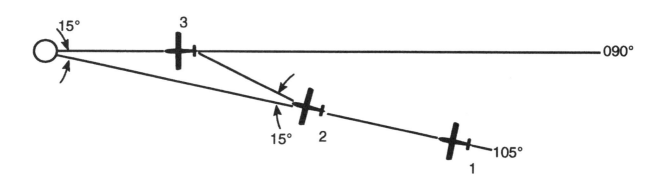

Figure 2-9. Isosceles Triangle.

2-67   PLT014
Inbound on the 040 radial, a pilot selects the 055 radial, turns 15° to the left, and notes the time. While maintaining a constant heading, the pilot notes the time for the CDI to center is 15 minutes. Based on this information, the ETE to the station is

A– 8 minutes.
B– 15 minutes.
C– 30 minutes.

2-67. Answer B. GFDICM 2C, IFH
When not on a heading perpendicular to a bearing or radial, the time to the station equals the time required to double the relative bearing or, in this case, the time required to achieve a 15° radial change. The heading change and the radial change must be the same. The estimated time to the VOR is 15 minutes.

2-68   PLT014
Inbound on the 090 radial, a pilot rotates the OBS 010° to the left, turns 010° to the right, and notes the time. While maintaining a constant heading, the pilot determines that the elapsed time for the CDI to center is 8 minutes. Based on this information, the ETE to the station is

A– 8 minutes.
B– 16 minutes.
C– 24 minutes.

2-68. Answer A. GFDICM 2C, IFH
When not on a heading perpendicular to a bearing or radial, the time to the station equals the time required to double the relative bearing or, in this case, the time required to achieve a 10° radial change. The heading change and radial change must be the same. The estimated time to the VOR is 8 minutes.

2-69   PLT014
Inbound on the 315 radial, a pilot selects the 320 radial, turns 5° to the left, and notes the time. While maintaining a constant heading, the pilot notes the time for the CDI to center is 12 minutes. The ETE to the station is

A– 10 minutes.
B– 12 minutes.
C– 24 minutes.

2-69. Answer B. GFDICM 2C, IFH
When not on a heading perpendicular to a bearing or radial, the time to the station equals the time required to double the relative bearing or, in this case, the time required to achieve a 5° radial change. The heading change and radial change must be the same. The estimated time to the VOR is 12 minutes.

2-70   PLT014
Inbound on the 190 radial, a pilot selects the 195 radial, turns 5° to the left, and notes the time. While maintaining a constant heading, the pilot notes the time for the CDI to center is 10 minutes. The ETE to the station is

A– 10 minutes.
B– 15 minutes.
C– 20 minutes.

2-70. Answer A. GFDICM 2C, IFH
When not on a heading perpendicular to a bearing or radial, the time to the station equals the time required to double the relative bearing or, in this case, the time required to achieve a 5° radial change. The heading change and radial change must be the same. The estimated time to the VOR is 10 minutes.

2-71   PLT507
How should the pilot make a VOR receiver check when the aircraft is located on the designated checkpoint on the airport surface?

A– Set the OBS on 180° plus or minus 4°; the CDI should center with a FROM indication.
B– Set the OBS on the designated radial. The CDI must center within plus or minus 4° of that radial with a FROM indication.
C– With the aircraft headed directly toward the VOR and the OBS set to 000°, the CDI should center within plus or minus 4° of that radial with a TO indication.

2-71. Answer B. GFDICM 2C, IFH
When making a VOR receiver check at a designated ground checkpoint, you must set the course selector to the specified radial and the CDI must center within ± 4° of the radial. If you are at the correct location, the TO/FROM will indicate FROM. You can find a list of designated ground checkpoints in the Airport/Facility Directory.

2-72   PLT507
When using VOT to make a VOR receiver check, the CDI should be centered and the OBS should indicate that the aircraft is on the

A– 090 radial.
B– 180 radial.
C– 360 radial.

2-72. Answer C. GFDICM 2C, AIM
A VOR test facility (VOT) emulates a 360° radial. Therefore, when conducting a VOT, the course selector should indicate 360° with a FROM indication, or 180° with a TO indication.

2-73   PLT507
When the CDI needle is centered during an airborne VOR check, the omnibearing selector should read.

A– within 4° of the selected radial.
B– within 6° of the selected radial.
C– 0° TO, only if you are due south of the VOR.

2-73. Answer B. GFDICM 2C, AIM
Airborne check points consist of certified radials that should be received at specific points over predetermined landmarks in the immediate vicinity of an airport. When making an airborne check, the course selector must indicate the designated radial and the CDI must be within 6° of the selected radial with a FROM indication.

THE FLIGHT ENVIRONMENT

SECTION A - AIRPORTS, AIRSPACE, AND FLIGHT INFORMATION

Chapter 3, Section A of the Instrument Commercial Manual contains essential information for instrument and commercial pilots. It emphasizes IFR operations and does not include VFR chart information, since this is considered private pilot knowledge. Nonetheless, a number of FAA commercial questions covering VFR charts appear here, since this material is most closely related to airports, airspace, and flight information.

AIRPORT MARKINGS

- Mandatory instruction signs, such as those marking hold lines consist of white lettering on a red background. A hold line painted on the pavement consists of four yellow lines, with the two dashed lines nearest the runway.
- A mandatory instruction sign has white lettering on a red background.
- Remain outside of the ILS hold line if asked to hold short of the ILS critical area, and completely pass this line when exiting the runway during ILS operations.

AIRSPACE
CONTROLLED AIRSPACE

- Controlled airspace includes Class A, B, C, D, and Class E airspace. It is where air traffic control service is available to pilots. When you are operating under IFR, you must comply with ATC clearances.
- You must have an operating transponder with Mode C (or Mode S) capability in Class A and B airspace and within 30 nautical miles of Class B primary airports. This equipment is also required in and above Class C airspace, and at or above 10,000 feet MSL, except at and below 2,500 feet AGL.
- Below 10,000 feet MSL, basic VFR visibility is 3 statute miles in controlled airspace and 1 mile in uncontrolled airspace. Cloud clearance requirements within 1,200 feet of the surface in uncontrolled airspace, and in Class B airspace, is simply clear of clouds. Otherwise, you must maintain 1,000 feet above, 500 feet below, and 2,000 feet horizontal distance from clouds. Above 10,000 feet MSL and more than 1,200 feet above the surface, required flight visibility increases to 5 miles in both controlled and uncontrolled airspace with 1 mile horizontal and 1,000-foot vertical separation required from clouds.

CLASS A AIRSPACE

Most Class A airspace extends from 18,000 feet MSL up to and including FL600. You are required to use an altimeter setting of 29.92 in. Hg., you must be rated and current for instrument flight, your aircraft must be equipped for IFR and you must be operating on an IFR clearance at an altitude assigned by ATC. DME is required at or above FL 240 where a VOR is required, with exceptions for in-flight failure.

CLASS B AIRSPACE

Most Class B airspace is from the surface to 10,000 feet MSL. You must be at least a private pilot, or a student pilot with the appropriate endorsement, and must receive an ATC clearance before entering this airspace. Some Class B areas completely prohibit student pilot operations. Among other requirements for flight within Class B airspace, your aircraft must be equipped with either a Mode S or a 4096-code transponder that has Mode C altitude reporting equipment

CLASS C AIRSPACE

- Class C airspace normally resides in 5 and 10 nautical mile circles extending outward from a primary airport. An outer area with radar coverage outside Class C airspace extends to 20 n.m. From 5 to 10 n.m. from the airport, Class C airspace generally begins at about 1,200 feet above the primary airport surface and extends to approximately 4,000 feet above the airport. Within 5 n.m. of the primary airport, Class C airspace is from the surface to about 4,000 feet AGL.

- Radio contact is encouraged within the 20 n.m. outer area and required prior to entering Class C airspace. If you depart a satellite airport within Class C airspace, you must establish two-way communication with ATC as soon as practicable after takeoff.

CLASS D AIRSPACE

- Class D airspace exists at airports with operating control towers which are not associated with Class B or C airspace. Normally, the upper limit of Class D airspace is about 2,500 feet above the surface of the primary airport and the lateral limits are approximately 4 nautical miles from the primary airport.

- Two-way radio communication with the control tower must be established prior to entering this airspace or taking off from the primary airport. Pilots taking off from satellite airports within Class D airspace must check in with the tower as soon as practicable.

- At part-time tower locations, Class D airspace normally becomes Class E airspace when the tower is closed, or Class G if weather observations and reporting are not available.

CLASS E AIRSPACE

- The remaining controlled airspace includes Federal airways, which are normally 8 nautical miles wide, begin at 1,200 feet AGL and extend up to 17,999 feet MSL. Transition areas are depicted with magenta shading on sectional charts, for certain airports with approved instrument approach procedures. These areas of Class E airspace typically begin at 700 feet AGL and extend to the overlying controlled airspace.

- At some nontower airports, Class E airspace extends upward from the surface, and typically encompasses a 4 n.m. circle around the airport, in addition to extensions to accommodate arrivals and departures. These are depicted with dashed magenta lines on VFR charts.

- At almost all remaining U.S. locations where Class E airspace is not designated at a lower altitude, it begins at 14,500 feet MSL (except within 1,500 feet of the surface) and extends up to 17,999 feet MSL.

SPECIAL VFR

When the weather is below basic VFR minimums, as indicated by daytime operation of a rotating beacon, you may obtain a special VFR (SVFR) clearance from the ATC facility controlling the airspace at selected airports. Ground (or flight) visibility must be at least 1 statute mile and you must remain clear of clouds. An instrument rating and IFR equipped airplane are required for SVFR after sunset and it is not allowed at airports indicating "No SVFR" on aeronautical charts.

CLASS G AIRSPACE

Class G airspace is that area which has not been designated as Class A, B, C, D, or E airspace. It is uncontrolled by ATC. For example, the airspace below a Class E airspace area or below a Victor airway is normally uncontrolled. Most Class G airspace terminates at the base of Class E airspace at 700 or 1,200 feet AGL, or at 14,500 feet MSL.

AIRCRAFT SPEED LIMITS

The speed limit is 250 knots indicated airspeed (KIAS) below 10,000 feet MSL and 200 KIAS within 4 nautical miles of the primary airport of Class C or Class D airspace within 2,500 feet of the surface. The 200 KIAS limit also applies to the airspace underlying Class B airspace or in a VFR corridor through such airspace. Aircraft that cannot safely operate at these speeds are exempt.

SPECIAL USE AIRSPACE

- Military operations areas (MOAs) separate certain military training activities from IFR traffic. You may be cleared IFR through an active MOA only if ATC can provide separation.
- Military training routes (MTRs) are depicted as thin, black, shaded lines on VFR charts. You could encounter military traffic exceeding 250 knots below 10,000 feet MSL along these routes.

OTHER AIRSPACE AREAS

An airport advisory area is within 10 statute miles of an airport with an FSS but no control tower. At these locations, the FSS provides local airport advisory (LAA) service.

OBSTRUCTION LIGHTING

Red or white beacons/flashing lights are used to mark man-made obstructions and hazards to aerial navigation when the obstruction is not in the vicinity of an airport. Steady red lights are used to mark obstructions and hazards in the vicinity of an airport, including end-of-runway lights.

LAND AND HOLD SHORT OPERATIONS (LAHSO)

LASHO clearances can be issued by ATC when the ceiling and visibility limits are above basic VFR minimums of 1,000 feet and 3 statute miles. It is the responsibility of the pilot-in-command to determine if the clearance can be safely executed, including determining that the available length of runway is adequate to adhere to the clearance.

FLIGHT INFORMATION
AIRPORT/FACILITY DIRECTORY

- The Airport/Facility Directory (A/FD) is a series of regional books with FAA information for public-use civil airports, associated terminal control facilities, air route traffic control centers, and radio aids to navigation.
- When planning night cross-country flights, airport and enroute lighting should be considered. This should include determining the availability and type of lighting at the destination, enroute, and alternate airports.

AERONAUTICAL INFORMATION MANUAL

The Aeronautical Information Manual (AIM) contains fundamental information required for both VFR and IFR flight operations within the National Airspace System. It is a major reference for this Study Guide

NOTICES TO AIRMEN

NOTAM(D) information is disseminated for all navigational facilities that are part of the National Airspace System, all public use airports, seaplane bases, and heliports listed in the Airport/Facility Directory. NOTAM(D) information includes items such as taxiway closures, construction activities near runways, snow conditions, and changes in the status of airport lighting, such as VASI, that do not affect instrument approach criteria. FDC NOTAMs are used to disseminate information that is regulatory in nature. Examples are amendments to aeronautical charts, changes to instrument approach procedures, and temporary flight restrictions.

3-1   PLT161
What designated airspace associated with an airport becomes inactive when the control tower at that airport is not in operation?

A– Class D, which then becomes Class C.
B– Class D, which then becomes Class E.
C– Class B.

3-1. Answer B. GFDICM 3A, FAR 1.1
An Airport Traffic Area (Class D Airspace) exists only when the control tower is in operation. When the tower closes the airspace becomes Class E.

3-2   PLT161
Excluding Hawaii, the vertical limits of the Federal Low Altitude airways extend from

A– 700 feet AGL up to, but not including, 14,500 feet MSL.
B– 1,200 feet AGL up to, but not including, 18,000 feet MSL.
C– 1,200 feet AGL up to, but not including, 14,500 feet MSL.

3-2. Answer B. GFDICM 3A, FAR 71.5c
Low altitude airways begin at 1,200 feet AGL, unless otherwise indicated on sectional charts, and end at the overlying Class A Airspace.

3-3   PLT161
In the contiguous U.S., excluding the airspace at and below 2,500 feet AGL, an operable coded transponder equipped with Mode C capability is required in all airspace above

A– 10,000 feet MSL.
B– 12,500 feet MSL.
C– 14,500 feet MSL.

3-3. Answer A. GFDICM 3A, FAR 91.215b
Encoding transponders are required in all airspace above 10,000 feet (except within 2,500 feet of the surface).

3-4   PLT161
What transponder equipment is required for airplane operations within Class B airspace? A transponder

A– with 4096 code or Mode S, and Mode C capability.
B– is required for airplane operations when visibility is less than 3 miles.
C– with 4096 code capability is required except when operating at or below 1,000 feet AGL under the terms of a letter of agreement.

3-4. Answer A. GFDICM 3A, FAR 91.215
Airplanes, helicopters, and any aircraft, must have an encoding transponder to operate in Class B Airspace.

3-5   PLT161
What is the maximum indicated airspeed authorized in the airspace underlying Class B airspace?

A– 156 knots.
B– 200 knots.
C– 230 knots.

3-5. Answer B. GFDICM 3A, FAR 91.117c
No person may operate an aircraft in the airspace underlying Class B airspace or in a VFR corridor designated through such Class B airspace at an indicated airspeed of more than 200 knots.

3-6   PLT161

Unless otherwise authorized or required by ATC, the maximum indicated airspeed permitted when at or below 2,500 feet AGL within 4 NM of the primary airport within Class C or D airspace is

A– 200 knots.
B– 180 knots.
C– 230 knots.

3-6. Answer A. GFDICM 3A, FAR 91.117c
Unless otherwise authorized or required by ATC, you may not operate an aircraft at or below 2,500 feet above the surface within 4 nautical miles of the primary airport of a Class C or Class D airspace area at a speed greater than 200 KIAS.

3-7   PLT161

Which is true regarding flight operations in Class B airspace?

A– The pilot must receive an ATC clearance before operating an aircraft in that area.
B– Solo student pilot operations are not authorized.
C– Flight under VFR is not authorized unless the pilot in command is instrument rated.

3-7. Answer A. GFDICM 3A, FAR 91.131
An ATC clearance is required prior to penetrating Class B airspace.

3-8   PLT161

Which is true regarding pilot certification requirements for operations in Class B airspace?

A– The pilot in command must hold at least a private pilot certificate with an instrument rating.
B– The pilot in command must hold at least a private pilot certificate.
C– Solo student pilot operations are not authorized.

3-8. Answer B. GFDICM 3A, FAR 91.131
Generally, the pilot in command must hold at least a private pilot certicate to operate an aircraft in Class B airspace.

3-9   PLT161

Which is true regarding flight operations in Class B airspace?

A– The aircraft must be equipped with an ATC transponder and altitude reporting equipment.
B– The pilot in command must hold at least a private pilot certificate with an instrument rating.
C– The pilot in command must hold at least a student pilot certificate.

3-9. Answer A. GFDICM 3A, FAR 91.131b, AIM
An encoding transponder with mode C is required in all Class B airspace. With limited exceptions allowing student pilot operations, a private pilot certificate, but not an instrument rating, is required.

3-10   PLT163
When operating an airplane for the purpose of takeoff or landing within Class D airspace under special VFR, what minimum distance from clouds and what visibility are required?

A– Remain clear of clouds, and the ground visibility must be at least 1 SM.
B– 500 feet beneath clouds, and the ground visibility must be at least 1 SM.
C– Remain clear of clouds, and the flight visibility must be at least 1 NM.

3-10. Answer A. GFDICM 3A, FAR 91.157, AIM
You may take off or land an airplane under special VFR with a ground visibility of at least 1 statute mile. If ground visibility is not reported, then flight visibility must be at least 1 statute mile.

3-11   PLT163
At some airports located in Class D airspace where ground visibility is not reported, takeoffs and landings under special VFR are

A– not authorized.
B– authorized by ATC if the flight visibility is at least 1 SM.
C– authorized only if the ground visibility is observed to be at least 3 SM.

3-11. Answer B. GFDICM 3A, FAR 91.157d
If ground visibility is not reported then flight visibility is used.

3-12   PLT161
To operate an airplane under SPECIAL VFR (SVFR) within Class D airspace at night, which is required?

A– The Class D airspace must be specifically designated as a night SVFR area.
B– The pilot must hold an instrument rating, but the airplane need not be equipped for instrument flight, as long as the weather will remain at or above SVFR minimums.
C– The pilot must hold an instrument rating, and the airplane must be equipped for instrument flight.

3-12. Answer C. GFDICM 3A, FAR 91.157e
Special VFR is not permitted between sunset and sunrise unless you have a current instrument rating and the aircraft is equipped for instrument flight. In addition, special VFR clearances are not issued to fixed-wing aircraft (day or night) at the nation's busier airports which are listed in Section 3 of Appendix D of FAR 91.

3-13   PLT162
When operating an aircraft in the vicinity of an airport with an operating control tower, in Class E airspace, a pilot must establish communications prior to

A– 8 NM, and up to and including 3,000 feet AGL.
B– 5 NM, and up to and including 3,000 feet AGL.
C– 4 NM, and up to and including 2,500 feet AGL.

3-13. Answer C. GFDICM 3A, FAR 91.127c
Sometimes, control towers are established in Class E airspace. These are normally non-FAA facilities and often exist on a temporary basis, such as managing traffic for a special event at the airport. You are obligated to communicate with these towers over about the same area as if Class D airspace existed there, establishing contact prior to approaching within 4 NM of the airport below 2,500 feet AGL.

3-14   PLT162

When approaching to land at an airport with an ATC facility, in Class D airspace, the pilot must establish communications prior to

A– 10 NM, up to and including 3,000 feet AGL.
B– 30 SM, and be transponder equipped.
C– 4 NM, up to and including 2,500 feet AGL.

3-14. Answer C. GFDICM 3A, FAR 91.129
Communications must be established prior to 4 nautical miles from the airport, up to and including 2,500 feet AGL. There is no transponder requirement for Class D airspace.

3-15   PLT161

Which is true regarding flight operations to or from a satellite airport, without an operating control tower, within the Class C airspace area?

A– Prior to entering that airspace, a pilot must establish and maintain communication with the ATC serving facility.
B– Aircraft must be equipped with an ATC transponder.
C– Prior to takeoff, a pilot must establish communication with the ATC controlling facility.

3-15. Answer B. GFDICM 3A, FAR 91.130, FAR 91.215
An altitude encoding transponder is required within Class C airspace. Communication with ATC is not always possible when on the ground at a satellite airport, which is why the regulations state that two-way radio communications with ATC must established as soon as practicable after departing.

3-16   PLT162

Which is true regarding flight operations to or from a satellite airport, without an operating control tower, within the Class C airspace area?

A– Prior to takeoff, a pilot must establish communication with the ATC controlling facility.
B– Prior to entering that airspace, a pilot must establish and maintain communication with the ATC serving facility.
C– Aircraft must be equipped with an ATC transponder.

3-16. Answer B. GFDICM 3A, FAR 91.130, FAR 91.215
Each person must establish two-way radio communications with the ATC facility prior to entering Class C airspace and thereafter, maintain those communications while within that airspace. Communication with ATC is not always possible when on the ground at a satellite airport, therefore two-way radio communications with ATC must established as soon as practicable after departing.

3-17   PLT162

Which is true regarding flight operations in Class A airspace?

A– Aircraft must be equipped with approved distance measuring equipment (DME).
B– Aircraft must be equipped with an approved ATC transponder and altitude reporting equipment.
C– Must conduct operations under instrument flight rules.

3-17. Answer C. GFDICM 3A, FAR 91.135
Each person operating an aircraft in Class A airspace must conduct that operation under instrument flight rules (IFR) and must receive an ATC clearance prior to enter the airspace. Obviously, each pilot must maintain two-way communications with ATC while operating in Class A airspace. DME is only required at or above FL240 where VOR is required.

3-18   PLT162

Which is true regarding flight operations in Class A airspace?

A– Aircraft must be equipped with approved distance measuring equipment (DME).
B– Aircraft must be equipped with an ATC transponder and altitude reporting equipment.
C– May conduct operations under visual flight rules.

3-18. Answer B. GFDICM 3A, FAR 91.135
Each person operating an aircraft in Class A airspace must conduct that operation under instrument flight rules (IFR) and must receive an ATC clearance prior to enter the airspace. Each aircraft must be equipped with an altitude encoding transponder. DME is only required at or above FL240 where VOR is required.

3-19   PLT141

Light beacons producing red flashes indicate

A– end of runway warning at departure end.
B– a pilot should remain clear of an airport traffic pattern and continue circling.
C– obstructions or areas considered hazardous to aerial navigation.

3-19. Answer C. GFDICM 3A, PHB
Flashing red lights, or beacons, are used to indicate obstructions or other areas considered hazardous to aerial navigation. End of runway warning lights at some airports are steady red while a flashing red light from a control tower indicates that an airport is unsafe-do not land.

3-20   PLT141

When planning a night cross-country flight, a pilot should check for the availability and status of

A– all VORs to be used en route.
B– airport rotating light beacons.
C– destination airport lighting systems.

3-20. Answer C. GFDICM 3A, PHB
It is recommended that prior to a night flight, and particularly a cross-country night flight, the pilot check the availability and status of lighting systems at the destination airport. This information can be found on aeronautical charts and in the Airport/Facility Directory.

3-21   PLT040

Which is true concerning the blue and magenta colors used to depict airports on Sectional Aeronautical Charts?

A– Airports with control towers underlying Class A, B, and C airspace are shown in blue, Class D and E airspace are magenta.
B– Airports with control towers underlying Class C, D, and E airspace are shown in magenta.
C– Airports with control towers underlying Class B, C, D, and E airspace are shown in blue.

3-21. Answer C. GFDPPM 4C, PHB
Airports with operating control towers are depicted in blue symbols, and underlie Class B, C, or D airspace. For questions regarding chart symbology, refer to a chart legend panel.

3-22   PLT040
(Refer to figure 3-1 on page 3-9.)
(Point 1) The floor of the Class E airspace above Georgetown Airport (Q61) is at

A– 3,823 feet MSL.
B– the surface.
C– 700 feet AGL.

3-22. Answer A. GFDPPM 4C, PHB
Class E airspace begins at 1,200 feet AGL on the UNshaded side of magenta areas. The airport elevation is 2,623 feet MSL. For questions regarding chart symbology, refer to a chart legend panel.

Figure 3-1. Sectional Chart Excerpt.

3-23   PLT040
(Refer to figure 3-1 on page 3-9.)
(Point 7) The floor of Class E airspace over the town of Woodland is

A– 700 feet AGL over part of the town and no floor over the remainder.
B– 1,200 feet AGL over part of the town and no floor over the remainder.
C– both 700 feet and 1,200 feet AGL.

3-23. Answer C. GFDPPM 4C, AIM
The floor is 700 feet AGL inside the magenta shaded area and 1,200 feet AGL outside it.

3-24   PLT040
(Refer to figure 3-1 on page 3-9.)
(Point 5) The floor of the Class E airspace over University Airport (0O5) is

A– the surface.
B– 700 feet AGL.
C– 1,200 feet AGL.

3-24. Answer B. GFDPPM 4C, AIM
This airport is inside a magenta shaded area, where the floor of controlled (Class E) airspace is 700 feet AGL.

3-25   PLT040
(Refer to figure 3-1 on page 3-9.)
(Point 8) The floor of the Class E airspace over the town of Auburn is

A– 1,200 feet MSL.
B– 1,200 feet AGL.
C– 700 feet AGL.

3-25. Answer C. GFDPPM 4C, AIM
Auburn is inside a magenta shaded area. Here, the floor of Class E (controlled) airspace is 700 feet AGL.

3-26   PLT064
(Refer to figure 3-2 on page 3-11.)
(Point 1) This thin black shaded line is most likely

A– an arrival route.
B– a military training route.
C– a state boundary line.

3-26. Answer B. GFDPPM 4C, AIM
State boundaries a thinner than this and solid black. This is actually a gray line, which depicts a military training route.

Figure 3-2. Sectional Chart Excerpt.

3-27   PLT064

(Refer to figure 3-2 on page 3-11.)

(Point 2) The 16 indicates

A–an antenna top at 1,600 feet AGL.

B– the maximum elevation figure for that quadrangle.

C– the minimum safe sector altitude for that quadrangle.

3-27. Answer B. GFDPPM 4C, AIM

This is the maximum elevation MSL including terrain and obstacles in the quadrangle bounded by ticked lines of latitude and longitude. It includes 200-300 feet safety margin for altimeter error. For questions regarding chart symbology, refer to a chart legend panel.

3-28   PLT040

(Refer to figure 3-3 on page 3-13.)

(Point 1) What minimum altitude is required to avoid the Livermore Airport (LVK) Class D airspace?

A–2,503 feet MSL.

B– 2,901 feet MSL.

C– 3,297 feet MSL.

3-28. Answer B. GFDPPM 4C, AIM

The top of the Class D airspace is indicated by the number [29] within the blue dashed circle.

Figure 3-3. Sectional Chart Excerpt.

3-29   PLT040
(Refer to figure 3-1 on page 3-9.)
(Point 9) The alert area depicted within the blue lines is an area in which

A– there is a high volume of pilot training activities or an unusual type of aerial activity, neither of which is hazardous to aircraft.
B– the flight of aircraft is prohibited.
C– the flight of aircraft, while not prohibited, is subject to restriction.

3-29. Answer A. GFDPPM 4C, FAR 1.1
An alert area is established to inform pilots of a specific area wherein a high volume of pilot training or an unusual type of aeronautical activity is conducted. However, unlike prohibited or restricted areas, there are no restrictions to flight in alert areas.

3-30   PLT040
When a dashed blue circle surrounds an airport on a sectional aeronautical chart, it will depict the boundary of

A– Special VFR airspace.
B– Class B airspace
C– Class D airspace.

3-30. Answer C. GFDICM 3A, AIM
A dashed blue circle indicates Class D airspace. Although a special VFR clearance is required here when certain weather conditions exist, there is no such designation as Special VFR airspace. For questions regarding chart symbology, refer to a chart legend panel.

3-31   PLT040
(Refer to figure 3-1 on page 3-9.)
(Point 4) The highest obstruction with high intensity lighting within 10 NM of Lincoln Regional Airport (LHM) is how high above the ground?

A– 1,254 feet.
B– 662 feet.
C– 299 feet.

3-31. Answer C. GFDPPM 4C, PHB
The only obstruction with high intensity lighting is 3 NM south of the airport. The top of the obstruction is at 409 feet MSL, and it is 299 feet high.

3-32   PLT101
(Refer to figure 3-1 on page 3-9.)
Mosier Airport is

A– an airport restricted to use by private and recreational pilots.
B– a restricted military stage field within restricted airspace.
C– a nonpublic use airport.

3-32. Answer C. GFDPPM 4C, PHB
Airports identified with the letter "R" enclosed in an open circle are non-public use (private) airports. Although landing at a private airport requires the owner's permission, you could use one in an emergency. For questions regarding chart symbology, refer to a chart legend panel.

3-33   PLT162
(Refer to figure 3-3 on page 3-13.)
(Point 2) After departing from Byron Airport
(C83) with a northeast wind, you discover you are
approaching Livermore Class D airspace and flight
visibility is approximately 2 1/2 miles. You must

A–stay below 700 feet to remain in Class G and land.
B–stay below 1,200 feet to remain in Class G.
C–contact Livermore ATCT on 119.65 and advise of
your intentions.

3-33. Answer A. GFDICM 3A, FAR 91.155
If you climb above 700 feet AGL, you will be in Class
E airspace, where required visibility is 3 miles. You
could request a special VFR clearance from Livermore
ATCT, but that frequency is 118.1, not 119.65.

3-34   PLT064
(Refer to figure 3-1 on page 3-9.)
(Point 4) The terrain at the obstruction approximately
8 NM east southeast of the Lincoln Airport is
approximately how much higher than the airport
elevation?

A–376 feet.
B–835 feet.
C–1,135 feet.

3-34. Answer B. GFDPPM 4C, FAR 91.95
The obstruction extends to 1,254 feet MSL. If you
subtract the obstruction's AGL height (300 feet) from
the MSL height, you can determine the MSL elevation
of the terrain. The answer is 954 (1,254 - 300 = 954).
The difference between this elevation and the airport
elevation is 835 feet (954 - 119 = 835). For questions
regarding chart symbology, refer to a chart legend
panel.

3-35   PLT040
(Refer to figure 3-3 on page 3-13.)
(Point 6) The Class C airspace at Metropolitan Oakland
International (OAK) which extends from the surface
upward has a ceiling of

A–both 2,100 feet and 3,000 feet MSL.
B–8,000 feet MSL.
C–2,100 feet AGL.

3-35. Answer A. GFDICM 3A, PHB
The "T/SFC" indicates the ceiling of the Oakland Class
C airspace is at the overlying San Francisco Class
B airspace. The Class B sectors here have altitudes
"80/21" and "80/30."

3-36   PLT040
(Refer to figure 3-2 on page 3-11.)
GIVEN:

Location -Madera Airport (MAE)
Altitude...1,000 ft AGL
Position...7 NM north of Madera (MAE)
Time...3 p.m. local
Flight visibility...1 SM

You are VFR approaching Madera Airport for a
landing from the north. You

A– are in violation of the CFR's; you need 3 miles of
visibility under VFR.
B– may descend to 800 feet AGL (Pattern Altitude)
after entering Class E airspace and continue to the
airport.
C– are required to descend to below 700 feet AGL to
remain clear of Class E airspace and may continue
for landing.

3-36. Answer C. GFDICM 3A, FAR 91.155
Class E airspace begins at 700 feet AGL over this
airport. You can operate VFR clear of clouds and land
with 1 mile of visibility during daylight hours if you stay
below this controlled airspace.

3-37   PLT140
Who has the final authority to accept or decline any
"land and hold short" (LAHSO) clearance?

A– Pilot-in-command.
B– ATC tower controller.
C– Airplane owner/operator.

3-37. Answer A. GFDICM 3A, AIM
The Pilot-in-Command (PIC) of an aircraft has the final
authority to accept or decline any LAHSO clearance. If
the PIC elects to decline the clearance, ATC must be
notified as soon as possible.

3-38   PLT140
When should pilots decline a "land and hold short"
(LAHSO) clearance?

A– When it will compromise safety.
B– If runway surface is contaminated.
C– Only when the tower controller concurs.

3-38. Answer A. GFDICM 3A, AIM
The Pilot-in-Command (PIC) of an aircraft has the final
authority to accept or decline a LAHSO clearance. If
the PIC determines that the LAHSO may compromise
safety in any way, the pilot should advise ATC that the
clearance is declined.

3-39   PLT140
What is the minimum visibility and ceiling required for
a pilot to receive a "land and hold short" clearance?

A– 3 statute miles and 1,500 feet.
B– 3 nautical miles and 1,000 feet.
C– 3 statute miles and 1,000 feet.

3-39. Answer C. GFDICM 3A, AIM
Pilots should only receive a LAHSO clearance when
there is a minimum ceiling of 1,000 feet and 3 statute
miles visibility. The intent of having "basic" VFR
weather conditions is to allow pilots to maintain
visual contact with other aircraft and ground vehicle
operations.

3-40   PLT140
Once a pilot-in-command accepts a "land and hold short" (LAHSO) clearance, the clearance must be adhered to, just as any other ATC clearance, unless

A– an amended clearance is obtained or an emergency occurs.
B– the wind changes or Available Landing Distance decreases.
C– Available Landing Distance decreases or density altitude increases.

3-40. Answer A. AIM
Once you accept a LAHSO clearance, you must adhere to it, just as you would any other ATC clearance, unless you obtain an amended clearance or an emergency occurs. A LAHSO clearance does not preclude a rejected landing.

3-41   PLT141
(Refer to figure 3-4 on page 3-17.)
This sign is an indication

A– of an area where aircraft are prohibited.
B– that the taxiway does not continue.
C– of the general taxiing direction to a taxiway.

3-41. Answer B. AOPA ASF Flash cards
The sign in the top half of the figure is a "taxiway ending" marker, which indicates that the taxiway does not continue beyond the sign. You may find such a sign at the far end of "T" intersection as an alert to turn left or right.

Figure 3-4. Taxiway Ending Marker.

SECTION B - AIR TRAFFIC CONTROL SYSTEM

Although no specific commercial FAA test questions are included in this section, important information pertaining to your commercial training is covered. Some of these topics are: ATC services, separation requirements, and the function of automatic terminal information service (ATIS).

PROCEDURES AT TOWER-CONTROLLED AIRPORTS

- Automatic terminal information service (ATIS) broadcasts are updated upon receipt of any official weather information. The absence of the sky condition and visibility on an ATIS broadcast specifically implies the ceiling is more than 5,000 feet AGL and the visibility is more than 5 statute miles.
- To relieve congestion on ground control frequencies, clearance delivery is used for ATC clearances at busier airports.
- At airports with an operating control tower, you are required to obtain a clearance before operating in a movement area, which is an area on the airport, other than a parking area and loading ramp, used for taxiing, takeoff, and landing. When departing from a runway intersection, always state your position when calling the tower for takeoff.

TERMINAL PROCEDURES

- Terminal radar service for VFR aircraft includes basic radar service, terminal radar service area (TRSA) service, Class C service, and Class B service.
- Basic radar service for VFR aircraft includes safety alerts, traffic advisories, and limited radar vectoring. Sequencing also is available at certain terminal locations.
- Departure control provides separation of all aircraft within Class B and Class C airspace.
- When calling out traffic, controllers describe the position of the traffic in terms of the 12-hour clock. For example, "traffic at 3 o'clock" indicates the aircraft lies off your right wing. Traffic advisories from ATC are based on your aircraft's actual ground track, not on your aircraft's heading.
- A local airport advisory (LAA) is provided by flight service at FSS airports not served by an operating control tower, or when the tower is closed. Although VFR participation LAA service is not mandatory, it is strongly encouraged that you report your position, aircraft type, and intentions when 10 miles from the airport, and request an airport advisory from the FSS.

SECTION C - ATC CLEARANCES

Chapter 3, Section C of the Instrument Commercial Manual contains information that is useful to both instrument and commercial pilots. Although this section emphasizes IFR operations, some clearances, such as to operate in Class B airspace, are also relevant to VFR operations. There no FAA commercial questions assigned to this section.

- An ATC clearance is an authorization for you to proceed under a specified set of conditions within controlled airspace.
- You may not deviate from an ATC clearance unless you experience an emergency or the clearance will cause you to violate a rule or regulation. If you deviate from an ATC clearance, you must notify ATC as soon as possible. If you are given priority over other aircraft you may be requested to submit a written report to the manager of the ATC facility within 48 hours.
- While operating under VFR, if ATC assigns an altitude or heading that will cause you to enter clouds, you should avoid the clouds and inform ATC that the altitude or heading will not permit VFR.
- Anytime you are in VFR conditions, it is your responsibility to see and avoid all other traffic, even if you have filed a flight plan.
- You must receive an ATC clearance before entering Class A or B airspace regardless of the weather and Class C, D, and E airspace when the weather is below VFR minimums.
- You may cancel a flight plan anytime you are operating under VFR conditions.

DEPARTURE

Chapter 4 covers such areas as IFR departure charts, IFR departure procedures, and IFR departure considerations. Most of this information is directed toward those preparing for an instrument rating.

SECTION A - DEPARTURE CHARTS

Chapter 4, Section A, covers IFR departure charts. Since this information is directed toward those preparing for an instrument rating, there are no commercial airplane FAA test questions assigned to this section.

SECTION B - DEPARTURE PROCEDURES

- When taxiing in a quartering headwind, turn the control yoke into the wind. When taxiing with a quartering tailwind, turn the control yoke away from the wind and push forward. Remember the saying "climb into the wind, dive away." Although it is not necessary to pull back on the yoke when taxiing a tricycle gear airplane into a headwind it is okay to do so and it is recommended for tailwheel airplanes.

- If an aircraft is equipped with anti-collision lights, the lights are required to be on anytime that the aircraft is operated both day and night. However, the lights may be turned off, if the pilot-in-command determines that, because of operating conditions, it would be in the interest of safety to do so.

4-1   PLT461
Pilots are required to have the anti-collision light system operating

A– anytime the pilot is in the cockpit.
B– during all types of operations, both day and night.
C– anytime an engine is in operation.

4-1. Answer B. FAR 91.209, AIM
Anti-collision lights are required to be operated during all types of operations (day and night) except when the pilot in command determines that, because of operating conditions, it would be in the interest of safety to turn the lights off.

CHAPTER 5

ENROUTE

SECTION A - ENROUTE AND AREA CHARTS

Chapter 5, Section A, covers such areas as IFR enroute and area charts. Since this information is directed toward those preparing for an instrument rating, there are no commercial airplane FAA test questions assigned to this section.

SECTION B - ENROUTE PROCEDURES

Chapter 5, Section B, covers such areas as IFR enroute procedures. However, there are several items relevant to the commercial pilot certificate and there are several FAA commercial airplane questions.

- The rate at which an airplane climbs is dependent on several factors. The most accurate way to determine a climb rate for a specific type of aircraft is to refer to the manufacturer's POH. The POH will provide graphical and textual information concerning the configuration, airspeed, and other factors affecting the rate of climb.
- You can determine if you are on a collision course with another aircraft if there is no apparent relative motion between your aircraft and the other aircraft.
- If you inadvertently drift off course during the enroute portion of your flight, first find the angle to correct back to a course paralleling your original course, then add to that the angle to converge back on course. Use the formula, Angle = (Miles Off Course x 60) ÷ Miles Flown.

5-1   PLT194

How can you determine if another aircraft is on a collision course with your aircraft?

A– The nose of each aircraft is pointed at the same point in space.

B– The other aircraft will always appear to get larger and closer at a rapid rate.

C– There will be no apparent relative motion between your aircraft and the other aircraft.

5-1. Answer C. GFDPPM 4A, AIM

If there is no apparent relative motion between your aircraft and another aircraft, you are probably on a collision course.

5-2   PLT001

You have flown 52 miles, are 6 miles off course, and have 118 miles yet to fly. To converge on your destination, the total correction angle would be

A–3°.
B–6°.
C–10°.

5-2. Answer C. GFDPPM 8C, PHB

The correction angle to fly directly to your destination can be easily determined with the calculator side of a mechanical flight computer, or by using two formulas. Using a mechanical computer, first set the distance off course (outer scale) over the distance flown (inner scale). Then find the degree of correction necessary to parallel the course under the speed index (7°). Next, set the distance off course (outer scale) over the distance remaining (inner scale). Then, find the additional degrees of correction to return to course (3°). The sum of the two correction angles is 10°.

You also can compute the correction angle arithmetically. An important rule of thumb for off-course problems is that one mile off course in 60 miles equals approximately one degree of drift. First, you must determine the correction angle that would parallel the original course using the following equation.

(Distance Off Course ÷ Distance Flown) × 60 = Degrees of turn to parallel original course

(6 n.m. ÷ 52 n.m.) × 60 = 6.92°

Second, you must determine the additional correction angle necessary to fly direct to the destination using the formula:

(Distance Off Course ÷ Distance Remaining) × 60 = Additional degrees of turn to fly directly to destination

(6 n.m. ÷ 118 n.m.) × 60 = 3.05°

The sum of these correction angles is approximately 10.0° (6.92 + 3.05 = 9.97).

5-3   PLT001

GIVEN:

Distance off course...9 miles
Distance flown...95 miles
Distance to fly...125 miles.

To converge at the destination, the total correction angle would be

A–4°.
B–6°.
C–10°.

5-3. Answer . GFDPPM 8, PHB

See explanation for Question 5-2. The sum of these correction angles is approximately 10° (5.7° + 4.3° = 10.0°).

5-4   PLT119

What is the general direction of movement of the other aircraft if during a night flight you observe a steady white light and a rotating red light ahead and at your altitude? The other aircraft is

A– headed away from you.
B– crossing to your left.
C– approaching you head-on.

5-4. Answer A. GFDPPM 4A, AFH

By interpreting the position lights on other aircraft, you can determine which direction the aircraft is heading. For example, if you see only a white light and a rotating beacon, you know an aircraft is heading away from you.

5-5   PLT194

When in the vicinity of a VOR which is being used for navigation on VFR flights, it is important to

A– make 90° left and right turns to scan for other traffic.
B– exercise sustained vigilance to avoid aircraft that may be converging on the VOR from other directions.
C– pass the VOR on the right side of the radial to allow room for aircraft flying in the opposite direction on the same radial.

5-5. Answer B. GFDPPM 4A, AIM

When flying in the vicinity of a VOR, you should be vigilant for other aircraft that may be converging on the VOR. This pertains to both VFR and IFR operations.

SECTION C - HOLDING PROCEDURES

Chapter 5, Section C, covers IFR holding procedures. Since this information is directed toward those preparing for an instrument rating, there are no commercial airplane FAA test questions assigned to this section.

CHAPTER
6

ARRIVAL

Chapter 6 covers IFR arrival charts and procedures. Since this information is directed toward those preparing for an instrument rating, there are no commercial airplane FAA test questions assigned to this chapter.

CHAPTER 7

APPROACH

Chapter 7 covers IFR approach charts and procedures. Since this information is directed toward those preparing for an instrument rating, there are no commercial airplane FAA test questions assigned to this chapter.

CHAPTER 8

INSTRUMENT APPROACHES

Chapter 8 covers VOR, NDB, ILS, GPS, and RNAV approach procedures. Since this information is directed toward those preparing for an instrument rating, there are no commercial airplane FAA test questions assigned to this chapter.

METEOROLOGY

SECTION A - WEATHER FACTORS

THE ATMOSPHERE

- The atmosphere commonly is divided into a number of layers according to its thermal characteristics. The lowest layer, the troposphere, is where most weather occurs.
- In the troposphere, temperatures decrease with altitude up to the tropopause, where an abrupt change in the temperature lapse rate occurs. The average height of the troposphere in the middle latitudes is 36,000 to 37,000 feet. The temperature in the lower part of the stratosphere (up to approximately 66,000 feet) experiences relatively small changes in temperature with an increase in altitude.

ATMOSPHERIC CIRCULATION

- Uneven heating of the earth's surface is the driving force behind all weather. The special characteristics of water also affect the release of heat into the atmosphere, and dramatically affect the weather.
- Atmospheric circulation patterns are caused by differences in pressure. Wind flows outward from high pressure areas to low pressure areas.
- Above the friction layer, the wind does not flow directly from a high to a low because of Coriolis force, which deflects air to the right in the northern hemisphere. The result is a wind that flows in a clockwise direction leaving a high and in a counterclockwise, or cyclonic, direction when entering a low.
- Near the surface, friction reduces the effects of Coriolis force and causes the wind to flow more directly from a high to low pressure area. This causes the wind to cross the isobars at an angle, rather than flowing parallel to them.
- A low pressure area, or trough, is an area of rising air, which results in generally unfavorable weather conditions. A high pressure area, or ridge, is characterized by descending air, which encourages dissipation of clouds and results in generally favorable weather conditions. Because of the wind circulation patterns, you will most likely experience a crosswind from the left when flying from a high to a low in the northern hemisphere, with stronger winds as you approach the low.
- Convective circulation patterns associated with sea breezes are caused by land absorbing and radiating heat faster than water. Cool air must sink to force warm air upward.
- Moisture is added to a parcel of air by evaporation and sublimation. The amount of water vapor that air can hold increases with temperature. When the temperature cools to the dewpoint, the air is saturated.
- At 100% humidity, water vapor condenses, forming clouds, fog or dew. Frost forms when the temperature of the collecting surface is below the dewpoint and the dewpoint is below freezing.
- Precipitation occurs when water vapor condenses out of the air and becomes heavy enough to fall to earth. The type of precipitation is influenced by the temperature and other conditions under which condensation occurs. Upward currents enhance the growth rate of precipitation.
- The presence of ice pellets normally indicates freezing rain at higher altitudes. The presence of wet snow indicates the temperature is above freezing at your flight altitude.
- Virga is best described as streamers of rain trailing beneath clouds which evaporate before reaching the ground.

CLOUDS

- Clouds occur when water vapor condenses. They are divided into four basic families: low, middle, high, and clouds with vertical development.
- Cumulus clouds are formed when unstable air is lifted. Stratiform clouds are formed when stable air is lifted. The lifting of moist, unstable air results in good visibility outside the cloud, showery precipitation, and turbulence. However, the lifting of moist, stable air results in continuous precipitation, little or no turbulence, and poor visibility.
- Towering cumulus clouds indicate convective turbulence. Fair weather cumulus clouds indicate turbulence at and below the cloud level. To estimate the bases of cumulus clouds, in thousands of feet, divide the temperature/dewpoint spread at the surface by 2.5°C (4.4°F). If using the quick estimate method, divide the temperature/ dewpoint spread by 4°F (2.2°C).
- The suffix nimbus, used in naming clouds, means a rain cloud.
- High clouds are composed mostly of ice crystals.

AIRMASSES AND FRONTS

- An airmass is a large body of air that covers an extensive area and has fairly uniform temperature and moisture content. A front is a discontinuity between two airmasses. A cold front occurs when cold air displaces warmer air. A warm front occurs when warm air overruns colder air.
- Cooling from below increases the stability of an airmass and warming from below decreases it. Steady precipitation, in contrast to showers, preceding a front is an indication of stratiform clouds with little or no turbulence.
- When a cold airmass moves over, or is heated by, a warm surface, the result is cumuliform clouds, turbulence, and good visibility. When the air is moist and unstable, the updrafts are particularly strong, resulting in cumulonimbus clouds.
- An occlusion occurs when a cold front overtakes another front. In a cold front occlusion, the air ahead of the warm front is warmer than the air behind the overtaking cold front.
- A frontal cyclone starts as a slow-moving cold front or stationary front and can end as a cold front occlusion with potentially severe weather.

HIGH ALTITUDE WEATHER

- A jetstream is defined as wind of 50 knots or greater. They are found in bands of strong westerly winds that occur at breaks in the tropopause in the northern hemisphere. While they can provide beneficial winds when flying west to east, they also can be associated with strong turbulence.
- The strength and location of the jetstream is normally weaker and farther north in the summer. During the winter months in the middle latitudes, the jet stream shifts toward the south and speed increases.

9-1   PLT492
Every physical process of weather is accompanied by or is the result of

A– a heat exchange.
B– the movement of air.
C– a pressure differential.

9-1. Answer A. GFDICM 9A, AW
Every physical process of weather is accompanied by, or is the result of, a heat exchange. This process happens as the earth's surface is cooled or heated, and when water changes from one physical state to another.

9-2   PLT492

What is the standard temperature at 10,000 feet?

A–-5°C.
B–-15°C.
C–+5°C.

9-2. Answer A. GFDICM 9A, AW

Standard temperature at sea level is 15°C. The standard, or average, lapse rate is approximately 2°C per 1,000 feet of altitude. To determine the standard temperature at 10,000 feet, multiply 10 by the lapse rate (2°C) and subtract the result from the sea level standard (15°C). The answer is -5°C (15 - (10 x 2).

9-3   PLT492

What is the standard temperature at 20,000 feet?

A–-15°C.
B–-20°C.
C–-25°C.

9-3. Answer C. GFDICM 9A, IFH

See explanation for Question 9-2. The answer is -25°C (15 - (20 x 2) = -25).

9-4   PLT301

Which conditions are favorable for the formation of a surface based temperature inversion?

A–Clear, cool nights with calm or light wind.
B– Area of unstable air rapidly transferring heat from the surface.
C– Broad areas of cumulus clouds with smooth, level bases at the same altitude.

9-4. Answer A. GFDICM 9A, AW

When temperature increases with altitude, a temperature inversion exists. One of the most familiar types of ground- or surface-based inversions forms in stable conditions from radiation cooling just above the ground on clear, cool nights with little wind.

9-5   PLT517

What causes wind?

A–The Earth's rotation.
B– Air mass modification.
C– Pressure differences.

9-5. Answer C. GFDICM 9A, AW

The uneven heating of the earth's surface creates circulation patterns, resulting in pressure differences. In an attempt to equalize the pressure between systems, air flows from system to system creating wind. The speed of the resulting wind depends on the strength of the pressure gradient.

9-6   PLT197

In the Northern Hemisphere, the wind is deflected to the

A–right by Coriolis force.
B–right by surface friction.
C–left by Coriolis force.

9-6. Answer A. GFDICM 9A, AW

The earth's rotation induces what is known as Coriolis force. This force deflects the wind to the right in the northern hemisphere and to the left in the southern hemisphere.

9-7   PLT517
Why does the wind have a tendency to flow parallel to the isobars above the friction level?

A–Coriolis force tends to counterbalance the horizontal pressure gradient.
B–Coriolis force acts perpendicular to a line connecting the highs and lows.
C–Friction of the air with the Earth deflects the air perpendicular to the pressure gradient.

9-7. Answer A. GFDICM 9A, AW
When pressure gradient force and Coriolis are balanced, airflow circulation aloft is parallel to the isobars. Within about 2,000 feet of the ground, surface friction slows the wind, and Coriolis force is weakened. Pressure gradient force then predominates, causing the wind to flow at an angle to the isobars.

9-8   PLT517
The wind system associated with a low-pressure area in the Northern Hemisphere is

A–an anticyclone and is caused by descending cold air.
B–a cyclone and is caused by Coriolis force.
C–an anticyclone and is caused by Coriolis force.

9-8. Answer B. GFDICM 9A, AW
See explanation for Question 9-7.

9-9   PLT197
What prevents air from flowing directly from high-pressure areas to low-pressure areas?

A–Coriolis force.
B–Surface friction.
C–Pressure gradient force.

9-9. Answer A. GFDICM 9A, AW
If the earth did not rotate, the pressure gradient force would propel wind directly from highs to lows. Instead, the earth's rotation introduces Coriolis force which deflects the wind to the right in the northern hemisphere.

9-10   PLT517
While flying cross-country, in the Northern Hemisphere, you experience a continuous left crosswind which is associated with a major wind system. This indicates that you

A–are flying toward an area of generally unfavorable weather conditions.
B–have flown from an area of unfavorable weather conditions.
C–cannot determine weather conditions without knowing pressure changes.

9-10. Answer A. GFDICM 9A, AW
High pressure systems circulate in a clockwise (anticyclonic) direction and are usually associated with favorable flying conditions. On the other hand, low pressure areas circulate in a counterclockwise direction and are associated with unfavorable flying conditions. If you experience a continuous left crosswind when flying, you are generally flying from an area of high pressure and good weather to an area of low pressure and bad weather.

9-11   PLT517

Which is true with respect to a high- or low-pressure system?

A–A high-pressure area or ridge is an area of rising air.

B–A low-pressure area or trough is an area of descending air.

C–A high-pressure area or ridge is an area of descending air.

9-11. Answer C. GFDICM 9A, AW

In high-pressure systems, air is moving outward, depleting the quantity of air. As a result, a high or ridge is characterized by descending air which favors generally good flying conditions. In low-pressure systems, the air is moving inward, converging to the center and rising. As a result, a low or trough is characterized by ascending air which generally produces unfavorable flying conditions.

9-12   PLT517

Which is true regarding high- or low-pressure systems?

A–A high-pressure area or ridge is an area of rising air.

B–A low-pressure area or trough is an area of rising air.

C–Both high- and low-pressure areas are characterized by descending air.

9-12. Answer B. GFDICM 9A, AW

See explanation for Question 9-11.

9-13   PLT517

When flying into a low-pressure area in the Northern Hemisphere, the wind direction and velocity will be from the

A–left and decreasing.

B–left and increasing.

C–right and decreasing.

9-13. Answer B. GFDICM 9A, AW

See explanation for Question 9-10. When flying into a low-pressure system, the wind direction will always be from the left and the wind speed will increase as you fly toward the system's center.

9-14   PLT492

Which is true regarding actual air temperature and dewpoint temperature spread? The temperature spread

A–decreases as the relative humidity decreases.

B–decreases as the relative humidity increases.

C–increases as the relative humidity increases.

9-14. Answer B. GFDICM 9A, AW

The difference between air temperature and dewpoint temperature is popularly called the "spread." As spread becomes less, relative humidity increases, and it is 100 when temperature and dew point are the same.

9-15   PLT517

The general circulation of air associated with a high-pressure area in the Northern Hemisphere is

A–outward, downward, and clockwise.

B–outward, upward, and clockwise.

C–inward, downward, and clockwise.

9-15. Answer A. GFDICM 9A, AW

In high-pressure systems, air circulates in a clockwise direction and moves outward, depleting the quantity of air. As a result, a high or ridge is characterized by descending air which favors generally good flying conditions. In low-pressure systems, the air circulates in a counterclockwise direction as it converges and rises. As a result, a low or trough is characterized by ascending air which generally produces unfavorable flying conditions.

9-16   PLT192
Virga is best described as

A– streamers of precipitation trailing beneath clouds
    which evaporates before reaching the ground.
B– wall cloud torrents trailing beneath cumulonimbus
    clouds which dissipate before reaching the ground.
C– turbulent areas beneath cumulonimbus clouds.

9-16. Answer A. GFDICM 9A
Virga are streamers of precipitation that trail below the
clouds, but evaporate before reaching the ground.

9-17   PLT512
Moisture is added to air by

A– sublimation and condensation.
B– evaporation and condensation.
C– evaporation and sublimation.

9-17. Answer C. GFDICM 9A, AW
Water vapor is added to the atmosphere by the
process of evaportation or sublimation. Evaporation
is the process of a liquid changing to a gaseous
state, and sublimation describes the process of solid
moisture (ice) changing to a gas.

9-18   PLT192
When conditionally unstable air with high-moisture
content and very warm surface temperature is forecast,
one can expect what type of weather?

A– Strong updrafts and stratonimbus clouds.
B– Restricted visibility near the surface over a large
    area.
C– Strong updrafts and cumulonimbus clouds.

9-18. Answer C. GFDICM 9A, AW
When unstable, moist air exists over a warm surface,
convective activity tends to force the moisture aloft
producing cumulus and/or cumulonimbus clouds.

9-19   PLT192
What is the approximate base of the cumulus clouds
if the temperature at 2,000 feet MSL is 10°C. and the
dewpoint is 1°C?

A– 3,000 feet MSL.
B– 4,000 feet MSL.
C– 6,000 feet MSL.

9-19. Answer C. GFDICM 9A, AW
To determine the base of a cloud layer, compute the
difference between the temperature and dewpoint
and divide the difference by the rate at which the
temperature and the dewpoint converge. In convective
conditions, the convergency rate is about 2.5°C per
1,000 feet. The result will approximate cloud bases
in thousands of feet. The answer is 6,000 feet (10 -
1 = 9 ÷ 2.5 = 3.6 or 3,600 + 2,000 = 5,600 feet) or
approximately 6,000 feet MSL.

9-20   PLT192
If clouds form as a result of very stable, moist air being
forced to ascend a mountain slope, the clouds will be

A– cirrus type with no vertical development or
    turbulence.
B– cumulus type with considerable vertical
    development and turbulence.
C– stratus type with little vertical development and
    little or no turbulence.

9-20. Answer C. GFDICM 9A, AW
Stable and unstable air have predictable characteristics
in terms of cloud types, precipitation, visibility,
turbulence, and icing. If either a stable or unstable
layer of air is lifted, the associated characteristics
remain. For example, if stable air is forced up a slope,
stratus-type clouds with little or no turbulence typically
form.

9-21   PLT192

What determines the structure or type of clouds which will form as a result of air being forced to ascend?

A– The method by which the air is lifted.
B– The stability of the air before lifting occurs.
C– The relative humidity of the air after lifting occurs.

9-21. Answer B. GFDICM 9A, AW
See explanation for Question 9-20.

9-22   PLT059

Refer to the excerpt from the following METAR report:
KTUS 08004KT 4SM HZ 26/04 A2995 RMK RAE36

At approximately what altitude AGL should bases of convective-type cumuliform clouds be expected?

A– 4,400 feet.
B– 8,800 feet.
C– 17,600 feet.

9-22. Answer B. GFDICM 9A, AW
Temperature and dewpoint converge at 2.5°C per 1,000 feet of altitude. The temperature/dewpoint spread at the surface, according to the METAR, is 26°C – 4°C = 22°C. The bases of cumulus clouds are at the altitude where the spread is zero:

22°C ÷ (2.5°C/1,000 feet) = 8,800 feet AGL.

9-23   PLT173

What are the characteristics of stable air?

A– Good visibility; steady precipitation; stratus clouds.
B– Poor visibility; steady precipitation; stratus clouds.
C– Poor visibility; intermittent precipitation; cumulus clouds.

9-23. Answer B. GFDICM 9A, AW
Stable and unstable air each have identifiable characteristics. For example, stable air is generally smooth, with layered or stratiform clouds. Visibility usually is restricted, with widespread areas of clouds and steady rain or drizzle.

9-24   PLT173

Which would decrease the stability of an air mass?

A– Warming from below.
B– Cooling from below.
C– Decrease in water vapor.

9-24. Answer A. GFDICM 9A, AW
As an airmass moves over a warmer surface, its lower layers are heated, and vertical movement of the air develops. This typically results in extreme instability.

9-25   PLT492

From which measurement of the atmosphere can stability be determined?

A– Atmospheric pressure.
B– The ambient lapse rate.
C– The dry adiabatic lapse rate.

9-25. Answer B. GFDICM 9A, AW
The ambient lapse rate can be used to determine the stability of the atmosphere. For example, moist air has less stability and a lower lapse rate than dry air.

9-26   PLT492
What type weather can one expect from moist, unstable air, and very warm surface temperatures?

A– Fog and low stratus clouds.
B– Continuous heavy precipitation.
C– Strong updrafts and cumulonimbus clouds.

9-26. Answer C. GFDICM 9A, AW
When moist, unstable air exists over a warm surface, convective activity will tend to force the moisture aloft producing cumulus and/or cumulonimbus clouds.

9-27   PLT173
Which would increase the stability of an air mass?

A– Warming from below.
B– Cooling from below.
C– Decrease in water vapor.

9-27. Answer B. GFDICM 9A, AW
See explanation for Question 9-24.

9-28   PLT192
The conditions necessary for the formation of stratiform clouds are a lifting action and

A– unstable, dry air.
B– stable, moist air.
C– unstable, moist air.

9-28. Answer B. GFDICM 9A, AW
Stratiform clouds are layered clouds that form in stable, moist air.

9-29   PLT192
Which cloud types would indicate convective turbulence?

A– Cirrus clouds.
B– Nimbostratus clouds.
C– Towering cumulus clouds.

9-29. Answer C. GFDICM 9A, AW
Towering cumulus clouds develop in moist, unstable air that is lifted. The combination of instability and the lifting action typically produce moderate to heavy convective turbulence with icing conditions.

9-30   PLT511
The formation of either predominantly stratiform or predominantly cumuliform clouds is dependent upon the

A– source of lift.
B– stability of the air being lifted.
C– temperature of the air being lifted.

9-30. Answer B. GFDICM 9A, AW
The formation of either stratiform or cumuliform clouds is dependent upon the stability of the air before it's lifted. For example, when stable air is lifted, stratiform clouds typically form, and when unstable air is lifted, cumuliform clouds usually form.

9-31   PLT511

Which combination of weather-producing variables would likely result in cumuliform-type clouds, good visibility, and showery rain?

A– Stable, moist air and orographic lifting.
B– Unstable, moist air and orographic lifting.
C– Unstable, moist air and no lifting mechanism.

9-31. Answer B. GFDICM 9A, AW
Both stable and unstable airmasses have distinguishable characteristics. Stable air is generally smooth, with layered or stratiform clouds, and visibility usually is restricted with widespread areas of clouds and steady rain or drizzle. Unstable air is typically turbulent, with cumuliform type clouds and good surface visibility outside areas of showery rain. When either type of airmass is lifted, their associated characteristics usually persist. If no lifting force is present the formation of clouds or precipitation is unlikely.

9-32   PLT511

What is a characteristic of stable air?

A– Stratiform clouds.
B– Fair weather cumulus clouds.
C– Temperature decreases rapidly with altitude.

9-32. Answer A. GFDICM 9A, AW
See explanation for Question 9-31.

9-33   PLT511

A moist, unstable air mass is characterized by

A– poor visibility and smooth air.
B– cumuliform clouds and showery precipitation.
C– stratiform clouds and continuous precipitation.

9-33. Answer B. GFDICM 9A, AW
See explanation for Question 9-31.

9-34   PLT511

When an air mass is stable, which of these conditions are most likely to exist?

A– Numerous towering cumulus and cumulonimbus clouds.
B– Moderate to severe turbulence at the lower levels.
C– Smoke, dust, haze, etc., concentrated at the lower levels with resulting poor visibility.

9-34. Answer C. GFDICM 9A, AW
A stable airmass is characterized by smooth air, stratiform clouds, and poor visibilities. The poor visibilities can be the result of extensive areas of continuous rain or a low level temperature inversion creating widespread areas of fog, haze, and low clouds.

9-35   PLT511

Which is a characteristic of stable air?

A– Cumuliform clouds.
B– Excellent visibility.
C– Restricted visibility.

9-35. Answer C. GFDICM 9A, AW
See explanation for Question 9-34.

9-36   PLT511
Which is a characteristic typical of a stable air mass?

A–Cumuliform clouds.
B– Showery precipitation.
C–Continuous precipitation.

9-36. Answer C. GFDICM 9A, AW
See explanation for Question 9-34. A stable airmass with sufficient moisture will typically create widespread areas of continuous precipitation.

9-37   PLT511
Which is true regarding a cold front occlusion? The air ahead of the warm front

A–is colder than the air behind the overtaking cold front.
B–is warmer than the air behind the overtaking cold front.
C–has the same temperature as the air behind the overtaking cold front.

9-37. Answer B. GFDICM 9A, AW
A frontal occlusion occurs when a fast-moving cold front catches up to a slow-moving warm front. The difference in temperature within each frontal system is a major factor that influences the type of front that develops. A cold front occlusion develops when the air ahead of the warm front is warmer than the overtaking cold front.

9-38   PLT511
Which are characteristics of a cold air mass moving over a warm surface?

A–Cumuliform clouds, turbulence, and poor visibility.
B–Cumuliform clouds, turbulence, and good visibility.
C– Stratiform clouds, smooth air, and poor visibility.

9-38. Answer B. GFDICM 9A, AW
The speed of a cold front usually dictates the type of weather associated with the front. However, there are some general weather characteristics that are found in most cold fronts. These include the development of cumulus clouds, turbulence, showery precipitation, strong, gusty winds, and good visibility after the front passes.

9-39   PLT203
Which feature is associated with the tropopause?

A–Constant height above the Earth.
B– Abrupt change in temperature lapse rate.
C–Absolute upper limit of cloud formation.

9-39. Answer B. GFDICM 9A, AW
The tropopause is a thin layer that acts as a boundary between the troposphere and the stratosphere and is characterized by an abrupt change in the temperature lapse rate.

9-40   PLT302
During the winter months in the middle latitudes, the jet stream shifts toward the

A–north and speed decreases.
B– south and speed increases.
C– north and speed increases.

9-40. Answer B. GFDICM 9A, AW
As the core of the jet stream moves south in the winter, its core rises, and its average speed usually increases.

9-41   PLT302
The strength and location of the jet stream is normally

A–weaker and farther north in the summer.
B– stronger and farther north in the winter.
C– stronger and farther north in the summer.

9-41. Answer A. GFDICM 9A, AW
See explanation for Question 9-40.

9-42   PLT206

Which is true regarding the development of convective circulation?

A–Cool air must sink to force the warm air upward.
B– Warm air is less dense and rises on its own accord.
C– Warmer air covers a larger surface area than the cool air; therefore, the warmer air is less dense and rises.

9-42. Answer A. GFDICM 9A, AW

Convective circulation results from cool, dense air sinking to the surface and forcing warm, less dense air upward.

9-43   PLT206

Convective circulation patterns associated with sea breezes are caused by

A–water absorbing and radiating heat faster than the land.
B– land absorbing and radiating heat faster than the water.
C– cool and less dense air moving inland from over the water, causing it to rise.

9-43. Answer B. GFDICM 9A, AW

Land surfaces warm and cool faster than water surfaces; therefore, land is warmer than water during the day. This creates the sea breeze, which is a wind that blows from the cool water to the warmer land.

SECTION B - WEATHER HAZARDS

THUNDERSTORMS

- When sufficient moisture is present, cumulus cloud build-ups indicate the presence of convective turbulence.
- Thunderstorm formation requires an unstable lapse rate, a lifting force, and a relatively high moisture level.
- The life cycle of a thunderstorm consists of three distinct stages. The cumulus stage is characterized by continuous updrafts. Thunderstorms reach the greatest intensity during the mature stage, which is signaled by the beginning of precipitation at the surface. As the storm dies during the dissipating stage, updrafts weaken and downdrafts become predominant.
- Airmass thunderstorms are relatively short-lived storms and are usually isolated or scattered over a large area. They form in convective currents, which are most active on warm summer afternoons when the winds are light. Severe thunderstorms contain wind gusts of 50 knots or more, hail 3/4 inch in diameter or larger, and/or tornadoes.
- Cumulonimbus clouds by themselves indicate severe turbulence. Other indications of turbulence are very frequent lightning and roll clouds.
- Some weather hazards associated with thunderstorms, such as lightning, hail, and turbulence, are not confined to the cloud itself. Wind shear areas can be found on all sides of a thunderstorm, as well as directly under it.
- Embedded thunderstorms are particularly dangerous to IFR pilots. Because they are obscured by massive cloud layers, they are more difficult to avoid.
- Airborne weather radar can help you avoid thunderstorms. However, it provides no assurance of avoiding IFR weather conditions. If using radar, avoid intense radar echoes by at least 20 miles and do not fly between them if they are less than 40 miles apart.
- A squall line is a narrow band of active thunderstorms that often forms 50 to 200 miles ahead of a fast moving cold front and contains some of the most severe types of weather-related hazards.
- If you encounter turbulence during flight, establish maneuvering or penetration speed, maintain a level flight attitude, and accept variations in airspeed and altitude. If encountering turbulence during the approach to a landing, it is recommended that you increase the airspeed slightly above normal approach speed to attain more positive control.

WAKE TURBULENCE

- Wake turbulence is created when an aircraft generates lift. The greatest vortex strength occurs when the generating aircraft is heavy, slow, in a clean configuration, and at a high angle of attack.
- Wingtip vortices can exceed the roll rate of an aircraft, especially when flying in the same direction as the generating aircraft.
- Wingtip vortices tend to sink below the flight path of the aircraft which generated them. They are most hazardous during light, quartering tailwind conditions. You should avoid the area below and behind an aircraft generating wake turbulence, especially at low altitude where even a momentary wake encounter could be hazardous.
- A helicopter can produce vortices similar to wingtip vortices of a large fixed-wing airplane.

OTHER TURBULENCE

- Turbulence that momentarily causes slight, erratic changes in altitude and/or attitude should be reported as light. Moderate turbulence causes noticeable changes in altitude and/or attitude, but aircraft control remains positive.
- Mechanical turbulence is often experienced in the traffic pattern when wind forms eddies as it blows over hangars, stands of trees, or other obstructions.
- Any front traveling at a speed of 30 knots or more produces at least a moderate amount of turbulence.
- Turbulence that is encountered above 15,000 feet AGL that is not associated with cumuliform cloudiness, including thunderstorms, is reported as clear air turbulence. Clear air turbulence often develops in or near the jet stream, which is a narrow band of high altitude winds near the tropopause.
- A common location of clear air turbulence is in an upper trough on the polar side of a jet stream. The jet stream and associated clear air turbulence can sometimes be visually identified in flight by long streaks of cirrus clouds.

- Strong mountain wave turbulence can be anticipated when the winds across a ridge are 40 knots or more, and the air is stable. The crests of mountain waves may be marked by lens-shaped, or lenticular, clouds. The presence of rotor clouds on the lee side of the mountain also indicates the possibility of strong turbulence.
- The greatest turbulence normally occurs as you approach the lee side of mountain ranges, ridges, or hilly terrain in strong headwinds.

WIND SHEAR

- Wind shear is a sudden, drastic change in wind speed and/or direction. It can exist at any altitude and may occur in a vertical or horizontal direction.
- Wind shear is often associated with a strong low-level temperature inversion with strong winds above the inversion, a jet stream, a thunderstorm, or a frontal zone.
- Wind shear can also occur prior to the passage of a warm front and following the passage of a cold front.
- During an approach, monitoring the power and vertical velocity required to remain on the proper glideslope is the most important and most easily recognized means of being alerted to possible wind shear. When the wind changes to more of a headwind, the aircraft initially tends to balloon above the glidepath, and then drop below the glidepath because of lower groundspeed. To correct, reduce power momentarily, and then increase it once established in the headwind conditions. The reverse actions are needed if flying into conditions of less headwind or more tailwind.
- Microbursts are one of the most dangerous sources of wind shear. A microburst is an intense, localized downdraft seldom lasting longer than 15 minutes from the time the burst first strikes the ground until dissipation. The maximum downdrafts encountered in a microburst may be as strong as 6,000 feet per minute.
- In a microburst, strong wind flows outward in every direction at the surface. An aircraft entering a microburst initially experiences a headwind, with increasing performance, and then a tailwind, with decreasing performance combined with a strong downdraft. If encountering a headwind of 45 knots within a microburst, you would expect a total shear across the microburst of 90 knots.
- When a squall is reported, you can expect a sudden increase in wind speed of at least 16 knots to a sustained wind speed of 22 knots or more for at least 1 minute.

RESTRICTIONS TO VISIBILITY

- Restrictions to visibility can include fog, haze, smoke, smog, and dust.
- Formation of fog is encouraged by the presence of small particles in the air on which condensation can occur. Industrial areas typically produce more fog since the burning of fossil fuels produces more of these condensation nuclei.
- Radiation fog forms over fairly flat land on clear, calm nights when the air is moist and there is a small temperature/ dewpoint spread.
- Advection fog is most likely to form in coastal areas when moist air moves over colder ground or water. It can appear suddenly during the day or night and is more persistent than radiation fog.
- Advection fog and upslope fog are both dependent upon wind for their formation. However, surface winds stronger than 15 knots tend to dissipate or lift advection fog into low stratus clouds.
- Volcanic ash clouds are highly abrasive to aircraft and engines, and they also restrict visibility.
- Precipitation-induced fog is most commonly associated with warm fronts and is a result of saturation due to evaporation of precipitation.
- Steam fog forms when very cold air moves over a warmer water surface.
- Restrictions to visibility, such as haze, create the illusion of being at a greater distance above the runway, which can cause a pilot to fly a lower-than-normal approach.
- When flying cross-country at night, the gradual disappearance of ground lights while at altitude indicates clouds and areas of reduced visibility below the aircraft.

ICING

- The three types of structural ice are rime, clear, and mixed.
- The accumulation of ice on an aircraft increases drag and weight and decreases lift and thrust.

- Ice pellets usually indicate the presence of freezing rain at a higher altitude. Freezing rain is hazardous because it is most likely to have the highest rate of accumulation of structural icing. The presence of freezing rain at your altitude indicates the temperature is above freezing at some higher altitude and could indicate that a warm front is about to pass.
- Since high clouds typically do not consist of liquid water, they are at least likely to contribute to aircraft structural icing.
- The freezing level is where the temperature is 0°C. You can estimate the freezing level by dividing the temperature in °C above zero, by the lapse rate of 2°C per 1000 feet.
- If froat is not removed from the wings before flight, it may cause an early airflow separation which decreases lift and increases drag. This causes the airplane to stall at a lower-than-normal angle of attack.

HYDROPLANING

- Hydroplaning occurs when the tires float on top of a thin layer of water on the runway. It results in poor or nil braking action at high speeds, and may result in an aircraft skidding off the side or end of the runway.
- High aircraft speed, standing water, slush, and a smooth runway texture are factors that are condusive to hydroplaning.

COLD WEATHER OPERATIONS

- During preflight in cold weather, crankcase breather lines should receive special attention because they are susceptible to being clogged by ice from crankcase vapors that have condensed and subsequently frozen.
- It is recommended that during cold weather operations, you should preheat the cabin, as well as the engine.

9-44   PLT220
When operating VFR at night, what is the first indication of flying into restricted visibility conditions?

A– Ground lights begin to take on an appearance of being surrounded by a halo or glow.
B– A gradual disappearance of lights on the ground.
C– Cockpit lights begin to take on an appearance of a halo or glow around them.

9-44. Answer B. GFDICM 9B, AFH
When operating VFR at night, one of the first indications of flying into areas of restricted visibility is the gradual disappearance of lights on the ground. The appearance of halos or a glow around ground lights indicates areas of ground fog or haze, which may obstruct visibility during the landing phase.

9-45   PLT120
The need to slow an aircraft below VA is brought about by the following weather phenomenon:

A– High density altitude which increases the indicated stall speed.
B– Turbulence which causes an increase in stall speed.
C– Turbulence which causes a decrease in stall speed.

9-45. Answer B. GFDICM 9B, PHB
When an airplane is flying at a high airspeed with a low angle of attack, and suddenly encounters a vertical current of air moving upward, the relative wind changes to an upward direction as it meets the wing. This increases the angle of attack of the wing, and can cause a momentary stall.

9-46   PLT344
Ice pellets encountered during flight normally are evidence that

A– a warm front has passed.
B– a warm front is about to pass.
C– there are thunderstorms in the area.

9-46. Answer B. GFDICM 9A, AW
In order for ice pellets to form, moisture (rain) must fall through colder air. Because of this, the presence of ice pellets at your altitude always indicates freezing rain aloft. This situation is most common just prior to the passage of a warm front when warm air extends up over the cold air preceding the front.

9-47   PLT511

What is indicated if ice pellets are encountered at 8,000 feet?

A– Freezing rain at higher altitude.
B– You are approaching an area of thunderstorms.
C– You will encounter hail if you continue your flight.

9-47. Answer A. GFDICM 9B, AW
See explanation for Question 9-46.

9-48   PLT344

Ice pellets encountered during flight are normally evidence that

A– a cold front has passed.
B– there are thunderstorms in the area.
C– freezing rain exists at higher altitudes.

9-48. Answer C. GFDICM 9A, AW
See explanation for Question 9-46.

9-49   PLT192

The presence of standing lenticular altocumulus clouds is a good indication of

A– lenticular ice formation in calm air.
B– very strong turbulence.
C– heavy icing conditions.

9-49. Answer B. GFDICM 9B, AW
Standing lenticular clouds form on the crests of waves created by barriers to wind flow such as mountain ranges. The clouds show little movement but can contain strong winds. The presence of these clouds is a good indication of very strong turbulence and should be avoided.

9-50   PLT192

The conditions necessary for the formation of cumulonimbus clouds are a lifting action and

A– unstable, dry air.
B– stable, moist air.
C– unstable, moist air.

9-50. Answer C. GFDICM 9B, AW
There are three conditions necessary to create cumulonimbus (thunderstorm) clouds. They include unstable air, a lifting force, and a high moisture content.

9-51   PLT226

Fog produced by frontal activity is a result of saturation due to

A– nocturnal cooling.
B– adiabatic cooling.
C– evaporation of precipitation.

9-51. Answer C. GFDICM 9B, AW
Precipitation fog typically forms as a result of frontal activity. As a cold front advances, warm air is pushed aloft over the cooler air below. If precipitation begins to fall through the cooler air, evaporation from the precipitation will saturate the cool air and fog typically will form.

9-52   PLT518

What is an important characteristic of wind shear?

A–It is present at only lower levels and exists in a horizontal direction.

B–It is present at any level and exists in only a vertical direction.

C–It can be present at any level and can exist in both a horizontal and vertical direction.

9-52. Answer C. GFDICM 9B, AW

Wind shear is a sudden, drastic shift in wind speed and/or direction that may occur at any altitude in a vertical or horizontal plane.

9-53   PLT518

Hazardous wind shear is commonly encountered

A–near warm or stationary frontal activity.

B–when the wind velocity is stronger than 35 knots.

C–in areas of temperature inversion and near thunderstorms.

9-53. Answer C. GFDICM 9B, AW

Hazardous wind shear is most commonly associated with temperature inversions, the jet stream, and thunderstorms and is less common in warm and stationary front activity.

9-54   PLT518

Low-level wind shear may occur when

A–surface winds are light and variable.

B–there is a low-level temperature inversion with strong winds above the inversion.

C–surface winds are above 15 knots and there is no change in wind direction and windspeed with height.

9-54. Answer B. GFDICM 9B, AW

When a temperature inversion forms with strong winds above, a wind shear zone can develop between the calm air in the inversion and stronger winds above. Eddies in the shear zone can cause airspeed fluctuations as you climb or descend through them.

9-55   PLT301

If a temperature inversion is encountered immediately after takeoff or during an approach to a landing, a potential hazard exists due to

A–wind shear.

B–strong surface winds.

C–strong convective currents.

9-55. Answer A. GFDICM 9B, AW

See explanation for Question 9-54. If you encounter a temperature inversion after takeoff or during an approach to landing, the abrupt change in wind direction and/or speed above the inversion can create a potential wind shear hazard.

9-56   PLT170
GIVEN:
Winds at 3,000 feet AGL...30 kts
Surface winds...calm

While on approach for landing, under clear skies with convective turbulence a few hours after sunrise, one should

A– increase approach airspeed slightly above normal to avoid stalling.
B– keep the approach airspeed at or slightly below normal to compensate for floating.
C– not alter the approach airspeed, these conditions are nearly ideal.

9-56. Answer A. GFDICM 9B, AW
The conditions indicated can create a wind shear hazard. When approaching to land in these conditions, it is recommended that the approach be flown at an airspeed slightly higher than normal to avoid stalling. If the wind shears from a strong headwind to no wind during descent, you could stall dangerously close to the ground.

9-57   PLT494
Convective currents are most active on warm summer afternoons when winds are

A– light.
B– moderate.
C– strong.

9-57. Answer A. GFDICM 9B, AW
Convective currents are created as the surface releases heat into the air. These currents are most common during hot summer afternoons when winds are light.

9-58   PLT501
When flying low over hilly terrain, ridges, or mountain ranges, the greatest potential danger from turbulent air currents will usually be encountered on the

A– leeward side when flying with a tailwind.
B– leeward side when flying into the wind.
C– windward side when flying into the wind.

9-58. Answer B. GFDICM 9B, AW
Turbulence created due to interference with normal wind flow is called mechanical turbulence. This type of turbulence is typically encountered when flying low on the leeward side of hilly terrain, ridges, or mountain ranges with a headwind.

9-59   PLT518
During an approach, the most important and most easily recognized means of being alerted to possible wind shear is monitoring the

A– amount of trim required to relieve control pressures.
B– heading changes necessary to remain on the runway centerline.
C– power and vertical velocity required to remain on the proper glidepath.

9-59. Answer C. GFDICM 9B, AC 00-54
On every approach you should closely monitor the power and vertical velocity required to remain on the proper glide path. If either of these appear abnormal, you should be alert for wind shear.

9-60   PLT518
During departure, under conditions of suspected low-level wind shear, a sudden decrease in headwind will cause

A– a loss in airspeed equal to the decrease in wind velocity.
B– a gain in airspeed equal to the decrease in wind velocity.
C– no change in airspeed, but groundspeed will decrease.

9-60. Answer A. GFDICM 9B, AC 00-54
Anytime you experience a sudden decrease in headwind, you will experience a performance decrease. This will equate to a loss of airspeed equal to the decrease in wind velocity and a corresponding loss of lift.

9-61   PLT344
Which situation would most likely result in freezing precipitation? Rain falling from air which has a temperature of

A– 32°F or less into air having a temperature of more than 32°F.
B– 0°C or less into air having a temperature of 0°C or more.
C– more than 32°F into air having a temperature of 32°F or less.

9-61. Answer C. GFDICM 9B, AW
In order for precipitation to begin falling as a liquid and then freeze, rain typically must begin falling in air that is above freezing and continue falling through air that is below freezing.

9-62   PLT261
Which statement is true concerning the hazards of hail?

A– Hail damage in horizontal flight is minimal due to the vertical movement of hail in the clouds.
B– Rain at the surface is a reliable indication of no hail aloft.
C– Hailstones may be encountered in clear air several miles from a thunderstorm.

9-62. Answer C. GFDICM 9B, AW
When hail is created in a thunderstorm, the existing updrafts can lift the hail to the top of the thunderstorm where strong upper-level winds can carry it several miles downwind.

9-63   PLT261
Hail is most likely to be associated with

A– cumulus clouds.
B– cumulonimbus clouds.
C– stratocumulus clouds.

9-63. Answer B. GFDICM 9B, AW
Hail is most commonly associated with cumulonimbus clouds (thunderstorms).

9-64   PLT511

The most severe weather conditions, such as destructive winds, heavy hail, and tornadoes, are generally associated with

A–slow-moving warm fronts which slope above the tropopause.

B–squall lines.

C–fast-moving occluded fronts.

9-64. Answer B. GFDICM 9B, AW

A squall line is a narrow band of active thunderstorms which normally contains some of the most severe weather conditions.

9-65   PLT495

Of the following, which is accurate regarding turbulence associated with thunderstorms?

A–Outside the cloud, shear turbulence can be encountered 50 miles laterally from a severe storm.

B–Shear turbulence is encountered only inside cumulonimbus clouds or within a 5-mile radius of them.

C–Outside the cloud, shear turbulence can be encountered 20 miles laterally from a severe storm.

9-65. Answer C. GFDICM 9B, AW

Thunderstorms typically contain many severe weather hazards including lightning, hail, turbulence, gusty surface winds, and tornados. These hazards are not confined to the cloud itself. For example, you can encounter turbulence in VFR conditions as far as 20 miles from the storm.

9-66   PLT105

If airborne radar is indicating an extremely intense thunderstorm echo, this thunderstorm should be avoided by a distance of at least

A–20 miles.

B–10 miles.

C–5 miles.

9-66. Answer A. GFDICM 9B, AW

If the aircraft you are flying is equipped with airborne radar, you can use it to avoid thunderstorms. A good rule of thumb is to avoid any intense thunderstorm echoes by at least 20 miles.

9-67   PLT475

Which statement is true regarding squall lines?

A–They are always associated with cold fronts.

B–They are slow in forming, but rapid in movement.

C–They are nonfrontal and often contain severe, steady-state thunderstorms.

9-67. Answer C. GFDICM 9B, AW

A squall line is a non-frontal, narrow band of active thunderstorms that typically contain some of the most intense weather hazards known to aircraft. They can develop ahead of a cold front in moist, unstable air, but they may also develop in unstable air far removed from any front.

9-68   PLT475

Which statement is true concerning squall lines?

A–They form slowly, but move rapidly.

B–They are associated with frontal systems only.

C–They offer the most intense weather hazards to aircraft.

9-68. Answer C. GFDICM 9B, AW

See explanation for Question 9-67.

9-69   PLT495
Select the true statement pertaining to the life cycle of a thunderstorm.

A– Updrafts continue to develop throughout the dissipating stage of a thunderstorm.
B– The beginning of rain at the Earth's surface indicates the mature stage of the thunderstorm.
C– The beginning of rain at the Earth's surface indicates the dissipating stage of the thunderstorm.

9-69. Answer B. GFDICM 9B, AW
There are three stages in the life cycle of a thunderstorm; cumulus, mature, and dissipating.

9-70   PLT495
What visible signs indicate extreme turbulence in thunderstorms?

A– Base of the clouds near the surface, heavy rain, and hail.
B– Low ceiling and visibility, hail, and precipitation static.
C– Cumulonimbus clouds, very frequent lightning, and roll clouds.

9-70. Answer C. GFDICM 9B, AC 00-24B
Potentially hazardous turbulence is present in all thunderstorms. Some visual signs that can indicate extreme turbulence include the presence of cumulonimbus

9-71   PLT495
Which weather phenomenon signals the beginning of the mature stage of a thunderstorm?

A– The start of rain.
B– The appearance of an anvil top.
C– Growth rate of cloud is maximum.

9-71. Answer A. GFDICM 9B, AW
There are three stages in the life cycle of a thunderstorm; they are the cumulus stage, mature stage, and dissipating stage. The cumulus stage is characterized by strong updrafts reaching speeds in excess of 3,000 feet per minute causing a rapid growth rate. The mature stage signifies the beginning of downdrafts and can be identified by the presence of rain falling at the surface and the formation of a roll cloud. The dissipating stage consists primarily of downdrafts and the formation of an anvil.

9-72   PLT495
What feature is normally associated with the cumulus stage of a thunderstorm?

A– Roll cloud.
B– Continuous updraft.
C– Beginning of rain at the surface.

9-72. Answer B. GFDICM 9B, AW
See explanation for Question 9-71.

9-73   PLT495

During the life cycle of a thunderstorm, which stage is characterized predominately by downdrafts?

A– Mature.
B– Developing.
C– Dissipating.

9-73. Answer C. GFDICM 9B, AW

See explanation for Question 9-71.

9-74   PLT105

What minimum distance should exist between intense radar echoes before any attempt is made to fly between these thunderstorms?

A– 20 miles.
B– 30 miles.
C– 40 miles.

9-74. Answer C. GFDICM 9B, AW

If the aircraft you are flying is equipped with airborne radar, you can use it to avoid thunderstorms. A good rule of thumb is to avoid any intense thunderstorm echoes by at least 20 miles and never fly between two cells if they are less than 40 miles apart.

9-75   PLT226

Which in-flight hazard is most commonly associated with warm fronts?

A– Advection fog.
B– Radiation fog.
C– Precipitation-induced fog.

9-75. Answer C. GFDICM 9B, AW

Precipitation-induced fog may form when precipitation falls through a layer of cooler air near the surface and evaporates, saturating the cool air. The conditions required to produce this type of fog are commonly associated with warm fronts.

9-76   PLT105

Which is true regarding the use of airborne weather-avoidance radar for the recognition of certain weather conditions?

A– The radarscope provides no assurance of avoiding instrument weather conditions.
B– The avoidance of hail is assured when flying between and just clear of the most intense echoes.
C– The clear area between intense echoes indicates that visual sighting of storms can be maintained when flying between the echoes.

9-76. Answer A. GFDICM 9B, AW

Airborne weather radar is designed for avoiding severe weather, not for penetrating it. Weather radar detects drops of precipitation, not the minute drops associated with cloud formations. Therefore, weather radar provides no assurance of avoiding instrument meteorological conditions.

9-77   PLT226

A situation most conducive to the formation of advection fog is

A– a light breeze moving colder air over a water surface.
B– an air mass moving inland from the coastline during the winter.
C– a warm, moist air mass settling over a cool surface under no-wind conditions.

9-77. Answer B. GFDICM 9B, AW

Advection fog is caused when a low layer of warm, moist air moves over a cooler land or water surface. It is most common along the coast where sea breezes transport air from the warm water to cool land.

9-78   PLT263
Advection fog has drifted over a coastal airport during the day. What may tend to dissipate or lift this fog into low stratus clouds?

A– Nighttime cooling.
B– Surface radiation.
C– Wind 15 knots or stronger.

9-78. Answer C. GFDICM 9B, AW
Once advection fog forms, winds of approximately 15 knots or stronger will usually lift the fog sufficiently to create stratus clouds.

9-79   PLT226
What lifts advection fog into low stratus clouds?

A– Nighttime cooling.
B– Dryness of the underlying land mass.
C– Surface winds of approximately 15 knots or stronger.

9-79. Answer C. GFDICM 9B, AW
See explanation for Question 9-78.

9-80   PLT226
In what ways do advection fog, radiation fog, and steam fog differ in their formation or location?

A– Radiation fog is restricted to land areas; advection fog is most common along coastal areas; steam fog forms over a water surface.
B– Advection fog deepens as windspeed increases up to 20 knots; steam fog requires calm or very light wind; radiation fog forms when the ground or water cools the air by radiation.
C– Steam fog forms from moist air moving over a colder surface; advection fog requires cold air over a warmer surface; radiation fog is produced by radiational cooling of the ground.

9-80. Answer A. GFDICM 9B, AW
Radiation fog is typically restricted to land areas because water surfaces cool little from nighttime radiation. Because advection fog requires the movement of warm, moist air over a cooler land or water surface, it is most common along the coast. Steam fog occurs as cool air moves over warmer water, so its development is restricted to water surfaces.

9-81   PLT226
With respect to advection fog, which statement is true?

A– It is slow to develop, and dissipates quite rapidly.
B– It forms almost exclusively at night or near daybreak.
C– It can appear suddenly during day or night, and it is more persistent than radiation fog.

9-81. Answer C. GFDICM 9B, AW
A unique characteristic of advection fog is that it can form rapidly during the day or night, and it tends to be more persistent and extensive than radiation fog.

9-82   PLT302

A common location of clear air turbulence is

A– in an upper trough on the polar side of a jet stream.
B– near a ridge aloft on the equatorial side of a high-pressure flow.
C– south of an east/west oriented high-pressure ridge in its dissipating stage.

9-82. Answer A. GFDICM 9B, AW
Clear air turbulence (CAT) is often associated with a jet stream that is interacting with a large mountain range or deep low pressure system. It is commonly located in an upper trough on the polar or cold side of a jet stream where the wind speed gradient is greater.

9-83   PLT302

The jet stream and associated clear air turbulence can sometimes be visually identified in flight by

A– dust or haze at flight level.
B– long streaks of cirrus clouds.
C– a constant outside air temperature.

9-83. Answer B. GFDICM 9B, AW
Clear air turbulence associated with a jet stream can sometimes be visually identified in flight by long streaks of cirrus clouds.

9-84   PLT516

The conditions most favorable to wave formation over mountainous areas are a layer of

A– stable air at mountaintop altitude and a wind of at least 20 knots blowing across the ridge.
B– unstable air at mountaintop altitude and a wind of at least 20 knots blowing across the ridge.
C– moist, unstable air at mountaintop altitude and a wind of less than 5 knots blowing across the ridge.

9-84. Answer A. GFDICM 9B, AW
The formation of a strong mountain wave requires stable air blowing across a ridge at a speed of at least 20 knots.

9-85   PLT059

What wind conditions would you anticipate when squalls are reported at your destination?

A– Rapid variations in windspeed of 15 knots or more between peaks and lulls.
B– Peak gusts of at least 35 knots combined with a change in wind direction of 30° or more.
C– Sudden increases in windspeed of at least 16 knots to a sustained speed of 22 knots or more for at least 1 minute.

9-85. Answer C. GFDICM 9B, AW
A squall is defined as an abrupt windspeed increase of at least 16 knots to a sustained speed of 22 knots or more, lasting at least one minute.

9-86   PLT518

The minimum vertical wind shear value critical for probable moderate or greater turbulence is

A– 4 knots per 1,000 feet.
B– 6 knots per 1,000 feet.
C– 8 knots per 1,000 feet.

9-86. Answer B. GFDICM 9B, AWS

The tropopause data chart contains four panels: the observed tropopause data, a maximum wind prog, a height/vertical wind shear prog, and a high level significant weather prog. The height/vertical wind shear prog depicts the height of the tropopause in terms of pressure altitude and vertical wind shear in knots per 1,000 feet. As a general rule you should expect moderate or greater turbulence when the vertical wind shear is six knots or more.

9-87   PLT116

A pilot reporting turbulence that momentarily causes slight, erratic changes in altitude and/or attitude should report it as

A– light chop.
B– light turbulence.
C– moderate turbulence.

9-87. Answer B. GFDICM 9B, AIM

Light turbulence causes slight erratic changes in altitude or attitude and slight strain against seat belts.

9-88   PLT116

When turbulence causes changes in altitude and/or attitude, but aircraft control remains positive, that should be reported as

A– light.
B– severe.
C– moderate.

9-88. Answer C. GFDICM 9B, AIM

See explanation for Question 9-87.

9-89   PLT116

Turbulence that is encountered above 15,000 feet AGL not associated with cumuliform cloudiness, including thunderstorms, should be reported as

A– severe turbulence.
B– clear air turbulence.
C– convective turbulence.

9-89. Answer B. GFDICM 9B, AIM

Clear air turbulence (CAT) can take place at any altitude and its presence carries no visual warning. CAT may be caused by wind shear, convective currents, or obstructions to normal wind flow. According to the AIM, turbulence not associated with cumuliform clouds, including thunderstorms, should be reported as clear air turbulence preceded by the appropriate intensity.

9-90   PLT302

Which type of jetstream can be expected to cause the greater turbulence?

A– A straight jetstream associated with a low-pressure trough.

B– A curving jetstream associated with a deep low-pressure trough.

C– A jetstream occurring during the summer at the lower latitudes.

9-90. Answer B. GFDICM 9B, AC 00-30A

The turbulence associated with a jet stream can be very strong, and because it often occurs in clear air, it is difficult to forecast accurately. As a rule of thumb, clear air turbulence can be expected when a curving jet steam is found north of a deep low pressure system.

9-91   PLT302

A strong wind shear can be expected

A– in the jetstream front above a core having a speed of 60 to 90 knots.

B– if the 5°C isotherms are spaced between 7° to 10° of latitude.

C– on the low-pressure side of a jet stream core where the speed at the core is stronger than 110 knots.

9-91. Answer C. GFDICM 9B, AC 0030A

Strong clear air turbulence and strong wind shear can be expected on the low-pressure side of a jet stream core where the speed at the core is stronger than 110 knots.

9-92   PLT116

The Low Level Wind Shear Alert System (LLWAS) provides wind data and software process to detect the presence of a

A– rotating column of air extending from a cumulonimbus cloud.

B– change in wind direction and/or speed within a very short distance above the airport.

C– downward motion of the air associated with continuous winds blowing with an easterly component due to the rotation of the Earth.

9-92. Answer B. GFDICM 9B, AIM

Wind shear is defined as a change in wind speed and/or direction in a short distance resulting in a tearing or shearing effect. It can exist in a horizontal or vertical direction and occasionally in both.

9-93   PLT263

One of the most dangerous features of mountain waves is the turbulent areas in and

A– below rotor clouds.

B– above rotor clouds.

C– below lenticular clouds.

9-93. Answer A. GFDICM 9B, AW

There are three types of clouds associated with mountain wave activity. They are lenticular clouds, cap clouds, and rotor clouds. Lenticular clouds usually mark the crests of mountain waves. These clouds form in the updrafts and dissipate in the downdrafts so they have a stationary appearance as the wind blows through them. Rotor clouds may also form on the downwind side of the mountain and cap clouds may obscure the mountain peaks. One of the most dangerous features of mountain waves is the turbulent areas in and below rotor clouds.

9-94   PLT170
When turbulence is encountered during the approach to a landing, what action is recommended and for what primary reason?

A– Increase the airspeed slightly above normal approach speed to attain more positive control.
B– Decrease the airspeed slightly below normal approach speed to avoid overstressing the airplane.
C– Increase the airspeed slightly above normal approach speed to penetrate the turbulence as quickly as possible.

9-94. Answer A. GFDICM 9B, AFH
If you encounter turbulence while making an approach to landing, it is a good practice to make the approach at a slightly higher-than-normal airspeed to allow for more positive control of the airplane.

9-95   PLT170
Which type of approach and landing is recommended during gusty wind conditions?

A– A power-on approach and power-on landing.
B– A power-off approach and power-on landing.
C– A power-on approach and power-off landing.

9-95. Answer A. GFDICM 9B, AFH
When making an approach in gusty winds, it is best to make a power-on approach and landing at an airspeed slightly above normal. This will provide for better control of the aircraft throughout the landing.

9-96   PLT132
A pilot is entering an area where significant clear air turbulence has been reported. Which action is appropriate upon encountering the first ripple?

A– Maintain altitude and airspeed.
B– Adjust airspeed to that recommended for rough air.
C– Enter a shallow climb or descent at maneuvering speed.

9-96. Answer B. GFDICM 9B, PHB
Anytime you encounter turbulence, or expect to encounter turbulence, you should slow the airplane to maneuvering speed (V_A) or the recommended rough air penetration speed.

9-97   PLT132
If severe turbulence is encountered during flight, the pilot should reduce the airspeed to

A– minimum control speed.
B– design-maneuvering speed.
C– maximum structural cruising speed.

9-97. Answer B. GFDICM 9B, PHB
See explanation for Question 9-96.

9-98   PLT493
Frost covering the upper surface of an airplane wing usually will cause

A–the airplane to stall at an angle of attack that is higher than normal.
B–the airplane to stall at an angle of attack that is lower than normal.
C–drag factors so large that sufficient speed cannot be obtained for takeoff.

9-98. Answer B. GFDICM 9B, FTP
Frost interferes with the smooth flow of air over the wings and can cause early airflow separation. This results in a loss of lift, and the wing stalls at a lower than normal angle of attack.

9-99   PLT501
Which is the best technique for minimizing the wing-load factor when flying in severe turbulence?

A–Change power settings, as necessary, to maintain constant airspeed.
B–Control airspeed with power, maintain wings level, and accept variations of altitude.
C–Set power and trim to obtain an airspeed at or below maneuvering speed, maintain wings level, and accept variations of airspeed and altitude.

9-99. Answer C. GFDICM 9B, AIM
Anytime you experience turbulence, or expect it, you should slow the aircraft to maneuvering speed or less. In addition, you should try to maintain a wings-level flight attitude and accept variations in airspeed and altitude.

9-100   PLT509
Choose the correct statement regarding wake turbulence.

A–Vortex generation begins with the initiation of the takeoff roll.
B–The primary hazard is loss of control because of induced roll.
C–The greatest vortex strength is produced when the generating airplane is heavy, clean, and fast.

9-100. Answer B. GFDICM 9B, AIM
Large aircraft can produce wake turbulence that could induce uncontrolled roll rates in smaller aircraft. Vortex generation begins as soon as the aircraft's wing begins producing lift, not when it begins its takeoff roll. The greatest vortex strength is produced when the generating airplane is heavy, clean, and slow, not heavy, clean, and fast.

9-101   PLT509
During a takeoff made behind a departing large jet airplane, the pilot can minimize the hazard of wingtip vortices by

A–being airborne prior to reaching the jet's flightpath until able to turn clear of its wake.
B–maintaining extra speed on takeoff and climbout.
C–extending the takeoff roll and not rotating until well beyond the jet's rotation point.

9-101. Answer A. GFDICM 9B, AIM
If taking off behind a large aircraft, you can minimize the chance of flying into wake turbulence by making sure you lift off prior to the preceding aircraft's flightpath and remain above the flightpath until able to turn clear.

9-102   PLT509
Which procedure should you follow to avoid wake turbulence if a large jet crosses your course from left to right approximately 1 mile ahead and at your altitude?

A–Make sure you are slightly above the path of the jet.
B– Slow your airspeed to V_A and maintain altitude and course.
C– Make sure you are slightly below the path of the jet and perpendicular to the course.

9-102. Answer A. GFDICM 9B, AIM
As wake turbulence is generated in flight, it tends to sink at a rate of 400 to 500 feet per minute. Because of this, anytime you anticipate crossing a large aircraft's flightpath, you should cross above its path.

9-103   PLT509
To avoid possible wake turbulence from a large jet aircraft that has just landed prior to your takeoff, at which point on the runway should you plan to become airborne?

A–Past the point where the jet touched down.
B– At the point where the jet touched down, or just prior to this point.
C– Approximately 500 feet prior to the point where the jet touched down.

9-103. Answer A. GFDICM 9B, AIM
When taking off behind a large aircraft that has just landed, you should plan on becoming airborne beyond the point where the large aircraft touched down. Beyond this point, the jet's wake turbulence will be greatly diminished.

9-104   PLT509
When landing behind a large aircraft, which procedure should be followed for vortex avoidance?

A–Stay above its final approach flightpath all the way to touchdown.
B– Stay below and to one side of its final approach flightpath.
C– Stay well below its final approach flightpath and land at least 2,000 feet behind.

9-104. Answer A. GFDICM 9B, AIM
When landing behind a large aircraft, it is best to stay above its flight path all the way to touchdown.

9-105   PLT265
With respect to vortex circulation, which is true?

A–Helicopters generate downwash turbulence, not vortex circulation.
B– The vortex strength is greatest when the generating aircraft is flying fast.
C– Vortex circulation generated by helicopters in forward flight trail behind in a manner similar to wingtip vortices generated by airplanes.

9-105. Answer C. GFDICM 9B, AIM
In forward flight, departing or landing helicopters produce a pair of strong, high-speed trailing vortices similar to wingtip vortices of larger fixed-wing aircraft.

9-106   PLT265

Which is true with respect to vortex circulation?

A– Helicopters generate downwash turbulence only, not vortex circulation.

B– The vortex strength is greatest when the generating aircraft is heavy, clean, and slow.

C– When vortex circulation sinks into ground effect, it tends to dissipate rapidly and offer little danger.

9-106. Answer B. GFDICM 9B, AIM

Whenever an airplane generates lift, air spills over the wingtips causing wingtip vortices. The greatest vortex strength occurs when the generating aircraft is heavy, clean and slow.

9-107   PLT493

During preflight in cold weather, crankcase breather lines should receive special attention because they are susceptible to being clogged by

A– congealed oil from the crankcase.

B– moisture from the outside air which has frozen.

C– ice from crankcase vapors that have condensed and subsequently frozen.

9-107. Answer C. GFDICM 9B, AC 91-13C

Crankcase breather lines are susceptible to being clogged by ice formed when crankcase vapors condense after engine shutdown. The clogged lines prevent the release of air from the crankcase.

9-108   PLT126

Which is true regarding preheating an aircraft during cold weather operations?

A– The cabin area as well as the engine should be preheated.

B– The cabin area should not be preheated with portable heaters.

C– Hot air should be blown directly at the engine through the air intakes.

9-108. Answer A. GFDICM 9B, AC 91-13C

Preheating the cabin as well as the engine is recommended to ensure the proper operation of instruments, many of which are adversely affected by cold temperatures.

SECTION C - PRINTED REPORTS AND FORECASTS

METARS

- An aviation routine weather report (METAR) is an observation of surface weather written in a standard format which typically contains 10 or more separate elements.
- A non-routine aviation weather report (SPECI) is issued when a significant change in one or more of the elements of a METAR has occurred.
- Prevailing visibility is the greatest distance an observer can see and identify objects through at least half of the horizon.
- When a squall (SQ) is reported, you can expect a sudden increase in wind speed of at least 16 knots to a sustained wind speed of 22 knots or more for at least 1 minute.
- Runway visual range (RVR) is based on what a pilot in a moving aircraft should see when looking down the runway. If included in a METAR, RVR is reported following prevailing visibility.
- A ceiling is the height above ground level of the lowest layer of clouds aloft which is reported as broken (BKN) or overcast (OVC), or the vertical visibility (VV) into an obscuration. For example, VV008 indicates that the sky is obscured with a vertical visibility of 800 feet.
- If the top of a layer is known, you can easily determine its thickness by adding the airport's elevation (MSL) to the height of the cloud base (AGL) found in a METAR observation, then subtract the height of the cloud tops.
- The beginning of the remarks section is indicated by the code RMK. The remarks section reports weather considered significant to aircraft operations, which are not covered in the previous sections of the METAR.

RADAR WEATHER REPORTS

- Radar weather reports (SDs) define general areas of precipitation, particularly thunderstorms.
- The abbreviation MT is used to denote maximum tops of the precipitation in the clouds. Heights are reported in hundreds of feet MSL followed by the radial and distance in nautical miles from the reporting location.

PILOT WEATHER REPORTS

- The bases and tops of cloud layers, in-flight visibility, icing conditions, wind shear, and turbulence may be included in a pilot weather report (PIREP).
- PIREPs are the best source for current weather between reporting stations.

TERMINAL AERODROME FORECASTS

- Terminal aerodrome forecasts (TAFs) are issued 4 times per day, and predict the weather at a specific airport for a 24-hour period of time. A TAF should be your primary source of weather information for your destination.
- In a TAF, the contraction VRB indicates that the wind direction is variable. A calm wind (3 knots or less) is indicated by 00000KT.
- P6SM in a terminal aerodrome forecast implies that the prevailing visibility is expected to be greater than 6 statute miles.
- The letters SKC are used in a terminal aerodrome forecast to indicate "sky clear."
- The letters WS indicate that low-level wind shear which is not associated with convective activity may be present during the valid time of the forecast. For example, WS005/27050KT indicates that the wind at 500 feet AGL is 270° at 50 knots.
- The term PROB40 2102 +TSRA in a terminal aerodrome forecast indicates that there is approximately a 40% probability of thunderstorms with heavy rain between 2100Z and 0200Z.

AVIATION AREA FORECASTS

- Aviation area forecasts are issued three times each day and generally include a total forecast period of 18 hours. They cover a geographical group of states or well known areas.

- An aviation area forecast (FA) is a good source of information for weather at airports which do not have terminal aerodrome forecasts, as well as for enroute weather.
- The VFR clouds and weather section of an aviation area forecast summarizes sky conditions, cloud heights, visibility, obstructions to vision, precipitation, and sustained surface winds of 20 knots or greater.
- When the wind is forecast to be 20 knots or greater the categorical outlook in the aviation area forecast includes the contraction WND.

WINDS AND TEMPERATURES ALOFT FORECASTS

- An estimate of wind direction in relation to true north, wind speed in knots, and the temperature in degrees Celsius for selected altitudes can be found in the winds and temperatures aloft forecast (FD).
- A winds and temperatures aloft forecast (FD) does not include winds within 1,500 feet of the station elevation. Likewise temperatures for the 3,000-foot level or for a level within 2,500 feet of the station elevation are omitted.
- Wind direction and speed information on an FD are shown by a four-digit code. The first two digits are the wind direction in tens of degrees. Wind speed is shown by the second two digits. The last two digits indicate the temperature in degrees Celsius. All temperatures above 24,000 feet are negative and the minus sign is omitted.
- To decode a forecast of winds between 100 and 199 knots, subtract 50 from the two-digit direction code and multiply by 10. Then, add 100 to the two-digit wind speed code. The code 9900 indicates the winds are light and variable.

SEVERE WEATHER

- A convective outlook (AC) forecasts general thunderstorm activity for the next 24-hour period.
- Severe weather watch bulletins (WW) are issued only when required. They outline areas of possible severe thunderstorms or tornadoes.

9-109   PLT059

The remarks section of the Aviation Routine Weather Report (METAR) contains the following coded information. What does it mean?

RMK FZDZB42 WSHFT 30 FROPA

A– Freezing drizzle below 4,200 feet and wind shear.
B– Wind shift at three zero due to frontal passage.
C– Freezing drizzle with cloud bases below 4,200 feet.

9-109. Answer B. GFDICM 9C, AIM

To help you develop a better picture of the weather, some METARs include a remarks section. The remarks are generally limited to operationally significant weather, and may include the beginning and ending times of certain weather phenomena. In this example, freezing drizzle (FZDZ) began at 42 minutes past the hour (B42), and a wind shift occurred at thirty minutes past the hour. The contraction for frontal passage (FROPA) may be added when there is reasonable certainty that the wind shift was the result of frontal passage.

9-110   PLT059

What is meant by the Special METAR weather observation for KBOI?

SPECI KBOI 091854Z 32005KT 1 1/2SM RA BR OVC007 17/16 A2990 RMK RAB12

A– Rain and fog obscuring two-tenths of the sky; rain began at 1912Z.
B– Rain and mist obstructing visibility; rain began at 1812Z.
C– Rain and overcast at 1200 feet AGL.

9-110. Answer B. GFDICM 9C, PHB

The last section of the METAR is the remarks section which reports operationally significant weather, and may include the beginning and ending times of certain weather phenomena. In this example, rain (RA) and mist (BR) are included in the body of the report with rain beginning at 12 minutes past the hour (RAB12) in the remarks.

9-111   PLT059

The station originating the following METAR observation has a field elevation of 3,500 feet MSL. If the sky cover is one continuous layer, what is the thickness of the cloud layer? (Top of overcast reported at 7,500 feet MSL).

METAR KHOB 151250Z 17006KT 4SM OVC005 13/11 A2998

A–2,500 feet.
B–3,500 feet.
C–4,000 feet.

9-111. Answer B. GFDICM 9C, AIM

The notation "OVC005" in the body of the report, indicates that the base of the overcast is at 500 feet AGL. The report of 7,500 feet overcast (probably from a pilot report) indicates the top of the overcast is at 7,500 feet MSL. To determine the thickness of the cloud layer, you must first add the height of the cloud base (500 feet AGL) and the field elevation (3,500 feet MSL) to determine the cloud base height MSL. By subtracting the base of the cloud layer (4,000 feet MSL) from the top of the cloud layer (7,500 feet MSL), you can determine the thickness of the layer is 3,500 feet (7,500 - 4,000 = 3,500 feet).

9-112   PLT061

What significant cloud coverage is reported by this pilot report?

KMOB UA/OV 15NW MOB 1340Z/SK OVC 025/045 OVC 090

A–Three (3) separate overcast layers exist with bases at 250, 7,500 and 9,000 feet.
B–The top of the lower overcast is 2,500 feet; base and top of second overcast layer is 4,500 and 9,000 feet, respectively.
C–The base of the second overcast layer is 2,500 feet; top of second overcast layer is 7,500 feet; base of third layer is 9,000 feet.

9-112. Answer B. GFDICM 9C, AIM

In this example, the "UA" indicates routine PIREP information follows. The pilot reported the top of the lower overcast layer at 2,500 feet as indicated by the notation "SK OVC 025/." The rest of the notation, "/045 OVC 090," indicates that the base and top of the second layer at 4,500 feet and 9,000 feet MSL respectively.

9-113   PLT514

To best determine observed weather conditions between weather reporting stations, the pilot should refer to

A–pilot reports.
B–Area Forecasts.
C–prognostic charts.

9-113. Answer A. GFDICM 9C, AWS

Pilot reports (PIREPs) are the only means of directly determining cloud tops, icing conditions, and turbulence. In addition, PIREPs are the best source for observed weather between reporting points.

9-114   PLT037
Which is true concerning the radar weather report (SD) for KOKC?

KOKC 1934 LN 8TRW++/+ 86/40 164/60 199/115 15W L2425 MT 570 AT 159/65 2 INCH HAIL RPRTD THIS CELL

A– There are three cells with tops at 11,500, 40,000, and 60,000 feet.
B– The line of cells is moving 060° with winds reported up to 40 knots.
C– The maximum tops of the cells is 57,000 feet located 65 NM southeast of the station.

9-114. Answer C. GFDICM 9C, PHB
When reading a radar weather report (SD), maximum tops are identified by the abbreviation "MT," followed by the radial and distance (in nautical miles) from the radar facility. This report indicates that the maximum tops are at 57,000 feet MSL located on the 159° radial (south-southeast) at 65 n.m.

9-115   PLT072
What is the meaning of the terms PROB40 2102 +TSRA as used in a Terminal Aerodrome Forecasts (TAF)?

A– Probability of heavy thunderstorms with rain showers below 4000 feet at time 2102.
B– Between 2100Z and 0200Z there is a forty percent (40%) probability of thunderstorms with heavy rain.
C– Beginning at 2102Z forty percent (40%) probability of heavy thunderstorms and rain showers.

9-115. Answer B. GFDICM 9C, AIM
The probability group (PROB40) in a TAF is used to indicate there is between a 30% and 49% probability of thunderstorms or precipitation events and associated conditions occurring in the forecast period. This is followed by beginning and ending time and then by the conditions that are expected. In this example, there is approximately a 40 percent probability of a thunderstorm and heavy rain between 2100Z and 0200Z. There is no mention of showers (SH).

9-116   PLT072
What does the contraction VRB in the Terminal Aerodrome Forecast (TAF) mean?

A– Wind speed is variable throughout the period.
B– Cloud base is variable.
C– Wind direction is variable.

9-116. Answer C. GFDICM 9C, PHB
In a Terminal Aerodrome Forecast (TAF), the contraction "VRB" in the wind section indicates the wind direction is expected to be variable. Variable applies to the wind direction, not speed.

9-117   PLT072
Which statement pertaining to the following Terminal Aerodrome Forecast (TAF) is true?

TAF KMEM 091135Z 0915 15005KT 5SM HZ BKN060 FM1600 VRB04KT P6SM SKC

A– Wind in the outlook period implies surface winds are forecast to be greater than 5 KTS
B– wind direction is from 160° at 4 KTS and reported visibility is 6 statute miles.
C– SKC in the valid period indicates no significant weather and sky clear.

9-117. Answer C. GFDICM 9C, AIM
In a Terminal Aerodrome Forecast (TAF), FM is used to indicate that a change in the existing weather is expected, with the hour of the expected change following "FM." In this example, at Memphis International from 1600Z until the end of the forecast period, the wind is forecast to be variable at 4 knots (VRB04KT), visibility greater than 6 statute miles (P6SM), and the sky is clear (SKC).

9-118   PLT072

The visibility entry in a Terminal Aerodrome Forecast (TAF) of P6SM implies that the prevailing visibility is expected to be greater than

A– 6 nautical miles.
B– 6 statute miles.
C– 6 kilometers.

9-118. Answer B. GFDICM 9C, PHB

When the expected prevailing visibility is 6 miles or less it is included in the forecast, followed by "SM" to indicate statute miles. Visibilities greater than 6 statute miles are indicated in the forecast by Plus 6SM (P6SM).

9-119   PLT288

Terminal Aerodrome Forecasts (TAF) are issued how many times a day and cover what period of time?

A– Four times daily and are usually valid for a 24 hour period.
B– Six times daily and are usually valid for a 24 hour period including a 4-hour categorical outlook.
C– Four times daily and are valid for 12 hours including a 6-hour categorical outlook.

9-119. Answer A. GFDICM 9C, PHB

TAFs generally are issued four times a day, beginning at 0000Z, 0600Z, 1200Z, and 1800Z. Each report is valid for a 24-hour period. The basic sequence of a TAF provides forecast wind, visibility, weather, and sky conditions.

9-120   PLT291

Which information section is contained in the Aviation Area Forecast (FA)?

A– Winds aloft, speed and direction.
B– VFR Clouds and Weather (VFR CLDS/WX).
C– In-Flight Aviation Weather Advisories.

9-120. Answer B. GFDICM 9C, AWS

Issued three times each day for six regions in the contiguous U.S., an Aviation Area Forecast contains a heading section, precautionary statements section, a synopsis section, and a VFR Clouds and Weather section.

9-121   PLT291

The section of the Aviation Area Forecast (FA) entitled VFR Clouds and Weather contains a summary of

A– forecast sky cover, cloud tops, visibility, and obstructions to vision along specific routes.
B– only those weather systems producing liquid or frozen precipitation, fog, thunderstorms, or IFR ceilings.
C– sky condition, cloud heights, visibility, obstructions to vision, precipitation, and sustained surface winds of 20 knots or greater.

9-121. Answer C. GFDICM 9C, AWS

The VFR Clouds and Weather section of the area forecast describes the location and movement of frontal systems and circulation patterns. References to low ceilings and/or visibilities, strong winds, or other phenomena may be included. In addition, a forecast of conditions which meet marginal VFR (MVFR) criteria or better also is included.

9-122   PLT291

The Aviation Weather Center (AWC) prepares FAs for the contiguous U.S.

A–twice each day.

B–three times each day.

C–every 6 hours unless significant changes in weather require it more often.

9-122. Answer B. GFDICM 9C, AWS

Aviation Area forecasts (FAs) are issued for six regions in the contiguous United States three times each day.

9-123   PLT284

What values are used for Winds Aloft Forecasts?

A–True direction and MPH.

B–True direction and knots.

C–Magnetic direction and knots.

9-123. Answer B. GFDICM 9C, AWS

Winds and temperatures aloft forecasts report wind direction in relation to true north and wind speed in knots.

SECTION D - GRAPHIC WEATHER PRODUCTS
SURFACE ANALYSIS CHART

- The solid lines that depict sea level pressure patterns are called isobars. When they are close together, the pressure gradient is stronger and the wind velocities are stronger.
- A surface analysis chart is a good source for general weather information over a wide area, depicting the actual positions of fronts, pressure patterns, temperatures, dewpoint, wind, weather, and obstructions to vision at the valid time of the chart.
- A dashed line on a surface analysis chart indicates a weak pressure gradient.

WEATHER DEPICTION CHART

- The weather depiction chart provides a graphic display of VFR and IFR weather, as well as the type of precipitation.
- A ( ]) plotted to the right of a station circle on the weather depiction chart means the station is an automated observation location.
- When total sky cover is FEW or scattered, the height shown on the weather depiction chart is the base of the lowest layer.

RADAR SUMMARY CHART

- Radar summary charts are the only weather charts which show lines and cells of thunderstorms as well as other heavy precipitation. You can also determine the tops and bases of the echoes, the intensity of the precipitation, and the echo movement.
- A radar summary chart is most effective when used in combination with other charts, reports, and forecasts.

CONSTANT PRESSURE ANALYSIS CHART

- A constant pressure analysis chart provides observed winds aloft, temperature and dewpoint information.You can also use this chart to determine temperatures.
- Hatching on a constant pressure analysis chart indicates wind speeds between 70 and 110 knots.

WINDS AND TEMPERATURES ALOFT FORECASTS

An estimate of wind direction in relation to true north, wind speed in knots, and the temperature in degrees Celsius for selected altitudes can be found in the winds and temperatures aloft forecast (FD).

LOW AND HIGH LEVEL SIGNIFICANT WEATHER PROGNOSTIC CHARTS

- A low-level significant weather prognostic chart depicts weather conditions forecast to exist at 12, and 24 hours in the future. This chart is valid up to 24,000 feet MSL.
- In a high-level significant weather prognostic chart the areas enclosed in scalloped lines indicate that you should expect cumulonimbus clouds (CBs), icing, and moderate or greater turbulence.
- A high-level significant weather prognostic chart forecasts clear air turbulence, tropopause height, sky coverage, embedded thunderstorms, and jet stream velocities between 24,000 feet MSL and 63,000 feet MSL.

COMPOSITE MOISTURE STABILITY CHART

- A freezing level panel of the composite moisture stability chart is an analysis of observed freezing level data from upper air observations.

• The difference found by subtracting the temperature of a parcel of air theoretically lifted from the surface to 500 millibars and the existing temperature at 500 millibars is called the lifted index.

9-124   PLT287
With regard to windflow patterns shown on surface analysis charts; when the isobars are

A–close together, the pressure gradient force is slight and wind velocities are weaker.
B–not close together, the pressure gradient force is greater and wind velocities are stronger.
C–close together, the pressure gradient force is greater and wind velocities are stronger.

9-124. Answer C. GFDICM 9D, AW
The closer the spacing of isobars, the stronger the pressure gradient force. The stronger the pressure gradient force, the greater the wind velocities.

9-125   PLT287
On a Surface Analysis Chart, the solid lines that depict sea level pressure patterns are called

A–isobars.
B–isogons.
C–millibars.

9-125. Answer A. GFDICM 9D, AWS
On surface analysis charts, points of equal pressure are connected with solid lines. These lines are referred to as isobars.

9-126   PLT287
Dashed lines on a Surface Analysis Chart, if depicted, indicate that the pressure gradient is

A–weak.
B–strong.
C–unstable.

9-126. Answer A. GFDICM 9D, AW
On surface analysis charts, points of equal pressure are connected with solid lines. These lines are referred to as isobars. If the isobars on surface analysis charts are dashed the pressure gradient is weak.

9-127   PLT287
Which chart provides a ready means of locating observed frontal positions and pressure centers?

A–Surface Analysis Chart.
B–Constant Pressure Analysis Chart.
C–Weather Depiction Chart.

9-127. Answer A. GFDICM 9D, AW
In addition to depicting frontal positions and pressure centers, the surface analysis chart depicts such things as sea level pressure patterns, temperature and dewpoint, wind direction and speed, local weather, and obstructions to vision at the valid time of the chart.

9-128   PLT287
On a Surface Analysis Chart, close spacing of the isobars indicates

A–weak pressure gradient.
B–strong pressure gradient.
C–strong temperature gradient.

9-128. Answer B. GFDICM 9D, AW
Close spacing of isobars indicates the pressure gradient is strong, while a weak pressure gradient is identified by a dashed isobar. Temperature gradients are not identified on surface analysis charts.

9-129   PLT287

The Surface Analysis Chart depicts

A– frontal locations and expected movement, pressure centers, cloud coverage, and obstructions to vision at the time of chart transmission.
B– actual frontal positions, pressure patterns, temperature, dewpoint, wind, weather, and obstructions to vision at the valid time of the chart.
C– actual pressure distribution, frontal systems, cloud heights and coverage, temperature, dewpoint, and wind at the time shown on the chart.

9-129. Answer B. GFDICM 9D, AW
See explanation for Question 9-127.

9-130   PLT289

Which provides a graphic display of both VFR and IFR weather?

A– Surface Weather Map.
B– Radar Summary Chart.
C– Weather Depiction Chart.

9-130. Answer C. GFDICM 9D, AW
You can think of the weather depiction chart as an abbreviated version of the surface analysis chart.
It provides a simplified station model and a graphic depiction of VFR, marginal VFR, and IFR weather conditions. For example, IFR conditions are indicated by shaded areas, MVFR conditions are identified with contoured lines without shading, and VFR areas have no contours.

9-131   PLT289

When total sky cover is few or scattered, the height shown on the Weather Depiction Chart is the

A– top of the lowest layer.
B– base of the lowest layer.
C– base of the highest layer.

9-131. Answer B. GFDICM 9D, AW
As with the hourly observation, the weather depiction chart indicates the base of the lowest layer of clouds.

9-132   PLT353

What information is provided by the Radar Summary Chart that is not shown on other weather charts?

A– Lines and cells of hazardous thunderstorms.
B– Ceilings and precipitation between reporting stations.
C– Areas of cloud cover and icing levels within the clouds.

9-132. Answer A. GFDICM 9D, AW
The radar summary chart provides a graphic depiction of areas of precipitation, individual thunderstorms cells, lines of cells, and areas of thunderstorm activity. The chart also shows size, shape, and intensity of returns, as well as the intensity trend and direction of movement.

9-133   PLT286

Which weather chart depicts conditions forecast to exist at a specific time in the future?

A– Freezing Level Chart.
B– Weather Depiction Chart.
C– 12-Hour Significant Weather Prognostic Chart.

9-133. Answer C. GFDICM 9D, AW
The low-level significant weather prognostic chart depicts conditions forecast to exist 12 and 24 hours into the future.

9-134   PLT068

What weather phenomenon is implied within an area enclosed by small scalloped lines on a U.S. High-Level Significant Weather Prognostic Chart?

A– Cirriform clouds, light to moderate turbulence, and icing.

B– Cumulonimbus clouds, icing, and moderate or greater turbulence.

C– Cumuliform or standing lenticular clouds, moderate to severe turbulence, and icing.

9-134. Answer B. GFDICM 9D, AW

The high-level significant weather prognostic chart presents a forecast of thunderstorms, tropical cyclones, severe squalls, moderate or greater turbulence, widespread duststorms and sandstorms, tropopause heights, and the location of jet streams. The scalloped lines on this chart are used to enclose areas that have sandstorms, duststorms, and cumulonimbus clouds. Enclosed areas of cumulonimbus clouds also imply the presence of moderate or greater turbulence and icing conditions.

9-135   PLT286

The U.S. High-Level Significant Weather Prognostic Chart forecasts significant weather for what airspace?

A– 18,000 feet to 45,000 feet.

B– 24,000 feet to 45,000 feet.

C– 24,000 feet to 63,000 feet.

9-135. Answer C. GFDICM 9D, AW

The high-level significant prog chart is valid from 400 millibars (24,000 feet) to 70 millibars (63,000 feet).

9-136   PLT286

What is the upper limit of the Low Level Significant Weather Prognostic Chart?

A– 30,000 feet.

B– 24,000 feet.

C– 18,000 feet.

9-136. Answer B. GFDICM 9D, AW

The low-level significant weather prog is prepared by the National Meteorological Center, and is valid for use up to 24,000 feet.

9-137   PLT070

A freezing level panel of the composite moisture stability chart is an analysis of

A– forecast freezing level data from surface observations.

B– forecast freezing level data from upper air observations.

C– observed freezing level data from upper air observations.

9-137. Answer C. GFDICM 9D, AW

The composite moisture stability chart contains four panels: stability, freezing level, precipitable water, and average relative humidity. The freezing level panel is an analysis of observed freezing level data from upper air observations.

9-138   PLT070

The difference found by subtracting the temperature of a parcel of air theoretically lifted from the surface to 500 millibars and the existing temperature at 500 millibars is called the

A– lifted index.
B– negative index.
C– positive index.

9-138. Answer A. GFDICM 9D, AW

The stability panel of the composite moisture stability chart outlines areas of stable and unstable air. The lifted index is found by subtracting the temperature of a parcel of air that is theoretically lifted from the surface to 500 millibars (18,000 feet MSL) from the existing temperature at 500 millibars. The result can be zero, positive, or negative. A zero value indicates neutral stability, while a positive value means stable air. A negative value indicates the air is unstable. The greater the value, the greater the stability or instability.

9-139   PLT283

Hatching on a Constant Pressure Analysis Chart indicates

A– hurricane eye.
B– windspeed 70 knots to 110 knots.
C– windspeed 110 knots to 150 knots.

9-139. Answer B. GFDICM 9D, AW

The constant pressure analysis chart is an upper air weather map on which all information is referenced to a specified pressure level. It is issued twice daily for each of five pressure altitude levels from 850 millibars (5,000 feet) to 200 millibars (39,000 feet). Cross-hatching is used on 300- and 200-millibar charts to denote wind speeds of 70 to 110 knots.

9-140   PLT283

What flight planning information can a pilot derive from Constant Pressure Analysis Charts?

A– Winds and temperatures aloft.
B– Clear air turbulence and icing conditions.
C– Frontal systems and obstructions to vision aloft.

9-140. Answer A. GFDICM 9D, AW

Each reporting location on a constant pressure chart includes information on the observed temperature and temperature/dewpoint spread, wind direction and speed, height of the pressure surface, and changes in height over the previous 12 hours. The constant pressure chart is most useful for quickly determining winds and temperatures aloft for your flight.

9-141   PLT283

From which of the following can the observed temperature, wind, and temperature/dewpoint spread be determined at a specified altitude?

A– Stability Charts.
B– Winds Aloft Forecasts.
C– Constant Pressure Analysis Charts.

9-141. Answer C. GFDICM 9D, AW

See explanation for Question 9-140.

SECTION E - SOURCES OF WEATHER INFORMATION

- Enroute flight advisory service (EFAS) provides enroute aircraft with timely and meaningful weather advisories pertinent to the type of flight intended, route, and altitude.

- EFAS is obtained by contacting flight watch, using the name of the ARTCC facility identification in your area, your aircraft identification, and name of the nearest VOR, on 122.0 MHz below FL180.

- In-flight aviation weather advisories consisting of AIRMETs, SIGMETs, and convective SIGMETs are forecasts that advise enroute aircraft of the development of potentially hazardous weather, and information on volcanic eruptions that are occurring or expected to occur. All in-flight advisories in the contiguous U.S. are issued by the National Aviation Weather Advisory Unit in Kansas City, MO. All in-flight advisories use the same location identifiers (either VORs, airports, or well-known geographic areas) to describe the hazardous weather areas.

- Convective SIGMETs contain either an observation and a forecast, or just a forecast, for tornadoes, significant thunderstorm activity, or hail 3/4 inch or greater in diameter.

- A center weather advisory (CWA) is an unscheduled advisory issued by an ARTCC to alert pilots of existing or anticipated adverse weather conditions within the next two hours. A CWA may be issued prior to an AIRMET or SIGMET when PIREPs suggest AIRMET or SIGMET conditions exist. Even if adverse weather is not sufficiently intense or widespread for a SIGMET or AIRMET, a CWA may be issued if conditions are expected to affect the safe flow of air traffic within the ARTCC area of responsibility.

- AIRMETs and CWAs provide an enroute pilot with information about moderate icing, moderate turbulence, winds of 30 knots or more at the surface, and extensive mountain obscurement.

- Weather advisory broadcasts, including severe weather forecast alerts (AWW), convective SIGMETs, and SIGMETs, are provided by ARTCCs on all frequencies, except emergency, when any part of the area described is within 150 miles of the airspace under their jurisdiction.

- The hazardous inflight weather advisory service (HIWAS) is a continuous broadcast of in-flight weather advisories over selected VORs of SIGMETs, convective SIGMETs, AIRMETs, AWWs, and CWAs.

- A transcribed weather broadcast (TWEB) provides specific information concerning expected sky cover, cloud tops, visibility, weather, and obstructions to vision in a route format. To obtain continuous transcribed information, including winds aloft and route forecasts for a cross-country flight, you could monitor a TWEB on a low-frequency radio receiver. TWEB mostly has been replaced by HIWAS.

9-142   PLT515

The Hazardous Inflight Weather Advisory Service (HIWAS) is a broadcast service over selected VORs that provides

A– SIGMETs, CONVECTIVE SIGMETs and AIRMETs at 15 minutes and 45 minutes past the hour.

B– SIGMETs and AIRMETs at 15 minutes and 45 minutes past the hour for the first hour after issuance.

C– continuous broadcast of inflight weather advisories.

9-142. Answer C. GFDICM 9E, AIM

HIWAS is a recorded summary of AIRMETs, SIGMETs, Convective SIGMETs, Servere Weather Forecast Weather Alerts (AWWs), Center Weather Advisories (CWAs), and urgent PIREPs that is continuously broadcast over selected VORs.

9-143   PLT515
The Telephone Information Briefing Service (TIBS) provided by AFSSs includes

A–recorded weather briefing service for the local area, usually within 50 miles and route forecasts.
B–continuous recording of meteorological and/or aeronautical information available by telephone.
C–weather information service on a common frequency (122.0 mHz).

9-143. Answer B. GFDICM 9E, AIM
The Telephone Information Briefing Service (TIBS) provides continuous telephone recordings of meteorological and/or aeronautical information.

9-144   PLT294
In-Flight Aviation Weather Advisories include what type of information?

A–Forecasts for potentially hazardous flying conditions for enroute aircraft.
B–State and geographic areas with reported ceilings and visibilities below VFR minimums.
C–IFR conditions, turbulence, and icing within a valid period for the listed states.

9-144. Answer A. GFDICM 9B
In-Flight Aviation Weather Advisories are forecasts to advise enroute aircraft of potentially hazardous weather. Included are convective SIGMETs, SIGMETs, and AIRMETs, using VORs, airports, or other well known geographic areas to describe the location of hazardous weather along a route.

9-145   PLT294
What type of Inflight Weather Advisories provides an en route pilot with information regarding the possibility of moderate icing, moderate turbulence, winds of 30 knots or more at the surface and extensive mountain obscurement?

A–Convective SIGMETs and SIGMETs.
B–Severe Weather Forecast Alerts (AWW) and SIGMETs.
C–AIRMETs and Center Weather Advisories (CWA).

9-145. Answer C. GFDICM 9B
An AIRMET is an advisory of significant weather including moderate icing, moderate turbulence, sustained surface winds of 30 knots or more, ceilings less than 1000 feet and/or visibility less than 3 miles over 50 percent of the area, and extensive mountain obscuration. When appropriate Center Weather Advisories include AIRMETs.

9-146   PLT294
What single reference contains information regarding a volcanic eruption, that is occurring or expected to occur?

A–In-Flight Weather Advisories.
B–Terminal Area Forecasts (TAF).
C–Weather Depiction Chart.

9-146. Answer A. GFDICM 9B
In-Flight Weather Advisories include AIRMETs, SIGMETs, and Convective SIGMETs. Of these only SIGMETs report volcanic activity.

9-147   PLT513

Which forecast provides specific information concerning expected sky cover, cloud tops, visibility, weather, and obstructions to vision in a route format?

A– Area Forecast.
B– Terminal Forecast.
C– Transcribed Weather Broadcast.

9-147. Answer C. GFDICM 9E, AIM
Transcribed Weather Broadcasts (TWEBs) provide route-oriented data which is broadcast over designated NDB and VOR navigation facilities. Information contained in a TWEB forecast includes ceilings and sky cover, cloud tops, visibility, and obstructions to vision.

9-148   PLT513

To obtain a continuous transcribed weather briefing including winds aloft and route forecasts for a cross-country flight, a pilot could monitor

A– a TWEB on a low-frequency and/or VOR receiver.
B– the regularly scheduled weather broadcast on a VOR frequency.
C– a high-frequency radio receiver tuned to En Route Flight Advisory Service.

9-148. Answer A. GFDICM 9E, AIM
Transcribed Weather Broadcasts (TWEBs) provide route-oriented data which is broadcast over designated NDB and VOR navigation facilities. Information contained in a TWEB forecast includes ceilings and sky cover, cloud tops, visibility, and obstructions to vision.

9-149   PLT290

SIGMETs are issued as a warning of weather conditions which are hazardous

A– to all aircraft.
B– particularly to heavy aircraft.
C– particularly to light airplanes.

9-149. Answer A. GFDICM 9E, AIM
SIGMETs (WSs) are issued for hazardous weather (other than convective activity) which is considered significant to all aircraft. SIGMET criteria include the following: severe, extreme, or clear air turbulence; severe icing, or wide spread duststorms, sandstorms, or volcanic ash lowering surface and/or in-flight visibilities to less than three miles.

9-150   PLT290

Which correctly describes the purpose of Convective SIGMETs (WST)?

A– They consist of an hourly observation of tornadoes, significant thunderstorm activity, and large hailstone activity.
B– They contain both an observation and a forecast of all thunderstorm and hailstone activity. The forecast is valid for 1 hour only.
C– They consist of either an observation and a forecast or just a forecast for tornadoes, significant thunderstorm activity, or hail greater than or equal to 3/4 inch in diameter.

9-150. Answer C. GFDICM 9E, AIM
A convective SIGMET (WST) is issued for hazardous convective weather. They include any of the following phenomena: tornadoes, lines of thunderstorms, embedded thunderstorms, thunderstorms over a wide area, hail greater than or equal to three-fourths of an inch in diameter, and/or wind gusts to 50 knots or greater.

9-151   PLT515

En route Flight Advisory Service (EFAS) is a service that provides en route aircraft with timely and meaningful weather advisories pertinent to the type of flight intended, route, and altitude. This information is received by

A– listening to en route VORs at 15 and 45 minutes past the hour.

B– contacting flight watch, using the name of the ARTCC facility identification in your area, your aircraft identification, and name of nearest VOR, on 122.0 MHz below 17,500 feet MSL.

C– contacting the AFSS facility in your area, using your airplane identification, and the name of the nearest VOR.

9-151. Answer B. GFDICM 9E, PHB

(EFAS) En route Flight Advisory Service is available on a request basis and is transmitted on the discrete frequency of 122.0 MHz not over VORs.

9-152   PLT116

Weather Advisory Broadcasts, including Severe Weather Forecast Alerts (AWW), Convective SIGMETs, and SIGMETs, are provided by

A– ARTCCs on all frequencies, except emergency, when any part of the area described is within 150 miles of the airspace under their jurisdiction.

B– AFSSs on 122.2 MHz and adjacent VORs, when any part of the area described is within 200 miles of the airspace under their jurisdiction.

C– selected low-frequency and/or VOR navigational aids.

9-152. Answer A. GFDICM 9E, AIM

According to the Aeronautical Information Manual, Weather Advisory Broadcasts are transmitted on all frequencies except 121.5 MHz when the area of adverse weather is within 150 miles, not 200 miles, of the area of the ARTCC's jurisdiction.

CHAPTER 10

FLIGHT CONSIDERATIONS

SECTION A - IFR EMERGENCIES

Chapter 10, Section A, covers IFR emergencies. Commercial pilots should also be familiar with these procedures. Because you have probably covered this material in your IFR training, there are only a few FAA test questions assigned to this section.

DISTRESS AND URGENCY CONDITIONS

- The Aeronautical Information Manual defines an emergency as a condition of distress or urgency. Pilots in distress are threatened by serious and/or imminent danger and require immediate assistance. An urgency situation, such as low fuel quantity, requires timely but not immediate assistance.
- In an emergency, you may deviate from any rule in FAR Part 91 to the extent necessary to meet the emergency. ATC may request a detailed report of an emergency when priority assistance has been given, even though no rules have been violated.
- If you are disoriented while flying, a flight service specialist may be able to locate you with VHF/DF equipment. To use this service you must have an operative VHF two-way radio.

COMMUNICATION PROCEDURES

- The frequency of 121.5 MHz may be used to declare an emergency in the event you are unable to contact ATC on other frequencies.
- In a distress situation, begin your initial call with the word "MAYDAY," preferably repeated three times. Use "PANPAN" in the same manner in an urgency situation.
- Your transponder may be used to declare an emergency by squawking code 7700.
- A special emergency is a condition of air piracy and should be indicated by squawking code 7500 on your transponder.

MINIMUM FUEL

- If your remaining fuel quantity is such that you can accept little or no delay, you should alert ATC with a minimum fuel advisory. Declaring minimum fuel to ATC indicates an emergency situation is possible should any undue delay occur.
- If the remaining usable fuel supply suggests the need for traffic priority to ensure a safe landing, you should declare an emergency due to low fuel and report fuel remaining in minutes.

INSTRUMENT FAILURE

During an instrument failure your first priority is to fly the airplane, navigate accurately, and then communicate with ATC

COMMUNICATION FAILURE

- You can use your transponder to alert ATC to a radio communication failure by squawking code 7600.
- During a communication failure in VFR conditions, remain in VFR conditions, land as soon as practicable, and call ATC.

ENGINE FAILURE

- In the event of complete engine failure the pilot must first remember to fly the airplane and establish the recommended glide speed.
- If a loss of power or system failure occurs and diverting to an alternate is the best course of action, quickly apply rule of thumb computations, estimates and other appropriate methods in order to quickly divert to the alternate.
- If a total loss of engine power occurs at night, consider making an approach to unlighted areas if the condition of the nearby terrain is unknown. However, plan the landing to be as close to public access as possible to allow for rescue or help, if needed.

10-1   PLT208

After experiencing a powerplant failure at night, one of the primary considerations should include

A– turning off all electrical switches to save battery power for landing.

B– planning the emergency approach and landing to an unlighted portion of an area.

C– Maneuvering to, and landing on a lighted highway or road.

10-1. Answer B. GFDPMM, AFH

Upon an airborne powerplant failure at night, one of the primary considerations should be to plan the emergency approach and landing to an unlighted area. Lighted areas typically indicate structures that may obstruct a landing area.

10-2   PLT208

When planning for an emergency landing at night, one of the primary considerations should include

A– selecting a landing area close to public access, if possible.

B– landing without flaps to ensure a nose-high landing attitude at touchdown.

C– turning off all electrical switches to save battery power for the landing.

10-2. Answer A. GFDICM 10A, AFH

When planning an emergency landing at night away from an airport, consider landing in an area close to public access. This may facilitate rescue or help, if needed.

10-3   PLT208

When diverting to an alternate airport because of an emergency, pilots should

A– rely upon radio as the primary method of navigation.

B– climb to a higher altitude because it will be easier to identify checkpoints.

C– apply rule-of-thumb computations, estimates, and other appropriate shortcuts to divert to the new course as soon as possible.

10-3. Answer C. GFDICM 10A, PHB

Because of the limitations in cockpit space and available equipment, and because the pilot's attention must be divided between solving the problem and operating the airplane, advantage must be taken of all possible short-cuts and rule-of-thumb computations when diverting to an alternate airport.

10-4 PLT172

To use VHF/DF facilities for assistance in locating your position, you must have an operative VHF

A– transmitter and receiver.
B– transmitter and receiver, and an operative ADF receiver.
C– transmitter and receiver, and an operative VOR receiver.

10-4. Answer A. GFDICM 10A, AFH

If you get disoriented while flying, a flight service specialist may be able to locate you with VHF direction finder (VHF/DF) equipment. To utilize these services, you must have an operative VHF two-way radio.

10-5 PLT208

A pilot's most immediate and vital concern in the event of complete engine failure after becoming airborne on takeoff is

A– maintaining a safe airspeed.
B– landing directly into the wind.
C– turning back to the takeoff field.

10-5. Answer A. GFDPPM M14, GFDICM 10A, AFH

Anytime you experience an engine failure, your most immediate concern should be to establish the manufacturer's recommended glide speed. This speed will allow the aircraft to glide the farthest and remain in positive control.

SECTION B - IFR DECISION MAKING

Chapter 10, Section B, covers IFR decision making. Since this information is directed toward those preparing for an instrument rating, there are no commercial airplane FAA test questions assigned to this chapter.

Commercial decision making is covered in Chapter 13, Section B.

SAFE HABIT PATTERNS

- Accidents are rarely attributed to a single cause, but are the result of a series of poor choices.
- You should consider filing a flight plan for every flight, and you should close that flight plan only when a safe landing is assured.
- Though you work closely with ATC, you remain the final authority as to the safety of the flight. You may also need to coordinate responsibility with other pilots that fly with you.

PERSONAL MINIMUMS CHECKLIST

- Developing a personal minimums checklist will assist you in determining the feasibility of a particular flight. You should take into account your currency and experience when deciding upon conditions in which you feel comfortable flying.
- Five hazardous attitudes affect your decisions, and you should examine your choices to ensure that you make the proper response when one of these attitudes affects your flight.

RESOURCE USE

- Effective use of resources occurs when you understand and utilize all the people and equipment available to you during a flight.
- Plan for each flight thoroughly before you leave the ground, including fuel requirements, alternates available, and missed approach instructions. It is also helpful to program any navigation information into your aircraft's equipment before engine start. The more you can rehearse ahead of time, the more prepared you will be in the event of a problem.
- During a high workload situation, identify the most important tasks and make those a priority. Do not allow yourself to fixate on an extraneous issue.

SECTION C - IFR FLIGHT PLANNING

Chapter 10, Section C, of the Instrument Commercial Manual covers IFR flight planning. Much of this information is useful to both instrument and commercial pilots. Although this section emphasizes IFR operations, the calculations required for VFR and IFR flight planning are similar, and there are a number of FAA commercial questions assigned to this section.

PREFLIGHT PLANNING

- Although weather information may be obtained from numerous sources including newspapers, television, and the internet, you should base any go/no-go decision on a flight service station or DUATS standard briefing.
- The navigation log is a convenient way for you to complete your preflight planning, organize your flight, and provide you with a concise textual description of your flight.
- During preflight preparation, weather report forecasts which are not routinely available at the local service outlet (AFSS) can best be obtained by means of contacting a weather forecast office (WFO).
- The most current en route and destination weather information for an instrument flight should be obtained from the FSS/AFSS.
- The hazardous inflight weather advisory service (HIWAS) is a broadcast service over selected VORs.
- True course measurements on a sectional aeronautical chart should be made at a meridian near the midpoint of the course because the angles formed by meridians and the course line vary from point to point.

DESCENT PLANNING

- If doing a time or fuel to descend problem, start by finding how long it will take to descend from the beginning altitude to the final altitude at the specified rate of descent. Once this time is computed, the fuel consumed can be calculated by multiplying the fuel flow by the time to descend. Remember to make sure the units of measurement are common or are converted when necessary.
- If given groundspeed and fuel flow and asked to compute time enroute, use your flight computer or simply divide distance (n.m.) by groundspeed (knots). This gives you the time in hours. Multiply by 60 to get time in minutes. To find fuel required, multiply the time (in hours) by the fuel flow (in units per hour).
- Some questions on the commercial test ask you to calculate wind speed and direction from course, heading, true airspeed and groundspeed. This is different than calculating groundspeed from winds, as you did on the private pilot test. Most newer electronic flight computers, as well as the classic E6B, can be used to perform these calculations.
- If given a time and fuel to climb problem, first, find the time it takes to climb from the initial altitude to the enroute altitude at the specified rate. To calculate the fuel consumed, multiply this time by the fuel flow. Again, remember to make sure the units of measurement are common or are converted when necessary.

10-6   PLT515
During preflight preparation, weather report forecasts which are not routinely available at the local service outlet (AFSS) can best be obtained by means of contacting

A– pilot's automatic telephone answering service.
B– air route traffic control center.
C– weather forecast office (WFO).

10-6. Answer C. GFDICM 10C, AIM
The weather forecast office prepares most weather forecasts that you use as a pilot. They are the logical source of additional information.

10-7   PLT515
The most current en route and destination weather information for an instrument flight should be obtained from the

A– ATIS broadcast.
B– Notices to Airmen publications.
C– AFSS.

10-7. Answer C. GFDICM 10C, AWS
Of all the different ways there are to obtain current and forecast weather information, flight service stations (FSSs) and automated flight service stations (AFSS) are still the best sources for obtaining this information.

10-8   PLT012
An airplane descends under the following conditions:
Cruising altitude...6,500 ft
Airport elevation...700 ft
Descends to...800 ft AGL
Rate of decent...500 ft/min
Average true airspeed...110 kts
True course...335°
Average wind velocity...060° at 15 kts
Variation 3°W; Deviation...+2°
Average fuel consumption...8.5 gal/hr.

Find the approximate time, compass heading, distance, and fuel consumed.

A– 10 minutes, 348°, 18 NM, 1.4 gallons.
B– 10 minutes, 355°, 17 NM, 2.4 gallons.
C– 12 minutes, 346°, 18 NM, 1.6 gallons.

10-8. Answer A. GFDICM 10C, PHB
First, determine the total height of the descent from 6,500 feet minus the airport elevation of 700 feet and the traffic pattern altitude of 800 feet (6,500 ft - 1,500 ft. = 5,000 feet). The time to descend is determined by dividing the height of the descent by the rate of descent (5,000 ft. ÷ 500 ft/min = 10 minutes. Now, enter the following given information into your flight computer to calculate true heading, and groundspeed.

1. Wind 060° at 15 kts.
2. True course 335°
3. True airspeed 110 kts.
   True heading = 343°

   Groundspeed = 108 kts.

Determine compass heading by adding the variation and deviation to the true heading (343° + 5° = 348°). Determine the distance by entering the time of 10 minutes and a groundspeed of 108 knots to get 18.0 n.m. Determine fuel consumption by entering the time of 10 minutes and a fuel flow of 8.5 gallons per hour to get 1.4 gallons.

10-9   PLT012

An airplane descends to an airport under the following conditions:

Cruising altitude...7,500 ft
Airport elevation...1,300 ft
Descends to...800 ft AGL
Rate of descent...300 ft/min
Average true airspeed...120 kts
True course...165°
Average wind velocity...240° at 20 kts
Variation...4°E
Deviation...-2°
Average fuel consumption...9.6 gal/hr

Determine the approximate time, compass heading, distance, and fuel consumed.

A– 16 minutes, 168°, 30 NM, 2.9 gallons.
B– 18 minutes, 164°, 34 NM, 3.2 gallons.
C– 18 minutes, 168°, 34 NM, 2.9 gallons.

10-9. Answer C. GFDICM 10C, PHB

First, determine the total height of the descent from 7,500 feet minus the airport elevation of 1,300 feet and the traffic pattern altitude of 800 feet AGL. (7,500 ft. - 2,100 ft. = 5,400 ft.). The time to descend is determined by dividing the height of the descent by the rate of descent (5,400 ft. ÷ 300 ft./min. = 18 minutes). Now, enter the following given information into your flight computer to calculate true heading and groundspeed.

1. Wind 240° at 20 kts.
2. True course 165°
3. True airspeed 120 kts.
   True heading = 174°

   Groundspeed = 113 kts.

Determine compass heading by subtracting the variation and compass deviation from the true heading (174° - 6° = 168°). Determine the distance by entering the time of 18 minutes and the groundspeed of 113 knots into your flight computer to get 34 n.m. Determine fuel consumption by entering the time of 18 minutes and a fuel flow of 9.6 gallons per hour to get 2.9 gallons.

10-10   PLT012

An airplane descends to an airport under the following conditions:

Cruising altitude...10,500 ft
Airport elevation...1,700 ft
Descends to...1,000 ft AGL
Rate of descent...600 ft/min
Average true airspeed...135 kts
True course...263°
Average wind velocity...330° at 30 kts
Variation...7° E
Deviation...+3°
Average fuel consumption...11.5 gal/hr

Determine the approximate time, compass heading, distance, and fuel consumed.

A–9 minutes, 274°, 26 NM, 2.8 gallons.
B– 13 minutes, 274°, 28 MN, 2.5 gallons.
C– 13 minutes, 271°, 26 NM, 2.5 gallons.

10-10. Answer C. GFDICM 10C, PHB

First, determine the total height of the descent from 10,500 feet minus the airport elevation of 1,700 feet and the traffic pattern altitude of 1,000 feet (10,500 ft. - 2,700 ft. = 7,800 ft.). The time to descend is determined by dividing the height of the descent (7,800 ft. ÷ 600 ft./min. = 13 min.) Now, enter the following given information into your flight computer to calculated true heading and groundspeed.

1. Wind 330° at 30 kts.
2. True course 263°
3. True airspeed 135 kts.
   True heading = 275°

   Groundspeed = 120 kts.

Determine compass heading by subtracting the variation (7°E) and adding the deviation (+3°) to the true heading (275° - 4° = 271°). Determine the distance by entering the time of 13 minutes and a ground speed of 120 knots to get 26.1 n.m. Determine fuel consumption by entering the time of 13 minutes and a fuel flow of 11.5 gal/hr to get 2.5 gallons.

10-11   PLT012
If fuel consumption is 80 pounds per hour and groundspeed is 180 knots, how much fuel is required for an airplane to travel 460 NM?

A– 205 pounds.
B– 212 pounds.
C– 460 pounds.

10-11. Answer A. GFDICM 10C, PHB
First, determine the time enroute by entering the groundspeed (180 kts.) and distance (460 n.m.) into your flight computer to get 2 hours 33 minutes. Then, enter the time (2:33:20) and fuel consumption rate (80 lbs/hr) into your flight computer to get 204.4 pounds of fuel.

10-12   PLT012
If an airplane is consuming 95 pounds of fuel per hour at a cruising altitude of 6,500 feet and the groundspeed is 173 knots, how much fuel is required to travel 450 NM?

A– 248 pounds.
B– 265 pounds.
C– 284 pounds.

10-12. Answer A. GFDICM 10C, PHB
First, determine the time enroute by entering the groundspeed (173 kts.) and distance (450 n.m.) into your flight computer to get 2 hours 36 minutes. Then, enter the time (2:36:04) and fuel consumption rate (95 lbs/hr) into your flight computer to get 247.1 pounds of fuel.

10-13   PLT012
If an airplane is consuming 12.5 gallons of fuel per hour at a cruising altitude of 8,500 feet and the groundspeed is 145 knots, how much fuel is required to travel 435 NM?

A– 27 gallons.
B– 34 gallons.
C– 38 gallons.

10-13. Answer C. GFDICM 10C, PHB
First, determine the time enroute by entering the groundspeed (145 kts.) and distance (435 n.m.) into your flight computer to get 3 hours even. Then, enter the time (3:00:00) and fuel consumption rate (12.5 lbs/hr) into your flight computer to get 37.5 gallons per hour.

10-14   PLT012
If an airplane is consuming 9.5 gallons of fuel per hour at a cruising altitude of 6,000 feet and the groundspeed is 135 knots, how much fuel is required to travel 490 NM?

A– 27 gallons.
B– 30 gallons.
C– 35 gallons.

10-14. Answer C. GFDICM 10C, PHB
First, determine the time enroute by entering the groundspeed (135 kts.) and distance (490 n.m.) into your flight computer to get 3 hours 37 minutes. Then, enter the time (3:37:47) and fuel consumption rate (9.5 gal/hr) into your flight computer to get 34.5 gallons of fuel.

10-15   PLT012
If an airplane is consuming 14.8 gallons of fuel per hour at a cruising altitude of 7,500 feet and the groundspeed is 167 knots, how much fuel is required to travel 560 NM?

A– 50 gallons.
B– 53 gallons.
C– 57 gallons.

10-15. Answer A. GFDICM 10C, PHB
First, determine the time enroute by entering the groundspeed (167 kts.) and distance (560 n.m.) into your flight computer to get 3 hours 21 minutes. Then, enter the time (3:21:12) and fuel consumption rate (14.8 gal/hr) into your flight computer to get 49.6 gallons of fuel.

10-16   PLT012

If fuel consumption is 14.7 gallons per hour and groundspeed is 157 knots, how much fuel is required for an airplane to travel 612 NM?

A–58 gallons.
B–60 gallons.
C–64 gallons.

10-16. Answer A. GFDICM 10C, PHB

First, determine the time enroute by entering the groundspeed (157 kts.) and distance (612 n.m.) into your flight computer to get 3 hours 53 minutes. Then, enter the time (3:53:53) and fuel consumption rate (14.7 gal/hr) into your flight computer to get 57.3 gallons of fuel.

10-17   PLT012
GIVEN:

True course...105°
True heading...085°
True airspeed...95 kts
Groundspeed...87 kts

Determine the wind direction and speed.

A–020° and 32 knots.
B–030° and 38 knots.
C–200° and 32 knots.

10-17. Answer A. GFDICM 10C, PHB

Enter the given information into your flight computer to get a wind direction of 020° and a wind speed of 33 knots.

10-18   PLT012
GIVEN:

True course...345°
True heading...355°
True airspeed...85 kts
Groundspeed...95 kts

Determine the wind direction and speed.

A–095° and 19 knots.
B–113° and 19 knots.
C–238° and 18 knots.

10-18. Answer B. GFDICM 10C, PHB

Enter the given information into your flight computer to get a wind direction of 112° and a wind speed of 19 knots.

10-19   PLT320

True course measurements on a Sectional Aeronautical Chart should be made at a meridian near the midpoint of the course because the

A–values of isogonic lines change from point to point.
B–angles formed by isogonic lines and lines of latitude vary from point to point.
C–angles formed by lines of longitude and the course line vary from point to point.

10-19. Answer C. GFDPPM 9A, PHB

Because lines of longitude (meridians) converge toward the poles, course measurement should be taken near the midpoint of the course rather than at the departure or destination point. This is because the angles formed by lines of longitude and your course line will vary from point to point.

10-20   PLT012
GIVEN:

Wind...175° at 20 kts
Distance...135 NM
True course...075°
True airspeed...80 kts
Fuel consumption...105 lb/hr

Determine the time en route and fuel consumption.

A– 1 hour 28 minutes and 73.2 pounds.
B– 1 hour 38 minutes and 158 pounds.
C– 1 hour 40 minutes and 175 pounds.

10-20. Answer C. GFDICM 10C, PHB
To solve this problem you must determine your groundspeed. To do this enter the wind direction (175°) and wind speed (20 kts.), true course (075°), and true airspeed (80 kts.) into your flight computer. Your groundspeed is 81 knots. To determine the estimated time enroute (ETE), divide the distance by your groundspeed. Your ETE is 1:40:00 (135 ÷ 81 = 1:40:00). To calculate your fuel consumption, multiply your ETE by the fuel consumption rate. The answer is 175 pounds (1:40:00 × 105 = 175).

10-21   PLT012
An airplane departs an airport under the following conditions:

Airport elevation...1,000 ft
Cruise altitude...9,500 ft
Rate of climb...500 ft/min
Average true airspeed...135 kts
True course...215°
Average wind velocity...290° at 20 kts
Variation...3° W; Deviation...-2°
Average fuel consumption...13 gal/hr

Determine the approximate time, compass heading, distance, and fuel consmed during the climb.

A– 14 minutes, 234°, 26 NM, 3.9 gallons.
B– 17 minutes, 224°, 36 NM, 3.7 gallons.
C– 17 minutes, 242°, 31 NM, 3.5 gallons.

10-21. Answer B. GFDICM 10C, PHB
First, determine the total height of the climb from the airport elevation of 1,000 feet to the cruise altitude of 9,500 feet (9,500 ft. - 1,000 ft. = 8,500 feet). The time to climb is determined by dividing the height of the climb by the rate of climb (8,500 ft. ÷ 500 ft/min = 17.0 minutes). Now enter the following given information into your flight computer to calculate true heading, and groundspeed.

1. Wind 290° at 20 kts.
2. True course 215°
3. True airspeed 135 kts.
   True heading = 223°

   Groundspeed = 128 kts.

Determine compass heading by adding the variation (3°W) and subtracting the deviation (-2°) to the true heading (223° + 3° - 2° = 224°). Determine the distance by entering the time of 17 minutes and a groundspeed of 128 knots to get 36.4 n.m. Determine fuel consumption by entering the time of 17 minutes and a fuel flow of 13.0 gallons per hour to get 3.7 gallons.

10-22   PLT012

An airplane departs an airport under the following conditions:

Airport elevation...1,500 ft
Cruise altitude...9,500 ft
Rate of climb...500 ft/min
Average true airspeed...160 kts
True course...145°
Average wind velocity...080° at 15 kts
Variation...5° E
Deviation...-3°
Average fuel consumption...14 gal/hr.

Determine the approximate time, compass heading, distance, and fuel consumed during the climb.

A– 14 minutes, 128°, 35 NM, 3.2 gallons.
B– 16 minutes, 132°, 41 NM, 3.7 gallons.
C– 16 minutes, 128°, 32 NM, 3.8 gallons.

10-22. Answer B. GFDICM 10C, PHB

First, determine the total height of the climb from the airport elevation of 1,500 feet to the cruise altitude of 9,500 feet (9,500 ft - 1,500 ft. = 8,000 feet). The time to climb is determined by dividing the height of the climb by the rate of climb (8,000 ft. ÷ 500 ft/min = 16.0 minutes). Now enter the following given information into your flight computer to calculate true heading, and groundspeed.

1. Wind 080° at 15 kts.
2. True course 145°
3. True airspeed 160 kts.
    True heading = 140°

    Groundspeed = 153 kts.

Determine compass heading by subtracting thevariation (5°E) and deviation (-3°) to the true heading (140° - 8° = 132°). Determine the distance by entering the time of 16 minutes and a groundspeed of 153 knots to get 40.8 n.m. Determine fuel consumption by entering the time of 16 minutes and a fuel flow of 14.0 gallons per hour to get 3.7 gallons.

ADVANCED SYSTEMS

CHAPTER 11

SECTION A - HIGH-PERFORMANCE POWERPLANTS

Chapter 11, Section A, of the Instrument/Commercial Manual contains essential information for commercial pilots. It emphasizes reciprocating powerplant operations and procedures. You may have covered much of this material in your training for a private pilot certificate, in which case you may find this section a useful review.

COMPLEX AIRPLANES

- A complex airplane is one that has retractable landing gear, flaps, and a controllable pitch propeller, whereas, a high-performance airplane is one that has an engine of more than 200 horsepower.
- Before increasing manifold pressure (MAP) or reducing r.p.m. on an aircraft that is equipped with a constantspeed propeller, you should verify that the resulting MAP will not cause engine damage.
- To increase power on an engine equipped with a constant-speed propeller, first increase the engine r.p.m. by advancing the propeller control and then advance the throttle to increase MAP. To decrease power, first decrease the MAP by retarding the throttle and then decrease the engine r.p.m. by retarding the propeller control.
- High engine oil temperature most likely is the indication of low oil level.
- Crankshaft counterweights designed to reduce engine vibration can be detuned by rapidly opening and closing the throttle.

OPERATION OF FUEL SYSTEMS

- The ratio of the weight of fuel and the weight of air entering a cylinder is known as the fuel/air ratio. The best power mixture is that fuel/air ratio at which the most power can be obtained for any given throttle setting.
- The application of carburetor heat enriches the fuel/air mixture, which can reduce power and decrease performance It may be necessary to adjust the mixture control when applying carburetor heat.
- An excessively rich mixture may cause spark plug fouling and a rough running engine at low r.p.m.
- When using the fuel flow indicator, you should be aware of a malfunction that may occur if a fuel nozzle becomes obstructed by dirt or other foreign debris. With a blocked nozzle, the injection system's pressure will rise, causing the indicator to show a higher-than-normal fuel flow value. In response, you may be tempted to lean the mixture further in order to obtain the desired flow rate.
- Fuel injection system vapor lock is caused by the fuel vaporizing in the injection system's lines and components. Without the flow of cooling air through the engine cowling, the engine's heat causes the fuel in the injection system to boil. The boiling fuel produces vapor that blocks fuel flow in the injection system.
- Fuel injection systems have an alternate air source that provides unfiltered, heated intake air to the engine in the event the main air source is obstructed by impact ice.

PREIGNITION AND DETONATION

- Preignition and detonation are the result of abnormal ignition and combustion. Frequency and severity of these conditions can be greatly reduced by using the correct fuel/air mixture and by monitoring the engine instruments to maintain the proper engine operating temperatures.
- Detonation is when the fuel air mixture in the cylinder instantaneously ignites instead of burning progressively and evenly.
- Preignition is the uncontrolled firing of the fuel/air charge in advance of normal spark ignition. This can be the result of hot spots or glowing carbon particles within the cylinder.

- Air-cooled reciprocating aircraft engines are dependent on the proper flow of lubricating oil to provide internal cooling. The circulation of the oil helps to disperse heat away from moving parts.

PROPELLERS

- The spiraling slipstream produced from a propeller around the fuselage of the aircraft strikes the left side of the vertical fin. This tends to cause the aircraft to turn left around the vertical axis, and roll to the right around the longitudinal axis.
- Propeller efficiency is the ratio of thrust horsepower to brake horsepower. A fixed-pitch propeller achieves its peak efficiency at a specific airspeed and r.p.m. while an aircraft with a constant-speed propeller will automatically adjust the propeller blade angle for any given throttle setting to attain the optimum efficiency.
- To obtain maximum power and thrust a controllable-pitch propeller should be set at a small angle of attack with a high r.p.m. setting.

11-1   PLT343

Before shutdown, while at idle, the ignition key is momentarily turned OFF. The engine continues to run with no interruption; this

A– is normal because the engine is usually stopped by moving the mixture to idle cut-off.
B– should not normally happen. Indicates a magneto not grounding in OFF position.
C– is an undesirable practice, but indicates that nothing is wrong.

11-1. Answer B. GFDPPM 2B, PHB
An engine that continues running after the ignition switch is turned to OFF may have a disconnected ground wire in the ignition switch.

11-2   PLT343

Leaving the carburetor heat on during takeoff

A– leans the mixture for more power on takeoff.
B– will decrease the takeoff distance.
C– will increase the ground roll.

11-2. Answer C. GFDPPM 11A, PHB
Carburetor heat causes a slight decrease in engine power, because the heated air is less dense than the outside air that would have been entering the engine.

11-3   PLT343

A way to detect a broken magneto primary grounding lead is to

A– idle the engine and momentarily turn the ignition off.
B– add full power, while holding the brakes, and momentarily turn off the ignition.
C– run on one magneto, lean the mixture, and look for a rise in manifold pressure.

11-3. Answer A. GFDPPM 2B, PHB
To check the ignition system for a broken ground wire, idle the engine before shutting it down and momentarily turn the ignition switch to OFF, then, turn the switch back to both. If the engine continues to run without hesitation the ground wire is broken. This check should be accomplished in accordance with the manufacturer's recommendations in the Aircraft Flight Manual or the Pilot's Operating Handbook.

11-4   PLT343
Fouling of spark plugs is more apt to occur if the aircraft

A– gains altitude with no mixture adjustment.
B– descends from altitude with no mixture adjustment.
C– throttle is advanced very abruptly.

11-4. Answer A. GFDPPM 11A, PHB
As altitude increases, the density of the air entering the carburetor decreases while the density of the fuel remains the same. This means that at higher altitudes the mixture becomes progressively richer. To maintain the correct fuel/air mixture, you must lean the mixture for flight at higher altitudes and you must remember to enrich the mixture during descent.

11-5   PLT343
The most probable reason an engine continues to run after the ignition switch has been turned off is

A– carbon deposits glowing on the spark plugs.
B– a magneto ground wire is in contact with the engine casing.
C– a broken magneto ground wire.

11-5. Answer C. GFDPPM 2B, PHB
The engine will continue to run with the ignition switch turned to the OFF position if a ground wire between the ignition switch and the magneto is broken.

11-6   PLT343
If the ground wire between the magneto and the ignition switch becomes disconnected, the engine

A– will not operate on one magneto.
B– cannot be started with the switch in the BOTH position.
C– could accidently start if the propeller is moved with fuel in the cylinder.

11-6. Answer C. GFDPPM 2B, PHB
If the ground wire between the magneto and the ignition switch is disconnected, the magneto may send a current to the spark plugs if any rotation of the crankshaft/propeller occurs. A small amount of fuel in the cylinders is all that is needed to start the engine in this situation.

11-7   PLT343
For internal cooling, reciprocating aircraft engines are especially dependent on

A– a properly functioning cowl flap augmenter.
B– the circulation of lubricating oil.
C– the proper freon/compressor output ratio.

11-7. Answer B. GFDPPM 2B, PHB
Oil provides two important functions in an engine, lubrication and cooling by reducing friction and removing some of the heat from the cylinders.

11-8   PLT249
The pilot controls the air/fuel ratio with the

A– throttle.
B– mixture control.
C– manifold pressure.

11-8. Answer B. GFDPPM 2B, AFH
To maintain the proper fuel/air mixture, you must be able to adjust the amount of fuel that is mixed with the incoming air. This is a function of the mixture control.

11-9   PLT350
Which statement best describes the operating principle of a constant-speed propeller?

A– As throttle setting is changed by the pilot, the prop governor causes pitch angle of the propeller blades to remain unchanged.
B– The propeller control regulates the engine RPM, and in turn, the propeller RPM.
C– A high blade angle, or increased pitch, reduces the propeller drag and allows more engine power for takeoffs.

11-9. Answer B. GFDICM 2B, PHB
The propeller control is used to set the engine RPM, which is the same as setting the propeller RPM.

11-10   PLT350
In aircraft equipped with constant-speed propellers and normally-aspirated engines, which procedure should be used to avoid placing undue stress on the engine components? When power is being

A– decreased, reduce the RPM before reducing the manifold pressure.
B– increased, increase the RPM before increasing the manifold pressure.
C– increased or decreased, the RPM should be adjusted before the manifold pressure.

11-10. Answer B. GFDICM 2B, PHB
When increasing power in an airplane with a constant speed propeller, first increase the RPM by decreasing the propeller blade angle, then advance the throttle to increase manifold pressure. When decreasing power, first retard the throttle to reduce manifold pressure, then decrease RPM by increasing the propeller blade angle.

11-11   PLT115
Detonation may occur at high-power settings when

A– the fuel mixture ignites instantaneously instead of burning progressively and evenly.
B– an excessively rich fuel mixture causes an explosive gain in power.
C– the fuel mixture is ignited too early by hot carbon deposits in the cylinder.

11-11. Answer A. GFDICM 11A, PHB
Detonation is the uncontrolled, explosive combustion of fuel. Normally, fuel burns evenly and progressively inside the combustion chamber. Detonation causes the fuel to explode, producing excessive pressures and temperatures within the engine.

11-12   PLT115
Detonation can be caused by

A– a "rich" mixture.
B– using a lower grade of fuel than recommended.
C– low engine temperatures.

11-12. Answer B. GFDICM 11A, PHB
Detonation is the uncontrolled, explosive combustion of fuel. Detonation is caused by several conditions such as using a fuel grade lower than recommended, high engine temperatures, a heavy engine load at a low RPM, or using a fuel/air mixture that is too lean.

11-13 PLT115

The uncontrolled firing of the fuel/air charge in advance of normal spark ignition is known as

A– instantaneous combustion.
B– detonation.
C– pre-ignition.

11-13. Answer C. GFDICM 11A, PHB

Preignition sometimes occurs when an excessively rich mixture causes residual fuel to form carbon deposits in the cylinder that are heated until they are glowing. Preignition can also occur from an excessively hot exhaust valve, or a cracked ceramic spark plug insulator, or almost any damage around the combustion chamber.These hot spots ignite the fuel/air mixture prematurely and cause a loss of performance, increase in operating temperatures and severe structural stresses on the engine.

11-14 PLT249

Fuel/air ratio is the ratio between the

A– volume of fuel and volume of air entering the cylinder.
B– weight of fuel and weight of air entering the cylinder.
C– weight of fuel and weight of air entering the carburetor.

11-14. Answer B. GFDPPM 11A, PHB

Fuel and air are mixed in the carburetor prior to entering the cylinders. The throttle is used to regulate the amount of airflow. For this mixture to burn efficiently, the ratio of air-to-fuel must be maintained within a specific range, such as 12:1, or 12 pounds of air and 1 pound of fuel.

11-15 PLT343

The mixture control can be adjusted, which

A– prevents the fuel/air combination from becoming too rich at higher altitudes.
B– regulates the amount of air flow through the carburetor's venturi.
C– prevents the fuel/air combination from becoming lean as the airplane climbs.

11-15. Answer A. GFDPPM 11A, PHB

The purpose of the mixture control is to prevent the mixture from becoming excessively rich at higher altitudes due to the decreasing density of the air.

11-16 PLT189

Which statement is true concerning the effect of the application of carburetor heat?

A– It enriches the fuel/air mixture.
B– It leans the fuel/air mixture.
C– It has no effect on the fuel/air mixture.

11-16. Answer A. GFDPPM 11A, PHB

Applying carburetor heat causes a slight decrease of engine power because the heated air is less dense than the outside air that would have been entering the engine. This enriches the mixture. When the same amount of fuel is mixed with less dense air (more fuel than air by weight), a richer mixture occurs.

11-17 PLT350

Propeller efficiency is the

A– ratio of thrust horsepower to brake horsepower.
B– actual distance a propeller advances in one revolution.
C– ratio of geometric pitch to effective pitch.

11-17. Answer A. GFDICM 11A, PHB

Propeller efficiency is the ratio of thrust horsepower to brake horsepower. Propeller efficiency varies between 50% and 87%, depending on how much the propeller slips.

11-18   PLT350

A fixed-pitch propeller is designed for best efficiency only at a given combination of

A– altitude and RPM.
B– airspeed and RPM.
C– airspeed and altitude.

11-18. Answer B. GFDICM 11A, PHB

A fixed-pitch propeller achieves peak efficiency only at a given combination of airspeed and r.p.m.

11-19   PLT351

The reason for variations in geometric pitch (twisting) along a propeller blade is that it

A– permits a relatively constant angle of incidence along its length when in cruising flight.
B– prevents the portion of the blade near the hub from stalling during cruising flight.
C– permits a relatively constant angle of attack along its length when in cruising flight.

11-19. Answer C. GFDICM 11A, PHB

Unlike an airfoil which moves the air at a uniform rate, propellers are rotating airfoils, and sections near the tip travel at a much faster speed than the sections near the hub. To compensate for this, each small section of the propeller blade is set at a different angle of attack to the plane of rotation. The gradual decrease in the blade angle (the propeller twist) on sections further away from the hub, allows the propeller to provide a relatively constant angle of attack and uniform thrust throughout most of the blade length.

11-20   PLT343

A detuning of engine crankshaft counterweights is a source of overstress that may be caused by

A– rapid opening and closing of the throttle.
B– carburetor ice forming on the throttle valve.
C– operating with an excessively rich fuel/air mixture.

11-20. Answer A. GFDICM 11A, AC 20-103

Many aircraft engines are equipped with balance weights as part of the crankshaft assembly. These counterweights can be detuned by rapidly opening and closing the throttle or excessive speed or power settings. When these counterweights are detuned, crankshaft vibrations leading to engine and/or crankshaft failure can result.

11-21   PLT343

The best power mixture is that fuel/air ratio at which

A– cylinder head temperatures are the coolest.
B– the most power can be obtained for any given throttle setting.
C– a given power can be obtained with the highest manifold pressure or throttle setting.

11-21. Answer B. GFDPPM 11A, PHB

When setting the mixture, you want to achieve a fuel/air ratio that provides the most power for any given throttle setting.

11-22   PLT189

Applying carburetor heat will

A– not affect the mixture.
B– lean the fuel/air mixture.
C– enrich the fuel/air mixture.

11-22. Answer C. GFDICM 11A, PHB

When carburetor heat is applied, warm air is introduced into the carburetor. Since heated air is less dense, the mixture is enriched.

11-23   PLT342

An abnormally high engine oil temperature indication may be caused by

A– a defective bearing.
B– the oil level being too low.
C– operating with an excessively rich mixture.

11-23. Answer B. GFDPPM 2B, PHB

High oil temperature indications can be caused by several factors, including a low oil quantity, a plugged oil line, or a defective temperature gauge.

11-24   PLT343

What will occur if no leaning is made with the mixture control as the flight altitude increases?

A– The volume of air entering the carburetor decreases and the amount of fuel decreases.
B– The density of air entering the carburetor decreases and the amount of fuel increases.
C– The density of air entering the carburetor decreases and the amount of fuel remains constant.

11-24. Answer C. GFDICM 11A, PHB

As altitude increases, air becomes less dense. However, the density of the fuel entering the carburetor at altitude remains the same. If the mixture control is not changed, the mixture could be enriched enough to cause engine roughness, reduced power, and spark plug fouling.

11-25   PLT343

Unless adjusted, the fuel/air mixture becomes richer with an increase in altitude because the amount of fuel

A– decreases while the volume of air decreases.
B– remains constant while the volume of air decreases.
C– remains constant while the density of air decreases.

11-25. Answer C. GFDICM 11A, PHB

See explanation for Question 11-24. As the air density decreases and the amount of fuel remains constant, the mixture becomes richer.

11-26   PLT343

The basic purpose of adjusting the fuel/air mixture control at altitude is to

A– decrease the fuel flow to compensate for decreased air density.
B– decrease the amount of fuel in the mixture to compensate for increased air density.
C– increase the amount of fuel in the mixture to compensate for the decrease in pressure and density of the air.

11-26. Answer A. GFDICM 11A, PHB

See explanation for Question 11-24. As the air density decreases with altitude, the fuel flow must be decreased to maintain the proper fuel/air ratio, or mixture.

11-27   PLT343

At high altitudes, an excessively rich mixture will cause the

A– engine to overheat.
B– fouling of spark plugs.
C– engine to operate smoother even though fuel consumption is increased.

11-27. Answer B. GFDICM 11A, PHB

A mixture that is too rich can foul the spark plugs, resulting in engine roughness.

11-28   PLT350

To establish a climb after takeoff in an aircraft equipped with a constant-speed propeller, the output of the engine is reduced to climb power by decreasing manifold pressure and

A–increasing RPM by decreasing propeller blade angle.

B–decreasing RPM by decreasing propeller blade angle.

C–decreasing RPM by increasing propeller blade angle.

11-28. Answer C. GFDICM 11A, AFH

Anytime you decrease power on an engine with a constant-speed propeller, you should reduce the manifold pressure first with the throttle, and the RPM second by increasing the propeller blade angle.

11-29   PLT350

To develop maximum power and thrust, a constant-speed propeller should be set to a blade angle that will produce a

A–large angle of attack and low RPM.

B–small angle of attack and high RPM.

C–large angle of attack and high RPM.

11-29. Answer B. GFDICM 11A, AFH

To achieve maximum power and thrust from an aircraft equipped with a constant-speed propeller, you must use a low blade angle that develops a high RPM.

11-30   PLT350

For takeoff, the blade angle of a controllable-pitch propeller should be set at a

A–small angle of attack and high RPM.

B–large angle of attack and low RPM.

C–large angle of attack and high RPM.

11-30. Answer A. GFDICM 11A, AFH

See explanation for Question 11-29. During takeoff it is important that you obtain the maximum performance from your aircraft. To do this with a constant-speed propeller, you should use a small propeller blade angle resulting in a high RPM.

SECTION B - ENVIRONMENTAL AND ICE CONTROL SYSTEMS

Chapter 11, Section B, covers systems found in advanced aircraft that you may fly as a commercial pilot. Although this information is important, there are no commercial FAA test questions assigned.

OXYGEN SYSTEMS

Make sure the oxygen system is filled with aviator's breathing oxygen. If you do not use this type of oxygen, it may contain too much moisture, which may cause valves and lines to freeze, possibly stopping the flow of oxygen.

CABIN PRESSURIZATION SYSTEMS

Pressurization is accomplished by pumping air into an aircraft that is adequately sealed to limit the rate at which air escapes from the cabin. By limiting the rate of airflow out of the cabin, the air pressure increases to produce a cabin environment equivalent to one encountered at a lower altitude.

ICE CONTROL SYSTEMS

Anti-icing equipment prevents the formation of ice; de-icing equipment removes ice once it has formed. Common anti-icing systems include heated wings and propellers, as well as systems for applying anti-ice fluids to wings and propellers. De-icing equipment typically consists of inflatable boots on leading edges of airfoils, designed to break off accumulated ice.

SECTION C - RETRACTABLE LANDING GEAR

- If there is moisture on the runway when taking off in freezing temperatures or possible ice accumulation climbing to or above the freezing level, it is wise to cycle the landing gear several times. Cycling the gear helps prevent ice from forming over the linkages and locking or sticking the gear in the retracted position.
- V_{LE} is the maximum landing gear extended speed.

11-31   PLT466
14 CFR part 1 defines V_{LE} as

A–maximum landing gear extended speed.
B–maximum landing gear operating speed.
C–maximum leading edge flaps extended speed.

11-31. Answer A. GFDICM 11A, FAR 1.2
V_{LE} is the maximum allowable speed with the landing gear extended. V_{LO} is the maximum landing gear operating speed.

11-32   PLT126
If necessary to take off from a slushy runway, the freezing of landing gear mechanisms can be minimized by

A–recycling the gear.
B–delaying gear retraction.
C–increasing the airspeed to V_{LE} before retraction.

11-32. Answer A. GFDICM 11C, AC 91-13C
In cold weather, moisture can splash onto gear linkages and freeze. If moisture is unavoidable, cycle the landing gear several times after takeoff to prevent a solid bond of ice from adhering to movable parts.

AERODYNAMICS AND PERFORMANCE LIMITATIONS

CHAPTER 12

SECTION A - ADVANCED AERODYNAMICS

Chapter 12, Section A is a review of basic aerodynamic principles and includes aerodynamic topics appropriate for a commercial pilot.

AERODYNAMIC FUNDAMENTALS

- The four fundamentals in maneuvering an aircraft are straight-and-level flight, turns, climbs, and descents.
- Opposing forces are equal in unaccelerated flight.
- When you initiate a climb or descent, you momentarily create an imbalance in the four forces, which causes the airplane to accelerate until the forces reach equilibrium again. For example, to climb you increase the angle of attack, creating an excess of lift. If thrust remains constant, the increase in induced drag slows the airplane. This reduced airspeed decreases the amount of lift, bringing lift and weight back into balance. Because the thrust vector is now inclined upward, a portion is acting to lift the airplane.

LIFT

- Lift is defined as the force acting perpendicular to the relative wind. Drag acts parallel to the flight path, in the same direction as the relative wind.
- Lift results from relatively high pressure below the wing's surface and lower air pressure above the wing's surface.
- There is a corresponding indicated airspeed for every angle of attack to generate sufficient lift to maintain altitude.
- To generate the same amount of lift at a higher altitude, an airplane must be flown at either a higher angle of attack or a higher true airspeed.
- When the angle of attack of a symmetrical airfoil is increased, the center of pressure will remain unaffected.
- Flaps increase the coefficient of lift, allowing the wing to produce the same amount of lift at a lower airspeed. Flaps also lower the stall speed.

DRAG

- At high angles of attack, pressure increases below the wing, and the increase in lift is accompanied by an increase in induced drag.
- Induced drag is a by-product of lift and is greatly affected by changes in airspeed.
- Ground effect decreases induced drag and increases lift at a given angle of attack. An airplane leaving ground effect will experience an increase in drag and will require more thrust.
- Parasite drag increases in proportion to the square of the airspeed, thus doubling the airspeed will quadruple parasite drag.
- Total drag is lowest at the airspeed which produces the highest ratio of lift to drag (L/D_{MAX}). At airspeeds below L/D_{MAX}, total drag increases due to induced drag, and at speeds above L/D_{MAX}, total drag increases because of parasite drag.
- The airspeed that gives the lowest total drag (L/D_{MAX}) will provide the best power-off glide range, as well as the greatest range. As aircraft weight decreases, the airspeed for L/D_{MAX} also decreases.

AIRCRAFT STABILITY

- An airplane with positive static stability tends initially to return to equilibrium if disturbed. An airplane that remains in a new attitude without returning toward equilibrium or moving farther away from equilibrium displays neutral static stability. If an airplane initially tends to move away from equilibrium when disturbed, it has negative static stability.
- Longitudinal dynamic stability is characterized by pitch oscillations that get smaller and eventually subside. Longitudinal dynamic instability is characterized by progressively steeper pitch oscillations.
- Longitudinal stability involves the motion of the airplane controlled by the elevator.

STALLS AND SPINS

- Total weight, load factor, power, and CG location affect stall speed.
- Stalling speed is most affected by load factor. In any situation involving increased load factor, such as a rapid pullout from a dive, the stall speed increases.
- Spin recovery may be difficult if the CG is too far aft and rotation is around the CG.
- Rectangular wings have a tendency to stall first at the wing root, with the stall progression toward the wingtip.

AERODYNAMICS AND FLIGHT MANEUVERS

- To maintain altitude while airspeed is being reduced, the angle of attack must be increased.
- Transitioning to a climb, angle of attack increases and lift momentarily increases.
- Approximate gliding distance can be found by multiplying your altitude AGL by the L/D ratio. Glide ratios for various angles of attack are obtained from an L/D graph.
- Load factor is the ratio between the lift generated by the wings at any given time divided by the total weight of the airplane. The design load factor takes into account the effects of acceleration on the contents of the airplane.
- As the angle of bank is increased, the vertical component of lift decreases because more of the total lift is directed horizontally. To compensate for the loss of part of the vertical component of lift in a turn, you must increase the angle of attack by using elevator back pressure.
- Load factor in turns increases at steeper bank angles, as does the stall speed. At a given bank angle, all airplanes experience the same load factor and the same percentage increase in stall speed over their wings-level stall speed. For example, any airplane in 60° banked coordinated, level turn experiences a 2-G load factor, which means the wings must support twice the weight of the loaded airplane.
- A given airspeed and bank angle will produce a specific rate and radius of turn in any airplane. In a coordinated, level turn, an increase in airspeed will increase the radius and decrease the rate of turn. Load factor is directly related to bank angle, so the load factor for a given bank angle is the same at any airspeed.
- V_{NO} is the maximum structural cruising speed during normal operations while V_{NE} is the never-exceed speed. Above V_{NE}, design limit load factors may be exceeded if gusts are encountered, causing structural damage or failure.

12-1   PLT310

The ratio between the total airload imposed on the wing and the gross weight of an aircraft in flight is known as

A–load factor and directly affects stall speed.
B–aspect load and directly affects stall speed.
C–load factor and has no relation with stall speed.

12-1. Answer A. GFDICM 12A, PHB

The ratio of the load imposed on the wings and the airplane's actual weight is the effective weight, or load factor. If a load factor of three is imposed on a 3,000-pound airplane, the load on the airframe is 9,000 pounds.

12-2   PLT310
Load factor is the lift generated by the wings of an aircraft at any given time

A–divided by the total weight of the aircraft.
B–multiplied by the total weight of the aircraft.
C–divided by the basic empty weight of the aircraft.

12-2. Answer A. GFDICM 12A, PHB
Load factor is the ratio between the load imposed on the wings and the airplane's actual weight.

12-3   PLT309
For a given angle of bank, in any airplane, the load factor imposed in a coordinated

A–is constant and the stall speed increases.
B–varies with the rate of turn.
C–is constant and the stall speed decreases.

12-3. Answer A. GFDICM 12A, PHB
Load factor remains constant for a given bank angle in a constant altitude turn and stall speed increases in proportion to the square root of the load factor. These relationships are the same for all aircraft.

12-4   PLT309
Airplane wing loading during a level coordinated turn in smooth air depends upon the

A–rate of turn.
B–angle of bank.
C–true airspeed.

12-4. Answer B. GFDICM 12A, PHB
Load factor increases with an increase in bank angle.

12-5   PLT312
In a rapid recovery from a dive, the effects of load factor would cause the stall speed to

A–increase.
B–decrease.
C–not vary.

12-5. Answer A. GFDICM 12A, PHB
A rapid pull-up from a dive increases the load factor or "G" forces imposed on the airplane, and stall speed increases in proportion to the square root of the load factor.

12-6   PLT309
If an aircraft with a gross weight of 2,000 pounds was subjected to a 60° constant-altitude bank, the total load would be

A–3,000 pounds.
B–4,000 pounds.
C–12,000 pounds.

12-6. Answer B. GFDICM 12A, PHB
At a bank angle of 60°, the load factor is two Gs, which means that the wings are supporting twice the weight of the airplane, or 4,000 pounds.

12-7   PLT348
While maintaining a constant angle of bank and altitude in a coordinated turn, an increase in airspeed will

A–decrease the rate of turn resulting in a decreased load factor.
B– decrease the rate of turn resulting in no change in load factor.
C– increase the rate of turn resulting in no change in load factor.

12-7. Answer B. GFDICM 12A, PHB
The rate of turn for a given bank angle varies with airspeed. If speed is increased at a constant bank angle, the rate of turn is reduced; however, changes in airspeed do not affect load factor.

12-8   PLT242
Lift on a wing is most properly defined as the

A–force acting perpendicular to the relative wind.
B– reduced pressure resulting from a laminar flow over the upper camber of an airfoil, which acts perpendicular to the mean camber.
C– differential pressure acting perpendicular to the chord of the wing.

12-8. Answer A. GFDICM 12A, PHB
Lift always acts perpendicular to the flight path, or relative wind, regardless of the wing's angle of attack. The production of lift requires relatively negative air pressure on the upper surface of the wing and positive air pressure on the bottom of the wing.

12-9   PLT309
While holding the angle of bank constant in a level turn, if the rate of turn is varied the load factor would

A–remain constant regardless of air density and the resultant lift vector.
B– vary depending upon speed and air density provided the resultant lift vector varies proportionately.
C– vary depending upon the resultant lift vector.

12-9. Answer A. GFDICM 12A, PHB
Load factor varies with bank angle and is not affected by air density or the resultant lift vector.

12-10   PLT237
In theory, if the airspeed of an airplane is doubled while in level flight, parasite drag will become

A–twice as great.
B– half as great.
C– four times greater.

12-10. Answer C. GFDICM 12A, PHB
Parasite drag varies proportionately to the square of the airspeed. Therefore if the airspeed is doubled, parasite drag increases four times.

12-11   PLT237
As airspeed decreases in level flight below that speed for maximum lift/drag ratio, total drag of an airplane

A–decreases because of lower parasite drag.
B– increases because of increased induced drag.
C– increases because of increased parasite drag.

12-11. Answer B. GFDICM 12A, PHB
If all other factors remain constant, induced drag varies inversely with the square root of the airspeed. For example, if airspeed is reduced by half, induced drag increases by a factor of four.

12-12   PLT311

If the airspeed is increased from 90 knots to 135 knots during a level 60° banked turn, the load factor will

A– increase as well as the stall speed.
B– decrease and the stall speed will increase.
C– remain the same but the radius of turn will increase.

12-12. Answer C. GFDICM 12A, PHB

The radius of turn for a given bank angle varies with airspeed. If speed is increased at a constant bank angle, the radius of turn is increased.

12-13   PLT310

Baggage weighing 90 pounds is placed in a normal category airplane's baggage compartment which is placarded at 100 pounds. If this airplane is subjected to a positive load factor of 3.5 Gs, the total load of the baggage would be

A– 315 pounds and would be excessive.
B– 315 pounds and would not be excessive.
C– 350 pounds and would not be excessive.

12-13. Answer B. GFDICM 12A, PHB

To find the weight of an object that is subject to a positive G force, multiply the weight of the object times the number of Gs. In this case, 90 pounds times 3.5 Gs equals 315 pounds. All airplanes are designed to meet certain strength requirements depending upon the intended use of the airplane. Normal aircraft are certificated with a maximum limit load factor of 3.8 positive Gs and 1.52 negative Gs.

12-14   PLT046

(Refer to figure 12-1 on page 12-6.)
At the airspeed represented by point A, in steady flight, the airplane will.

A– have its maximum L/D ratio.
B– have its minimum L/D ratio.
C– be developing its maximum coefficient of lift.

12-14. Answer A. GFDICM 12A, PHB

The intersection of the induced drag and parasite drag lines corresponds with a point on the total drag line where drag is at a minimum. This is also the point where the aircraft is operating at the best ratio of lift to drag, or L/D_{MAX}.

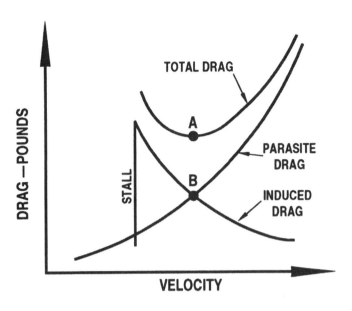

Figure 12-1. Drag vs. Speed.

12-15   PLT046
(Refer to figure 12-1 on page 12-6.)
At an airspeed represented by point B, in steady flight, the pilot can expect to obtain the airplane's maximum

A—endurance.
B—glide range.
C—coefficient of lift.

12-15. Answer B. GFDICM 12A, PHB
Point B corresponds to the airspeed where the airplane obtains the maximum ratio of lift to drag, L/D_{MAX}. This point provides both maximum range and the best power-off glide speed. Any increase or decrease from that specified for L/D_{MAX} will result in a reduced glide distance.

12-16   PLT247
Which statement is true relative to changing angle of attack?

A—An increase in angle of attack will decrease pressure below the wing, and increase drag.
B—An increase in angle of attack will increase drag.
C—A decrease in angle of attack will increase pressure below the wing, and decrease drag.

12-16. Answer B. GFDICM 12A, PHB
At higher angles of attack, more of the bottom surface of the wing is exposed to the relative wind which increases impact pressure. Induced drag also increases with an increase in angle of attack.

12-17   PLT473

Which is true regarding the use of flaps during level turns?

A– The lowering of flaps increases the stall speed.
B– The raising of flaps increases the stall speed.
C– Raising flaps will require added forward pressure on the yoke or stick.

12-17. Answer B. GFDICM 12A, PHB
Lowering flaps increases the coefficient of lift of the wing. It also lowers the stall speed. Therefore, raising the flaps increases the stall speed.

12-18   PLT266

One of the main functions of flaps during the approach and landing is to

A– decrease the angle of descent without increasing the airspeed.
B– provide the same amount of lift at a slower airspeed.
C– decrease lift, thus enabling a steeper-than-normal approach to be made.

12-18. Answer B. GFDICM 12A, PHB
Lowering flaps increases the coefficient of lift of the wing, which if all other variables remain constant, results in an overall increase in total lift produced by a wing.

12-19   PLT219

Name the four fundamentals involved in maneuvering an aircraft.

A– Power, pitch, bank, and trim.
B– Thrust, lift, turns, and glides.
C– Straight-and-level flight, turns, climbs, and descents.

12-19. Answer C. GFDICM 12A, AFH
The four fundamentals of flight include straight-and-level flight, climbs, turns, and descents.

12-20   PLT348

To increase the rate of turn and at the same time decrease the radius, a pilot should

A– increase the bank and decrease airspeed.
B– increase the bank and increase airspeed.
C– maintain the bank and decrease airspeed.

12-20. Answer A. GFDICM 12A, PHB
The rate of turn varies directly with bank angle and is inversely proportional to airspeed. The radius of turn is affected just the opposite by these two variables. Radius of turn varies directly with airspeed and is inversely proportional to bank angle.

12-21   PLT348

Which is correct with respect to rate and radius of turn for an airplane flown in a coordinated turn at a constant altitude?

A– For a specific angle of bank and airspeed, the rate and radius of turn will not vary.
B– To maintain a steady rate of turn, the angle of bank must be increased as the airspeed is decreased.
C– The faster the true airspeed, the faster the rate and larger the radius of turn regardless of the angle of bank.

12-21. Answer A. GFDICM 12A, PHB
Airspeed and bank angle are the two variables in determining rate and radius of turn. If these variables remain constant, rate and radius of turn will remain constant. The rate of turn varies directly with bank angle and is inversely proportional to airspeed.

12-22   PLT348

Why is it necessary to increase back elevator pressure to maintain altitude during a turn? To compensate for the

A– loss of the vertical component of lift.
B– loss of the horizontal component of lift and the increase in centrifugal force.
C– rudder deflection and slight opposite aileron throughout the turn.

12-22. Answer A. GFDICM 12A, PHB
In a level turn the total vertical component of lift no longer directly opposes gravity. Back pressure must be added to increase the amount of lift to compensate for the lost portion of the vertical component of lift.

12-23   PLT348

To maintain altitude during a turn, the angle of attack must be increased to compensate for the decrease in the

A– forces opposing the resultant component of drag.
B– vertical component of lift.
C– horizontal component of lift.

12-23. Answer B. GFDICM 12A, AFH
See explanation for Question 12-22.

12-24   PLT477

Stall speed is affected by

A– weight, load factor, and power.
B– load factor, angle of attack, and power.
C– angle of attack, weight, and air density.

12-24. Answer A. GFDICM 12A, AFH
The indicated stall speed is directly affected by weight, CG location, load factor, and power.

12-25   PLT168

By changing the angle of attack of a wing, the pilot can control the airplane's

A– lift, airspeed, and drag.
B– lift, airspeed, and CG.
C– lift and airspeed, but not drag.

12-25. Answer A. GFDICM 12A, PHB
When you change the angle of attack of the wing, you also change lift and drag forces. In general, increasing the angle of attack increases both lift and drag. If drag is increased without changing thrust, airspeed will decrease in level flight. Thus, the pilot can directly affect lift, and indirectly change drag and airspeed by changing the angle of attack.

12-26   PLT168

The angle of attack of a wing directly controls the

A– angle of incidence of the wing.
B– amount of airflow above and below the wing.
C– distribution of pressures acting on the wing.

12-26. Answer C. GFDICM 12A, PHB

There are regions of positive and negative pressure that move along the upper and lower surface of the wing as angle of attack is changed.

12-27   PLT237

In theory, if the angle of attack and other factors remain constant and the airspeed is doubled, the lift produced at the higher speed will be

A– the same as at the lower speed.
B– two times greater than at the lower speed.
C– four times greater than at the lower speed.

12-27. Answer C. GFDICM 12A, PHB

Lift is directly proportional to the square of the velocity. Therefore doubling the airspeed will quadruple (four times) the amount of lift being produced.

12-28   PLT236

An aircraft wing is designed to produce lift resulting from a difference in the

A– negative air pressure below and a vacuum above the wing's surface.
B– vacuum below the wing's surface and greater air pressure above the wing's surface.
C– higher air pressure below the wing's surface and lower air pressure above the wing's surface.

12-28. Answer C. GFDICM 12A, PHB

Production of lift requires relatively negative air pressure on the upper surface of the wing and positive air pressure on the lower surface.

12-29   PLT095

On a wing, the force of lift acts perpendicular to and the force of drag acts parallel to the

A– chord line.
B– flight path.
C– longitudinal axis.

12-29. Answer B. GFDICM 12A, PHB

Relative wind is parallel and opposite to the flight path of the airplane. Lift always acts perpendicular to the flight path (and to the relative wind), regardless of the wing's angle of attack. Also, drag acts opposite to the flight path.

12-30   PLT246

Which statement is true, regarding the opposing forces acting on an airplane in steady-state level flight?

A– These forces are equal.
B– Thrust is greater than drag and weight and lift are equal.
C– Thrust is greater than drag and lift is greater than weight.

12-30. Answer A. GFDICM 12A, PHB

Opposing aerodynamic forces are balanced in straight-and-level, unaccelerated flight. Lift opposes weight, thrust opposes drag, and the sum of opposing forces is zero.

12-31   PLT477

The angle of attack at which a wing stalls remains constant regardless of

A–weight, dynamic pressure, bank angle, or pitch attitude.
B–dynamic pressure, but varies with weight, bank angle, and pitch attitude.
C–weight and pitch attitude, but varies with dynamic pressure and bank angle.

12-31. Answer A. GFDICM 12A, PHB

For a given airfoil, a stall will always occur at the same angle of attack regardless of weight, dynamic pressure, bank angle, or pitch attitude. However, the indicated stall speed required to achieve the critical stall angle of attack will vary.

12-32   PLT240

In small airplanes, normal recovery from spins may become difficult if the

A–CG is too far rearward, and rotation is around the longitudinal axis.
B–CG is too far rearward, and rotation is around the CG.
C–spin is entered before the stall is fully developed.

12-32. Answer B. GFDICM 12A, PHB

Distribution of weight is a critical factor in spin recovery. Spins with aft CG positions are flatter than ordinary spins and may be extremely difficult or even impossible to recover from. A flat spin is characterized by a near level pitch and roll attitude with the spin axis near the CG of the airplane.

12-33   PLT240

Recovery from a stall in any airplane becomes more difficult when its

A–center of gravity moves aft.
B–center of gravity moves forward.
C–elevator trim is adjusted nosedown.

12-33. Answer A. GFDICM 12A, PHB

An airplane becomes less stable as the center of gravity moves aft. The airplane has less nose-down pitching moment. It is possible that the elevator would have insufficient authority to lower the nose and break the stall.

12-34   PLT131

An airplane leaving ground effect will

A–experience a reduction in ground friction and require a slight power reduction.
B–experience an increase in induced drag and require more thrust.
C–require a lower angle of attack to maintain the same lift coefficient.

12-34. Answer B. GFDICM 12A, PHB

During takeoffs or landings, when you are flying very close to the surface, the ground alters the three-dimensional airflow pattern around the airplane. This causes a reduction in upwash, downwash, and wingtip vortices, all of which contribute to induced drag. When an airplane climbs out of ground effect, these factors increase, thus increasing induced drag. To compensate for the increased induced drag, more thrust is required.

12-35   PLT237

If airspeed is increased during a level turn, what action would be necessary to maintain altitude? The angle of attack

A–and angle of bank must be decreased.
B–must be increased or angle of bank decreased.
C–must be decreased or angle of bank increased.

12-35. Answer C. GFDICM 12A, AFH

If you increase airspeed in a level turn, your vertical component of lift will increase. To maintain the same vertical lift component and prevent a climb, you must compensate by either increasing the angle of bank (changing part of the vertical lift component to the horizontal lift component), and/or by decreasing the angle of attack.

12-36   PLT477

The stalling speed of an airplane is most affected by

A– changes in air density.
B– variations in flight altitude.
C– variations in airplane loading.

12-36. Answer C. GFDICM 12A, AFH

The indicated stall speed can be affected by a number of things such as weight or load factor, center of gravity, and power.

12-37   PLT477

An airplane will stall at the same

A– angle of attack regardless of the attitude with relation to the horizon.
B– airspeed regardless of the attitude with relation to the horizon.
C– angle of attack and attitude with relation to the horizon.

12-37. Answer A. GFDICM 12A, AFH

For a given airfoil, a stall will always occur at the same angle of attack regardless of weight, dynamic pressure, bank angle, or pitch attitude.

12-38   PLT006

(Refer to figure 12-2 on page 12-12.)
If an airplane glides at an angle of attack of 10°, how much altitude will it lose in 1 mile?

A– 240 feet.
B– 480 feet.
C– 960 feet.

12-38. Answer B. GFDICM 12A, PHB

Glide distance is determined by the aircraft's maximum lift-to-drag ratio. To find the L/D_{MAX} value for a particular angle of attack, locate the horizontal base line at the bottom of the graph. These numbers correspond to the angle of attack in degrees. From zero, move right along the base line until you reach the number 10. Next, use the vertical reference line to move up the graph until you intersect the L/D_{MAX} curve.

The L/D ratio (11) can be determined by moving right along the horizontal reference line to the furthest right vertical line in bold. An 11:1 ratio means that for every 11 feet of horizontal glide distance, you will lose 1 foot in altitude. To find the total altitude lost in one mile, divide 5280 feet by the L/D ratio of 11. The answer is 480 feet (5280 ÷ 11 = 480).

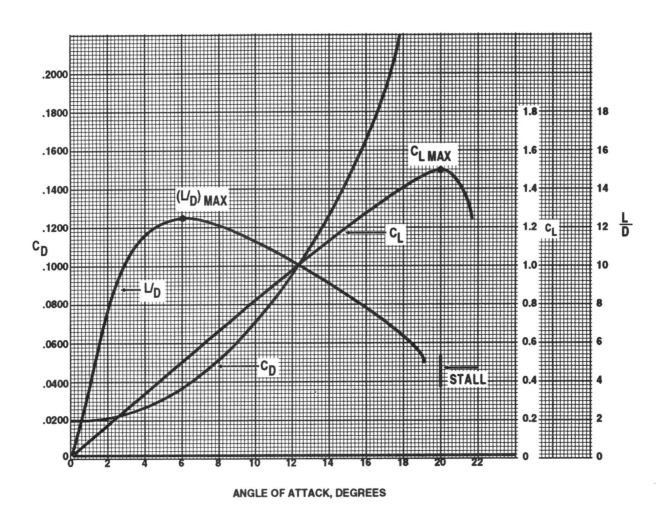

Figure 12-2. Angle of Attack, Degrees.

12-39   PLT006

(Refer to figure 12-2 on page 12-12.)
How much altitude will this airplane lose in 3 statute miles of gliding at an angle of attack of 8°?

A– 440 feet.
B– 880 feet.
C– 1,320 feet.

12-39. Answer C. GFDICM 12A, PHB

Glide distance is determined by the aircraft's maximum lift-to-drag ratio. To find the L/D$_{MAX}$ value for a particular angle of attack, locate the horizontal base line at the bottom of the graph. These numbers correspond to the angle of attack in degrees. From zero, move right along the base line until you reach the number eight. Next, use the vertical reference line to move up the graph until you intersect the L/D$_{MAX}$ curve.

The L/D ratio (12) can be determined by moving right along the horizontal reference line to the furthest right vertical line in bold. A 12:1 ratio means that for every 12 feet of horizontal glide distance, you will lose 1 foot in altitude. To find the total altitude lost in one mile, divide 5280 feet by the L/D ratio of 12. The answer is 440 feet (5280 ÷ 12 = 440). To find the total altitude lost in 3 miles, multiply 440 feet by a factor of three (440 x 3 = 1320).

12-40   PLT017
(Refer to figure 12-2 on page 12-12.)
The L/D ratio at a 2° angle of attack is approximately
the same as the L/D ratio for a

A–9.75° angle of attack.
B– 10.5° angle of attack.
C– 16.5° angle of attack.

12-40. Answer C. GFDICM 12A, PHB
To find the L/D_{MAX} value for a particular angle of
attack, locate the horizontal base line at the bottom
of the graph. These numbers correspond to the angle
of attack in degrees. From zero, move right along the
base line until you reach the number two. Next, use
the vertical reference line to move up the graph until
you intersect the L/D_{MAX} curve. Then move right until
you reintersect the back section of the L/D_{MAX} curve.
Now, follow the vertical reference line down to the
corresponding angle of attack (16.5°).

12-41   PLT131
If the same angle of attack is maintained in ground
effect as when out of ground effect, lift will

A–increase, and induced drag will decrease.
B– decrease, and parasite drag will increase.
C– increase, and induced drag will increase.

12-41. Answer A. GFDICM 12A, PHB
An aircraft maintaining the same angle of attack when
entering ground effect will experience an increase in
lift. At the same time, upwash, downwash, and wingtip
vortices decrease. Since these factors are associated
with induced drag, overall induced drag will decrease.

12-42   PLT303
What performance is characteristic of flight at
maximum lift/drag ratio in a propeller-driven airplane?
Maximum

A–gain in altitude over a given distance.
B– range and maximum distance glide.
C– coefficient of lift and minimum coefficient of drag.

12-42. Answer B. GFDICM 12A, PHB
Flying your aircraft at L/D_{MAX} provides both maximum
range and the best power-off glide speed. Any
decrease or increase in airspeed from that specified for
L/D_{MAX} will result in reduced range or gliding distance.

12-43   PLT303
Which is true regarding the forces acting on an aircraft
in a steady-state descent? The sum of all

A–upward forces is less than the sum of all downward
forces.
B– rearward forces is greater than the sum of all
forward forces.
C– forward forces is equal to the sum of all rearward
forces.

12-43. Answer C. GFDICM 12A, PHB
In a stabilized descent, the sum of the upward and
downward forces is zero. Likewise, forward and
rearward forces are also balanced and a condition of
equilibrium (similar to straight-and-level, unaccelerated
flight) exists.

12-44   PLT246

Which is true regarding the force of lift in steady, unaccelerated flight?

A– There is a corresponding indicated airspeed required for every angle of attack to generate sufficient lift to maintain altitude.

B– An airfoil will always stall at the same indicated airspeed; therefore, an increase in weight will require an increase in speed to generate sufficient lift to maintain altitude.

C– At lower airspeeds the angle of attack must be less to generate sufficient lift to maintain altitude.

12-44. Answer A. GFDICM 12A, PHB

For every angle of attack there is a corresponding indicated airspeed required to maintain altitude in steady, unaccelerated flight (all other factors being constant).

12-45   PLT246

During the transition from straight-and-level flight to a climb, the angle of attack is increased and lift

A– is momentarily decreased.

B– remains the same.

C– is momentarily increased.

12-45. Answer C. GFDICM 12A, PHB

Anytime there is a directional or velocity change in a flight path, an acceleration occurs. In order for an acceleration to occur there must be an imbalance in one or more of the four forces of flight. During the transition from straight-and-level flight to a climb, an increase in lift occurs when back elevator pressure is first applied. Because lift is momentarily greater then weight, the aircraft accelerates upwards. After the flight path is stabilized on the upward incline, the angle of attack and lift again stabilize at approximately the original value.

12-46   PLT018

(Refer to figure 12-3 on page 12-15.)
What is the stall speed of an airplane under a load factor of 2 Gs if the unaccelerated stall speed is 60 knots?

A– 66 knots.

B– 74 knots.

C– 84 knots.

12-46. Answer C. GFDICM 12A, PHB

To find the increase in stall speed at a 2-G load factor, enter the chart on the left and locate the load factor. Next, move right using the horizontal reference lines as a guide until you intersect the load factor curve. A 2-G load factor intersects at the 60% bank angle. From that intersection point use the vertical reference lines as a guide to move up until you intersect the stall speed increase curve. To determine the percent increase in stall speed you again use the horizontal reference lines as a guide to move back to the left vertical base line. In this case, a 40% increase is indicated. Now, multiply the stall speed by a 140% (60 × 1.4 = 84 knots).

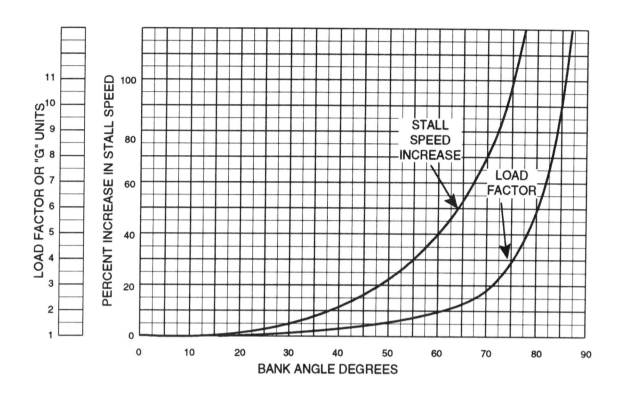

Figure 12-3. Stall Speed/Load Factor.

12-47   PLT018
(Refer to figure 12-3 on page 12-15.)
What increase in load factor would take place if the angle of bank were increased from 60° to 80°?

A– 3 Gs.
B– 3.5 Gs.
C– 4 Gs.

12-47. Answer C. GFDICM 12A, PHB
To find the increase in load factor from a 60° bank to a 80° bank, first locate the horizontal base line at the bottom of the graph. From zero move right along the base line until you reach 60°. Next, use the vertical reference lines as a guide to move up the graph until you intersect the load factor curve. Now, use the horizontal reference lines as a guide to read load factor from the scale on the left of the graph. In this case, there is a 2-G load factor at 60° of bank. Using the same procedure, you will find that the load factor at 80° of bank is approximately 6 G's. Finally, subtract the load factor at 60° bank from the load factor at 80° bank to find the increase (6 - 2 = 4).

12-48   PLT237
To generate the same amount of lift as altitude is increased, an airplane must be flown at

A– the same true airspeed regardless of angle of attack.
B– a lower true airspeed and a greater angle of attack.
C– a higher true airspeed for any given angle of attack.

12-48. Answer C. GFDICM 12A, PHB
In order to maintain lift at a higher altitude with the same angle of attack and wing area, a higher true airspeed is required because air density has decreased.

12-49   PLT131
To produce the same lift while in ground effect as when out of ground effect, the airplane requires

A–a lower angle of attack.
B–the same angle of attack.
C–a greater angle of attack.

12-49. Answer A. GFDICM 12A, PHB
If an aircraft maintains the same angle of attack when entering ground effect, the aircraft will experience an increase in lift. At the same time, upwash, downwash, and wingtip vortices decrease. Therefore, a lower angle of attack is required to produce the same amount of lift in ground effect.

12-50   PLT248
As the angle of bank is increased, the vertical component of lift

A–decreases and the horizontal component of lift increases.
B–increases and the horizontal component of lift decreases.
C–decreases and the horizontal component of lift remains constant.

12-50. Answer A. GFDICM 12A, PHB
As you increase bank, you are diverting part of the vertical lift component to the horizontal lift component.

12-51   PLT213
If the airplane attitude remains in a new position after the elevator control is pressed forward and released, the airplane displays

A–neutral longitudinal static stability.
B–positive longitudinal static stability.
C–neutral longitudinal dynamic stability.

12-51. Answer A. GFDICM 12A, PHB
Longitudinal stability involves the pitching motion, or tendency, of the airplane to move about its lateral axis. After elevator control pressures are released following a pitch displacement, and the airplane remains in the new pitch attitude, the airplane is exhibiting neutral longitudinal static stability.

12-52   PLT213
Longitudinal dynamic instability in an airplane can be identified by

A–bank oscillations becoming progressively steeper.
B–pitch oscillations becoming progressively steeper.
C–Trilatitudinal roll oscillations becoming progressively steeper.

12-52. Answer B. GFDICM 12A, PHB
Dynamic stability describes the time required for an airplane to respond to its static stability following a displacement from a condition of equilibrium. It is determined by the airplane's tendency to oscillate and damp out successive oscillations after initial displacement. If an aircraft is exhibiting longitudinal dynamic instability, it corrects itself but the aircraft enters a series of progressively steeper pitch oscillations.

12-53   PLT213
Longitudinal stability involves the motion of the airplane controlled by its

A–rudder.
B–elevator.
C–ailerons.

12-53. Answer B. GFDICM 12A, PHB
Longitudinal stability involves the pitching motion, or tendency, of the airplane to move about its lateral axis and the elevator controls an airplane's pitching moment.

12-54   PLT237

What changes in airplane longitudinal control must be made to maintain altitude while the airspeed is being decreased?

A– Increase the angle of attack to produce more lift than drag.

B– Increase the angle of attack to compensate for the decreasing lift.

C– Decrease the angle of attack to compensate for the increasing drag.

12-54. Answer B. GFDICM 12A, PHB

Lift varies in proportion to the square of the velocity. If the wing area remains constant, as the velocity decreases, angle of attack must increase to maintain the same amount of lift.

12-55   PLT480

If the airplane attitude initially tends to return to its original position after the elevator control is pressed forward and released, the airplane displays

A– positive dynamic stability.

B– positive static stability.

C– neutral dynamic stability.

12-55. Answer B. GFDICM 12A, PHB

Static stability is the initial tendency of an airplane to return to a state of equilibrium following a displacement from that condition. If positive static stability is present, an airplane has a tendency to return to the original point of equilibrium.

12-56   PLT243

A propeller, rotating clockwise as seen from the rear, creates a spiraling slipstream. The spiraling slipstream, along with torque effect, tends to rotate the airplane to the

A– right around the vertical axis, and to the left around the longitudinal axis.

B– left around the vertical axis, and to the right around the longitudinal axis.

C– left around the vertical axis, and to the left around the longitudinal axis.

12-56. Answer B. GFDICM 12A, PHB

As the slipstream produced by a clockwise rotating propeller (as seen from the rear) wraps around the fuselage, some of it strikes the left side of the vertical fin. This tends to rotate the airplane to the left around the vertical axis. Because the vertical fin is above the longitudinal axis, the spiraling slipstream also tends to rotate the aircraft to the right around the longitudinal axis.

12-57   PLT237

Which is true regarding aerodynamic drag?

A– Induced drag is created entirely by air resistance.

B– All aerodynamic drag is created entirely by the production of lift.

C– Induced drag is a by-product of lift and is greatly affected by changes in airspeed.

12-57. Answer C. GFDICM 12A, AFH

There are two types of drag; induced and parasite. Induced drag is a by-product of lift and decreases as airspeed increases. Parasite drag is created by the disruption of the flow of air around the airplane's surfaces. Unlike induced drag, parasite drag increases with increases in airspeed.

12-58   PLT373

Why should flight speeds above V_{NE} be avoided?

A– Excessive induced drag will result in structural failure.

B– Design limit load factors may be exceeded, if gusts are encountered.

C– Control effectiveness is so impaired that the aircraft becomes uncontrollable.

12-58. Answer B. GFDICM 12A, PHB

If you fly above the never-exceed speed, V_{NE}, you risk the possibility of exceeding limit load factors if gusts are encountered which can cause structural damage or failure.

12-59   PLT373

Maximum structural cruising speed is the maximum speed at which an airplane can be operated during

A– abrupt maneuvers.

B– normal operations.

C– flight in smooth air.

12-59. Answer B. GFDICM 12A, PHB

Maximum structural cruising speed, V_{NO}, is the top speed of the normal operating range and corresponds to the upper limit of the green arc on the airspeed indicator. You should not exceed this speed in rough air.

SECTION B - PREDICTING PERFORMANCE

FACTORS AFFECTING PERFORMANCE

- Air density decreases with air temperature and altitude. As air density decreases, engine performance decreases for both piston and gas turbine engines.
- A flight computer or a density altitude chart can be used to complete density altitude calculations based on pressure altitude and air temperature.
- Stall speed is affected by angle of bank, gross weight, and gear and flap position. Stall speed increases with bank and, on most propeller airplanes, decreases with high power settings because of additional airflow over the wings. You can see this relationship in tables provided by aircraft manufacturers.
- Headwind and crosswind components can be found using a wind component chart.
- An uphill runway slope increases takeoff distance because the airplane accelerates more slowly.

THE PILOT'S OPERATING HANDBOOK

- To estimate takeoff ground roll and distance to clear a 50-foot obstacle, use the takeoff distance charts. Most takeoff distance charts include variables for surface condition, headwind, and airport altitude above sea level.
- Climb performance charts provide information on time, fuel, and distance required to climb from one altitude to another. When using this chart you should remember to subtract the values for the starting altitude.

12-60   PLT018
(Refer to figure 12-4 on page 12-20.)
Select the correct statement regarding stall speeds.

A– Power-off stalls occur at higher airspeeds with the gear and flaps down.
B– In a 60° bank the airplane stalls at a lower airspeed with the gear up.
C– Power-on stalls occur at lower airspeeds in shallower banks.

12-60. Answer C. GFDICM 12B, PHB
A careful examination of the stall speed table shows that stall speeds are lower with power on and higher with power off. This results from the induced airflow over the wings created by the propeller generating thrust.

GROSS WEIGHT 2750 LBS		ANGLE OF BANK			
		LEVEL	30°	45°	60°
POWER		GEAR AND FLAPS UP			
ON	MPH	62	67	74	88
	KTS	54	58	64	76
OFF	MPH	75	81	89	106
	KTS	65	70	77	92
		GEAR AND FLAPS DOWN			
ON	MPH	54	58	64	76
	KTS	47	50	56	66
OFF	MPH	66	71	78	93
	KTS	57	62	68	81

Figure 12-4. Stall Speeds.

12-61   PLT018
(Refer to figure 12-4 on page 12-20.)
Select the correct statement regarding stall speeds. The airplane will stall

A– 10 knots higher in a power-on 60° bank with gear and flaps up than with gear and flaps down.

B– 25 knots lower in a power-off, flaps-up, 60° bank, than in a power-off, flaps-down, wings-level configuration.

C– 10 knots higher in a 45° bank, power-on stall than in a wings-level stall with flaps up.

12-61. Answer A. GFDICM 12B, PHB
According to the chart, the difference between the stall speed with power on in a 60° bank with gear and flaps up (76 kts.) and the stall speed with power on gear and flaps down (66 kts.) is 10 knots.

12-62   PLT074

(Refer to figure 12-5 on page 12-21.)
The horizontal line from point C to point E represents the

A– ultimate load factor.
B– positive limit load factor.
C– airspeed range for normal operations.

12-62. Answer B. GFDICM 12B, AFH

The horizontal scale indicates speed (V), and the vertical scale is load factor (G). Speed is plotted against the load factor or G-loading. The curved lines extending upward and downward from the load factor of zero are the positive and negative lift capability lines, The horizontal line at 3.8 Gs (point C to point E), and the line at -1.52 Gs (point I through point G), indicate the positive and negative load factor limits, respectively. Some of the vertical lines are labeled to identify specific aircraft speeds and are labeled.

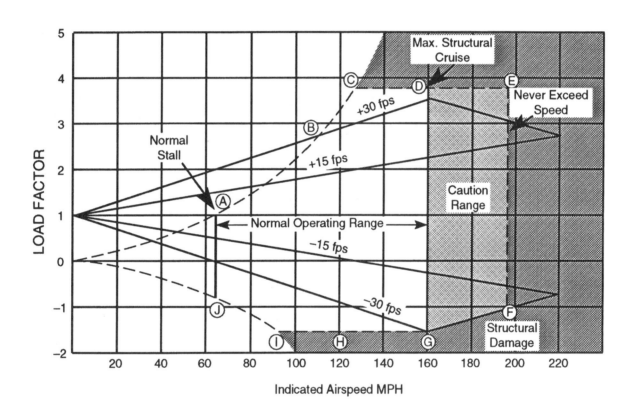

Figure 12-5. Velocity vs. G-Loads.

12-63   PLT074

(Refer to figure 12-5 on page 12-21.)
The vertical line from point E to point F is represented on the airspeed indicator by the

A– upper limit of the yellow arc.
B– upper limit of the green arc.
C– blue radial line.

12-63. Answer A. GFDICM 12B, AFH

See explanation for Question 12-62. The vertical line from point E to point F represents the upper limit of the yellow arc and is marked on the airspeed indicator with a red line (V$_{NE}$).

12-64   PLT312
(Refer to figure 12-5 on page 12-21.)
The vertical line from point D to point G is represented on the airspeed indicator by the maximum speed limit of the

A–green arc.
B–yellow arc.
C–white arc.

12-64. Answer A. GFDICM 12B, PHB
See explanation for Question 12-62. The vertical line from point D to point G represents the upper limit of the green arc and is the maximum structural cruising speed (V_{NO}).

12-65   PLT127
The performance tables of an aircraft for takeoff and climb are based on

A–pressure/density altitude.
B–cabin altitude.
C–true altitude.

12-65. Answer A. GFDICM 12B, PHB
Performance charts generally present information in either table or graph format. Most charts require pressure altitude and temperature to determine performance. This means the charts reflect density altitude.

12-66   PLT127
What effect, if any, would a change in ambient temperature or air density have on gas turbine engine performance?

A–As air density decreases, thrust increases.
B–As temperature increases, thrust increases.
C–As temperature increases, thrust decreases.

12-66. Answer C. GFDICM 12B, AFH
Density altitude is a factor which strongly affects the performance of gas-turbine engines. As ambient air temperatures increase, the density of the air decreases (increased density altitude). This results in less airmass passing through the engine inlet and, therefore, a decrease in thrust.

12-67   PLT005
GIVEN:
Pressure altitude...12,000 ft
True air temperature...+50°F

From the conditions given, the approximate density altitude is

A–11,900 feet.
B–14,130 feet.
C–18,150 feet.

12-67. Answer B. GFDICM 12B, AFH
This question requires you to compute density altitude. To do this use the following steps.

1. Enter pressure altitude (12,000 feet).
2. Enter the true air temperature (50°F/10°C).
3. Compute density altitude, 14,134 feet.

12-68   PLT005
GIVEN:
Pressure altitude...5,000 ft
True air temperature...+30°C

From the conditions given, the approximate density altitude is

A–7,200 feet.
B–7,800 feet.
C–9,000 feet.

12-68. Answer B. GFDICM 12B, AFH
This question requires you to compute density altitude. To do this use the following steps.

1. Enter pressure altitude (5,000 feet).
2. Enter the true air temperature (30°C/86°F).
3. Compute density altitude, 7,801 feet.

12-69   PLT005
GIVEN:
Pressure altitude...6,000 ft
True air temperature...+30°F

From the conditions given, the approximate density altitude is

A–9,000 feet.
B–5,500 feet.
C–5,000 feet.

12-69. Answer B. GFDICM 12B, AFH
This question requires you to compute density altitude. To do this use the following steps.

1. Enter pressure altitude (6,000 feet).
2. Enter the true air temperature (30°F/-1.1°C).
3. Compute density altitude, 5,496 feet.

12-70   PLT005
GIVEN:
Pressure altitude...7,000 ft
True air temperature...+15°C

From the conditions given, the approximate density altitude is

A–5,000 feet.
B–8,500 feet.
C–9,500 feet.

12-70. Answer B. GFDICM 12B, AFH
This question requires you to compute density altitude. To do this use the following steps.

1. Enter pressure altitude (7,000 feet).
2. Enter the true air temperature (15°C/59°F).
3. Compute density altitude, 8,595 feet.

12-71   PLT060
(Refer to figure 12-6 on page 12-24.)
GIVEN:
Fuel quantity...47 gal
Power-cruise (lean)...55 percent.

Approximately how much flight time would be available with a night VFR fuel reserve remaining?

A–3 hours 8 minutes.
B–3 hours 22 minutes.
C–3 hours 43 minutes.

12-71. Answer B. GFDICM 12B, PHB
Enter the Fuel Consumption vs. Brake Horsepower chart at the cruise (lean) curve. Find where the curve intersects the 55% maximum continuous power line, and move horizontally to the corresponding point on the fuel flow axis, approximately 11.4 gal/hr. Now, compute time available by using the known fuel quantity of 47 gallons and the fuel flow rate of 11.4 gal/hr to get 4 hours and 7 minutes. FAR 91.151 requires a fuel reserve of 45 minutes at normal cruise speed for night VFR flying. Subtract 45 minutes from your total time of 4:07 to get approximately 3 hours and 22 minutes of flight time available.

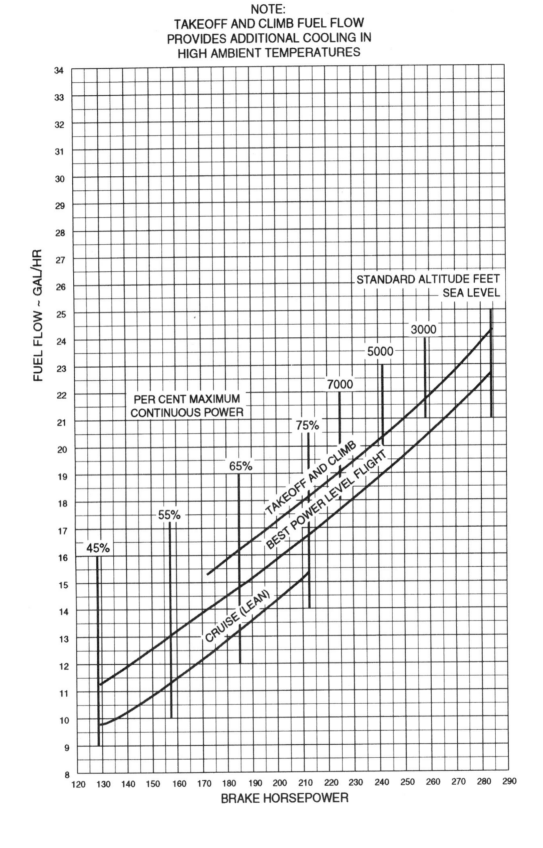

Figure 12-6. Fuel Consumption vs. Brake Horsepower.

12-72 PLT060
(Refer to figure 12-6 on page 12-24.)
GIVEN:
Fuel quantity...65 gal
Best power-level flight...55 percent.

Approximately how much flight time would be
available with a day VFR fuel reserve remaining?

A–4 hours 17 minutes.
B–4 hours 30 minutes.
C–5 hours 4 minutes.

12-72. Answer B. GFDICM 12B, PHB
Find the best power level flight curve and proceed
to where it intersects the 55% maximum continuous
power line. From that point, move to the corresponding
point on the fuel flow axis, 13 gallons per hour. Now,
compute the time available using the total fuel quantity
of 65 gallons and a fuel consumption rate of 13 gal/hr
The total flight time available is 5 hours. Part 91.151
requires 30 minutes of reserve fuel at normal cruise
speed for day VFR flying. Subtract 30 minutes from 5
hours to get 4 hours and 30 minutes of fuel available
after reserves.

12-73 PLT060
(Refer to figure 12-6 on page 12-24.)
Approximately how much fuel would be consumed
when climbing at 75 percent power for 7 minutes?

A–1.82 gallons.
B–1.97 gallons.
C–2.15 gallons.

12-73. Answer C. GFDICM 12B, PHB
Find the takeoff and climb curve and follow it to where
it intersects the vertical 75% maximum continuous
power line. From that point, move to the corresponding
point on the fuel flow axis, approximately 18.25 gal/hr.
Now, compute total fuel consumed using 7 minutes
and 18.25 gal/hr to get 2.13 gallons.

12-74 PLT060
(Refer to figure 12-6 on page 12-24.)
Determine the amount of fuel consumed during takeoff
and climb at 70 percent power for 10 minutes.

A–2.66 gallons.
B–2.88 gallons.
C–3.2 gallons.

12-74. Answer B. GFDICM 12B, PHB
Follow the takeoff and climb curve to where it
intersects the 70% maximum continuous power line.
Since this line is not drawn on the chart, you must
interpolate between the 65% and 75% lines. Now
move to the corresponding point on the fuel flow axis,
approximately 17.2 gal/hr. You can now compute the
amount of fuel consumed using the fuel consumption
rate of 17.2 gal/hr and a time of 10 minutes to get 2.87
gallons consumed in the takeoff and climb.

12-75 PLT060
(Refer to figure 12-6 on page 12-24.)
With 38 gallons of fuel aboard at cruise power (55
percent), how much flight time is available with night
VFR fuel reserve still remaining?

A–2 hours 34 minutes.
B–2 hours 49 minutes.
C–3 hours 18 minutes.

12-75. Answer A. GFDICM 12B, PHB
Follow the cruise (lean) curve to where it intersects
the 55% maximum continuous power line. Move
horizontally to the corresponding point on the fuel
flow axis, approximately 11.4 gal/hr. Now you can
compute total flight time using 38 gallons of fuel and a
fuel burn of 11.4 gal/hr to get 3 hours and 20 minutes.
Part 91.151 requires 45 minutes of reserve fuel for
night VFR flying. Subtract 45 minutes from 3 hours 20
minutes to get 2 hours and 35 minutes.

12-76   PLT012
(Refer to figure 12-7 on page 12-27.)
GIVEN:
Aircraft weight...3,800 lb
Airport pressure altitude...4,000 ft
Temperature...26°C

Using a normal climb, how much fuel would be used
from engine start to 12,000 feet pressure altitude?

A– 46 pounds.
B– 51 pounds.
C– 58 pounds.

12-76. Answer C. GFDICM 12B, PHB
Enter the table at the given aircraft weight of 3,800
pounds. Since the airport pressure altitude is 4,000
feet and not sea level, you must find how much fuel
would be burned climbing from sea level to 4,000 feet
(12 lbs.). Fuel used from sea level to 12,000 feet is 51
pounds. Therefore, fuel used from the airport to 12,000
feet is the difference, or 39 pounds.

Note 2 states that you must increase time, fuel, and
distance by 10% for each 10°C above standard
temperature, (1% change for every 1°C). Standard
temperature at sea level is 15°C and the standard
lapse rate is 2°C per each 1,000-foot increase in
altitude. Airport elevation is 4,000 feet and standard
temperature should be 7°C (4,000 ft. × 2°C/1,000 ft. =
8°C) and (15°C - 8°C = 7°C). Since it is actually 26°C,
there is a 19°C difference (26°C - 7°C = 19°C). The
19°C difference means a 19% increase in pounds of
fuel used, according to Note 2. Add 19% of 39 pounds
(39 × .19 = 7.41), for a total of 46.41 lbs (39 + 7.41).

Note 1 tells you to add 12 pounds for engine start, taxi
and takeoff. Final result is 58.41 pounds.

NORMAL CLIMB – 100 KIAS

CONDITIONS:
Flaps Up
Gear Up
2550 RPM
25 Inches MP or Full Throttle
Cowl Flaps Open
Standard Temperature

MIXTURE SETTING	
PRESS ALT	PPH
S.L. to 4000	108
8000	96
12,000	84

NOTES:
1. Add 12 pounds of fuel for engine start, taxi and takeoff allowance.
2. Increase time, fuel and distance by 10% for each 10 ˚C above standard temperature.
3. Distances shown are based on zero wind.

WEIGHT LBS	PRESS ALT FT	RATE OF CLIMB FPM	FROM SEA LEVEL		
			TIME MIN	FUEL USED POUNDS	DISTANCE NM
3800	S.L.	580	0	0	0
	2000	580	3	6	6
	4000	570	7	12	12
	6000	470	11	19	19
	8000	365	16	27	28
	10,000	265	22	37	40
	12,000	165	32	51	59
3500	S.L.	685	0	0	0
	2000	685	3	5	5
	4000	675	6	11	10
	6000	565	9	16	16
	8000	455	13	23	23
	10,000	350	18	31	33
	12,000	240	25	41	46
3200	S.L.	800	0	0	0
	2000	800	2	4	4
	4000	795	5	9	8
	6000	675	8	14	13
	8000	560	11	19	19
	10,000	445	15	25	27
	12,000	325	20	33	37

Figure 12-7. Fuel, Time, and Distance to Climb.

12-77   PLT012
(Refer to figure 12-7 on page 12-27.)
GIVEN:
Aircraft weight...3,500 lb
Airport pressure altitude...4,000 ft
Temperature...21°C

Using a normal climb, how much fuel would be used from engine start to 10,000 feet pressure altitude?

A– 23 pounds.
B– 31 pounds.
C– 35 pounds.

12-77. Answer C. GFDICM 12B, PHB
See the explanation for Question 12-76. Enter the table at 3,500 pounds. You need to find two values, fuel used from sea level to 4,000 feet and sea level to 10,000 feet. These figures are 11 pounds and 31 pounds, respectively. The difference is 20 pounds. Standard temperature at 4,000 feet should be 7°C (4,000 ft. × 2°C/1,000 ft. = 8°C) and (15°C - 8°C = 7°C). Subtract 7°C from the given field temperature of 21°C, to get a 14°C difference, so you will add 14% to the fuel used. Multiply 14% times 20 pounds to get 2.8 pounds, then add these two figures to get 22.8 pounds. Add 12 pounds for start, taxi, and takeoff to get a final answer of 34.8 pounds.

12-78   PLT012
(Refer to figure 12-8 on page 12-29.)
GIVEN:
Aircraft weight...3,200 lb
Airport pressure altitude...2,000 ft;
Temperature...27°C

Using a maximum rate of climb, how much fuel would be used from engine start to 6,000 feet pressure altitude?

A– 10 pounds.
B– 14 pounds.
C– 24 pounds.

12-78. Answer C. GFDICM 12B, PHB
See explanation for Question 12-76. Enter the table at 3,200 pounds aircraft weight. You need two figures, fuel used climbing from sea level to 2,000 feet and sea level to 6,000 feet, 4 pounds and 14 pounds of fuel respectively. The difference is 10 pounds of fuel used to climb from 2,000 feet to 6,000 feet. Standard temperature at 2,000 feet is 11°C (15°C - 2°C/1,000 ft. = 11°C). The actual temperature of 27°C is 16°C above standard, so you will increase the fuel used by 16%: (10 lbs × .16 = 1.6 lbs) and (10 lbs + 1.6 lbs = 11.6 lbs). Add 12 pounds for start, taxi, and takeoff (11.6 + 12 = 23.6).

MAXIMUM RATE OF CLIMB

CONDITIONS:
Flaps Up
Gear Up
2700 RPM
Full Throttle
Mixture Set at Placard Fuel Flow
Cowl Flaps Open
Standard Temperature

MIXTURE SETTING	
PRESS ALT	PPH
S.L.	138
4000	126
8000	114
12,000	102

NOTES:
1. Add 12 pounds of fuel for engine start, taxi and takeoff allowance.
2. Increase time, fuel and distance by 10% for each 10 °C above standard temperature.
3. Distances shown are based on zero wind.

WEIGHT LBS	PRESS ALT FT	CLIMB SPEED KIAS	RATE OF CLIMB FPM	FROM SEA LEVEL		
				TIME MIN	FUEL USED POUNDS	DISTANCE NM
3800	S.L.	97	860	0	0	0
	2000	95	760	2	6	4
	4000	94	660	5	12	9
	6000	93	565	9	18	14
	8000	91	465	13	26	21
	10,000	90	365	18	35	29
	12,000	89	265	24	47	41
3500	S.L.	95	990	0	0	0
	2000	94	885	2	5	3
	4000	93	780	5	10	7
	6000	91	675	7	16	12
	8000	90	570	11	22	17
	10,000	89	465	15	29	24
	12,000	87	360	20	38	32
3200	S.L.	94	1135	0	0	0
	2000	92	1020	2	4	3
	4000	91	910	4	9	6
	6000	90	800	6	14	10
	8000	88	685	9	19	14
	10,000	87	575	12	25	20
	12,000	86	465	16	32	26

Figure 12-8. Fuel, Time, Distance to Climb.

12-79   PLT012
(Refer to figure 12-8 on page 12-29.)
GIVEN:
Aircraft weight...3,800 lb
Airport pressure altitude...4,000 ft
Temperature...30°C.

Using a maximum rate of climb, how much fuel would be used from engine start to 10,000 feet pressure altitude?

A–28 pounds.
B–35 pounds.
C–40 pounds.

12-80   PLT015
(Refer to figure 12-9 on page 12-31.)
If the cruise altitude is 7,500 feet, using 64 percent power at 2500 RPM, what would be the range with 48 gallons of usable fuel?

A–635 miles.
B–645 miles.
C–810 miles.

12-79. Answer C. GFDICM 12B, PHB
See explanation for Question 12-76. Enter the table at 3,800 pounds and find the fuel used to climb from sea level to 4,000 feet and from sea level to 10,000 feet, 12 pounds and 35 pounds respectively. Then find the difference to determine fuel used to climb from 4,000 feet to 10,000 feet (35 lbs. - 12 lbs. = 23 lbs.). Fuel consumption increase due to nonstandard temperature is 23% (4,000 ft. x 2°C/1,000 ft. = 8°C) and (15°C - 8°C = 7°C) and (30°C - 7°C = 23°C). An increase of 23% times 23 pounds equals 5.29 pounds. Add this to 23 pounds to get 28.29. Now add 12 pounds for start up, taxi, and takeoff to obtain the final answer of 40.29.

12-80. Answer C. GFDICM 12B, PHB
Enter the table at 7,500 feet under altitude and find the 2,500 RPM line. (Note, this is also 64% power). At this power setting, range in the far right column (based on 48 gallons with no reserve) is 810 miles.

Gross Weight- 2300 Lbs.
Standard Conditions
Zero Wind Lean Mixture

					38 GAL (NO RESERVE)		48 GAL (NO RESERVE)	
					NOTE: Maximum cruise is normally limited to 75% power.			
ALT.	RPM	% BHP	TAS MPH	GAL/ HOUR	ENDR. HOURS	RANGE MILES	ENDR. HOURS	RANGE MILES
2500	2700	86	134	9.7	3.9	525	4.9	660
	2600	79	129	8.6	4.4	570	5.6	720
	2500	72	123	7.8	4.9	600	6.2	760
	2400	65	117	7.2	5.3	620	6.7	780
	2300	58	111	6.7	5.7	630	7.2	795
	2200	52	103	6.3	6.1	625	7.7	790
5000	2700	82	134	9.0	4.2	565	5.3	710
	2600	75	128	8.1	4.7	600	5.9	760
	2500	68	122	7.4	5.1	625	6.4	790
	2400	61	116	6.9	5.5	635	6.9	805
	2300	55	108	6.5	5.9	635	7.4	805
	2200	49	100	6.0	6.3	630	7.9	795
7500	2700	78	133	8.4	4.5	600	5.7	755
	2600	71	127	7.7	4.9	625	6.2	790
	2500	64	121	7.1	5.3	645	6.7	810
	2400	58	113	6.7	5.7	645	7.2	820
	2300	52	105	6.2	6.1	640	7.7	810
10,000	2650	70	129	7.6	5.0	640	6.3	810
	2600	67	125	7.3	5.2	650	6.5	820
	2500	61	118	6.9	5.5	655	7.0	830
	2400	55	110	6.4	5.9	650	7.5	825
	2300	49	100	6.0	6.3	635	8.0	800

Figure 12-9. Cruise and Range Performance.

12-81   PLT015
(Refer to figure 12-9 on page 12-31.)
What would be the endurance at an altitude of 7,500 feet, using 52 percent power?

NOTE: (With 48 gallons fuel-no reserve.)

A– 6.1 hours.
B– 7.7 hours.
C– 8.0 hours.

12-81. Answer B. GFDICM 12B, PHB
Enter the table at 7,500 feet altitude. Find 52% power then move across to the endurance column under 48 gallons to obtain the answer of 7.7 hours.

12-82   PLT015
(Refer to figure 12-9 on page 12-31.)
What would be the approximate true airspeed and fuel consumption per hour at an altitude of 7,500 feet, using 52 percent power?

A– 105 MPH TAS, 6.6 GPH.
B– 103 MPH TAS, 6.3 GPH.
C– 105 MPH TAS, 6.2 GPH.

12-82. Answer C. GFDICM 12B, PHB
Enter the table at 7,500 feet and find 52 percent power. Move to the right and find 105 MPH TAS and 6.2 GPH.

12-83   PLT012
(Refer to figure 12-10 on page 12-33.)
GIVEN:
Pressure altitude...18,000 ft
Temperature...-21°C
Power...2400 RPM - 28 inches MP
Recommended lean mixture
Usable fuel...425 lb.

What is the approximate flight time available under the given conditions? (Allow for VFR day fuel reserve.)

A– 3 hours 46 minutes.
B– 4 hours 1 minute.
C– 4 hours 31 minutes.

12-83. Answer B. GFDICM 12B, PHB
Enter the table at 2400 RPM. Move right along the line at 28 inches MP to the -21°C temperature columns. The corresponding fuel flow is 94 pounds per hour. Divide the usable fuel by the fuel flow to find total time (425 lbs ÷ 94 lb/hr = 4 hours 31 minutes). Subtract the day VFR fuel reserve of 30 minutes for a flight time of 4 hours 1 minute.

PRESSURE ALTITUDE 18,000 FEET

CONDITIONS:
4000 Pounds
Recommended Lean Mixture
Cowl Flaps Closed

```
┌─────────────────────────────────────────────┐
│                    NOTE                       │
│ For best fuel economy at 70% power or less,   │
│ operate at 6 PPH leaner than shown in this    │
│ chart or at peak EGT.                         │
└─────────────────────────────────────────────┘
```

RPM	MP	20 °C BELOW STANDARD TEMP -41 °C			STANDARD TEMPERATURE -21 °C			20 °C ABOVE STANDARD TEMP -1 °C		
		% BHP	KTAS	PPH	% BHP	KTAS	PPH	% BHP	KTAS	PPH
2500	30	---	---	---	81	188	106	76	185	100
	28	80	184	105	76	182	99	71	178	93
	26	75	178	99	71	176	93	67	172	88
	24	70	171	91	66	168	86	62	164	81
	22	63	162	84	60	159	79	56	155	75
2400	30	81	185	107	77	183	101	72	180	94
	28	76	179	100	72	177	94	67	173	88
	26	71	172	93	67	170	88	63	166	83
	24	66	165	87	62	163	82	58	159	77
	22	61	158	80	57	155	76	54	150	72
2300	30	79	182	103	74	180	97	70	176	91
	28	74	176	97	70	174	91	65	170	86
	26	69	170	91	65	167	86	61	163	81
	24	64	162	84	60	159	79	56	155	75
	22	58	154	77	55	150	73	51	145	65
2200	26	66	166	87	62	163	82	58	159	77
	24	61	158	80	57	154	76	54	150	72
	22	55	148	73	51	144	69	48	138	66
	20	49	136	66	46	131	63	43	124	59

Figure 12-10. Cruise Performance.

12-84   PLT012

(Refer to figure 12-10 on page 12-33.)
GIVEN:
Pressure altitude...18,000 ft
Temperature...-41°C
Power...2500
RPM - 26 inches MP
Recommended lean mixture
Usable fuel...318 lb

What is the approximate flight time available under the
given conditions? (Allow for VFR night fuel reserve.)

A– 2 hours 27 minutes.
B– 3 hours 12 minutes.
C– 3 hours 42 minutes.

12-85   PLT012

(Refer to figure 12-10 on page 12-33.)
GIVEN:
Pressure Altitude...18,000 ft
Temperature...-1°C
Power...2200
RPM - 20 inches MP
Best fuel economy
Usable fuel...344 lb.

What is the approximate flight time available under the
given conditions? (Allow for VFR day fuel
reserve.)

A– 4 hours 50 minutes.
B– 5 hours 20 minutes.
C– 5 hours 59 minutes.

12-84. Answer A. GFDICM 12B, PHB
Enter the table at 2500 RPM. Move right along the line
at 26 inches MP to the -41°C temperature columns.
The corresponding fuel flow is 99 pounds per hour.
Divide the usable fuel by fuel flow to find total time (318
lbs ÷ 99 lbs/hr = 3 hours 13 minutes). Subtract the
night VFR fuel reserve of 45 minutes, for a flight time of
2 hours 28 minutes.

12-85. Answer C. GFDICM 12B, PHB
Enter the table at 2200 RPM. Move right along the line
at 20 inches MP to the -1°C temperature columns. The
corresponding fuel flow is 59 pounds per hour. Divide
the useable fuel by fuel flow to find total time (344 lbs ÷
59 lbs/hr = 5 hours 59 minutes).

12-86   PLT012

(Refer to figure 12-11 on page 12-36.)

GIVEN:

Aircraft weight...3,400 lb

Airport pressure altitude...6,000 ft

Temperature at 6,000 ft...10°C

Using a maximum rate of climb under the given conditions, how much fuel would be used from engine start to a pressure altitude of 16,000 feet?

A– 43 pounds.

B– 45 pounds.

C– 49 pounds.

12-86. Answer A. GFDICM 12B, PHB

To determine the fuel used, you must subtract the fuel indicated at 6,000 feet from the fuel used to climb to 16,000 feet. Begin by entering the table at the given aircraft weight of 3,400 pounds, and move right to the pressure altitude column. Since a 6,000-foot pressure altitude is not listed, you will have to interpolate between the 4,000 and 8,000-foot levels. This results in 14 pounds of fuel. The 16,000-foot pressure altitude indicates 39 pounds of fuel used. Subtract these two values to determine the fuel used. The result is 25 pounds of fuel (39 - 14 = 25).

Note 2 states that you must increase time, fuel, and distance by 10% for each 10°C above standard temperature (1% change for every 1°C). Standard temperature at sea level is 15°C and the standard lapse rate is 2°C per 1,000-foot increase in altitude. This means the standard temperature for an airport at 6,000 feet is 3°C (15°C - 12°C = 3°C). Since there is a 7°C difference between the actual temperature and standard, the fuel used must be increased by 7%. This increase results in a fuel usage of 26.75 pounds (25 x 1.07 = 26.75).

Note 1 indicates you need to add 16 pounds for engine start, taxi and takeoff. This increases the amount of fuel used to 42.75 pounds (26.75 + 16 = 42.75).

MAXIMUM RATE OF CLIMB

CONDITIONS:
Flaps Up
Gear Up
2600 RPM
Cowl Flaps Open
Standard Temperature

PRESS ALT	MP	PPH
S.L. TO 17,000	35	162
18,000	34	156
20,000	32	144
22,000	30	132
24,000	28	120

NOTES:
1. Add 16 pounds of fuel for engine start, taxi and takeoff allowance.
2. Increase time, fuel and distance by 10% for each 10 °C above standard temperature.
3. Distances shown are based on zero wind.

WEIGHT LBS	PRESS ALT FT	CLIMB SPEED KIAS	RATE OF CLIMB FPM	FROM SEA LEVEL		
				TIME MIN	FUEL USED POUNDS	DISTANCE NM
4000	S.L.	100	930	0	0	0
	4000	100	890	4	12	7
	8000	100	845	9	24	16
	12,000	100	790	14	38	25
	16,000	100	720	19	52	36
	20,000	99	515	26	69	50
	24,000	97	270	37	92	74
3700	S.L.	99	1060	0	0	0
	4000	99	1020	4	10	6
	8000	99	975	8	21	13
	12,000	99	915	12	33	21
	16,000	99	845	17	45	30
	20,000	97	630	22	59	42
	24,000	95	370	30	77	60
3400	S.L.	97	1205	0	0	0
	4000	97	1165	3	9	5
	8000	97	1120	7	19	12
	12,000	97	1060	11	29	18
	16,000	97	985	15	39	26
	20,000	96	760	19	51	36
	24,000	94	485	26	65	50

Figure 12-11. Fuel, Time, and Distance to Climb.

12-87   PLT004
(Refer to figure 12-11 on page 12-36.)
GIVEN:
Aircraft weight...4,000 lb
Airport pressure altitude...2,000 ft
Temperature at 2,000 ft...32°C

Using a maximum rate of climb under the given
conditions, how much time would be required to climb
to a pressure altitude of 8,000 feet?

A– 7 minutes.
B– 8.4 minutes.
C– 11.2 minutes.

12-87. Answer B. GFDICM 12B, PHB
To determine the time to climb, you must subtract
the time indicated at 2,000 feet from the time to
climb to 8,000 feet. Enter the table at 4,000 pounds
and move to the pressure altitude column. Since a
2,000-foot pressure altitude is not listed, you will have
to interpolate. This results in a time of 2 minutes. The
8,000-foot pressure altitude indicates a time to climb of
9 minutes The difference is 7 minutes (9 - 2 = 7).

Note 2 states that you must increase time, fuel, and
distance by 10% for each 10°C above standard
temperature (1% change for every 1°C). Standard
temperature at sea level is 15°C and the standard
lapse rate is 2°C per 1,000-foot increase in altitude.
This means the standard temperature for an airport at
2,000 feet is 11°C (15°C - 4°C = 11°C). Since there is
a 21°C difference between the actual temperature and
standard, the time to climb must be increased by 21%.
This increase results in a time to climb of 8.47 minutes
(7 x 1.21 = 8.47).

12-88   PLT012
(Refer to figure 12-12 on page 12-38.)
GIVEN:
Aircraft weight...3,700 lb
Airport pressure altitude...4,000 ft
Temperature at 4,000 ft...21°C

Using a normal climb under the given conditions,
how much fuel would be used from engine start to a
pressure altitude of 12,000 feet?

A– 30 pounds.
B– 37 pounds.
C– 46 pounds.

12-88. Answer C. GFDICM 12B, PHB
To determine the fuel used, you must subtract the
fuel indicated at 4,000 feet from the fuel used to
climb to 12,000 feet. Begin by entering the table at
the given aircraft weight of 3,700 pounds, and move
right to the 4,000-foot pressure altitude line. Under
these conditions, 12 pounds of fuel is indicated. The
12,000-foot altitude indicates 37 pounds of fuel used.
Subtract these two values to determine the fuel used.
The result is 25 pounds of fuel (37 - 12 = 25).

Note 2 states that you must increase time, fuel,
and distance by 10% for each 7°C above standard
temperature. Standard temperature at sea level is
15°C and the standard lapse rate is 2°C per 1,000-foot
increase in altitude. This means the standard
temperature for an airport at 4,000 feet is 7°C (15°C -
8°C = 7°C). Since there is a 14°C difference between
the actual temperature and standard, the fuel used
must be increased by 20%. This increase results in a
fuel usage of 30 pounds (25 x 1.20 = 30).

Note 1 indicates you need to add 16 pounds for engine
start, taxi and takeoff. This increases the amount of
fuel used to 46 pounds (30 + 16 = 46).

NORMAL CLIMB – 110 KIAS

CONDITIONS:
Flaps Up
Gear Up
2500 RPM
30 Inches Hg
120 PPH Fuel Flow
Cowl Flaps Open
Standard Temperature

NOTES:
1. Add 16 pounds of fuel for engine start, taxi and takeoff allowance.
2. Increase time, fuel and distance by 10% for each 7 °C above standard temperature.
3. Distances shown are based on zero wind.

WEIGHT LBS	PRESS ALT FT	RATE OF CLIMB FPM	FROM SEA LEVEL		
			TIME MIN	FUEL USED POUNDS	DISTANCE NM
4000	S.L.	605	0	0	0
	4000	570	7	14	13
	8000	530	14	28	27
	12,000	485	22	44	43
	16,000	430	31	62	63
	20,000	365	41	82	87
	S.L.	700	0	0	0
3700	4000	665	6	12	11
	8000	625	12	24	23
	12,000	580	19	37	37
	16,000	525	26	52	53
	20,000	460	34	68	72
	S.L.	810	0	0	0
	4000	775	5	10	9
3400	8000	735	10	21	20
	12,000	690	16	32	31
	16,000	635	22	44	45
	20,000	565	29	57	61

Figure 12-12. Fuel, Time, and Distance to Climb.

12-89   PLT004

(Refer to figure 12-13 on page 12-40.)
GIVEN:

Airport pressure altitude...4,000 ft
Airport temperature...12°C
Cruise pressure altitude...9,000 ft
Cruise temperature...-4°C

What will be the distance required to climb to cruise
altitude under the given conditions?

A–6 miles.
B–8.5 miles.
C–11 miles.

12-89. Answer B. GFDICM 12B, PHB

To complete this problem, you must first determine
the distance required to climb from sea level to 9,000
feet then subtract the distance required to climb from
sea level to the airport elevation. Begin by entering
the graph at the outside air temperature for the
cruise altitude (-4°C). From this point proceed up the
graph parallel to the vertical reference lines until you
reach the corresponding point representing 9,000
feet (midway between the 8,000 and 10,000-foot
lines). From this point move to the right, paralleling
the horizontal reference lines until reaching the
corresponding point on the reference line for distance.
Now move downward, paralleling the vertical reference
lines until reaching the horizontal axis and determine
the corresponding distance (14 n.m.). Repeat the
above steps for the temperature (12°C) and elevation
(4,000 ft.) of the departure airport to determine that
5.5 nautical miles must be subtracted. The difference
of these two figures (14 n.m. - 5.5 n.m. = 8.5 n.m.)
represents the distance traveled climbing from 4,000
feet to 9,000 feet.

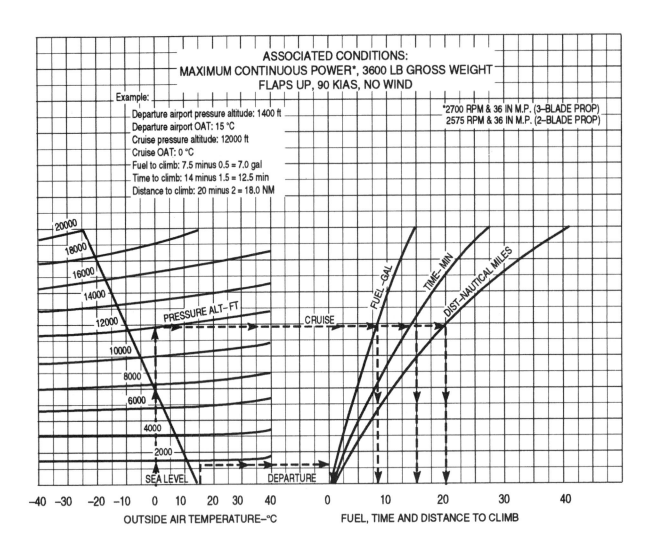

Figure 12-13. Fuel, Time, and Distance to Climb.

12-90   PLT129

What effect does an uphill runway slope have on takeoff performance?

A– Increases takeoff speed.
B– Increases takeoff distance.
C– Decreases takeoff distance.

12-90. Answer B. GFDICM 12B, PHB

When taking off on an uphill runway, aircraft acceleration is slower and the distance required to get airborne increases. If taking off on a downhill runway, aircraft acceleration will be enhanced and the distance required to get airborne will decrease. Runway slope has no effect on takeoff speed, although it would take longer (and more distance) to accelerate to takeoff speed.

12-91   PLT013

(Refer to figure 12-14 on page 12-42.)
Rwy 30 is being used for landing. Which surface wind would exceed the airplane's crosswind capability of 0.2 VSO, if VSO is 60 knots?

A– 260° at 20 knots.
B– 275° at 25 knots.
C– 315° at 35 knots.

12-91. Answer A. GFDICM 12B, PHB

In this example, the aircraft's maximum crosswind component is 12 knots (.2 × 60 = 12). To determine which of the indicated choices exceeds this value, calculate the angle between the wind and the runway for each possible answer. Then, enter the chart with the result and the wind speed. A wind of 260° at 20 knots gives you a crosswind component of 13 knots.

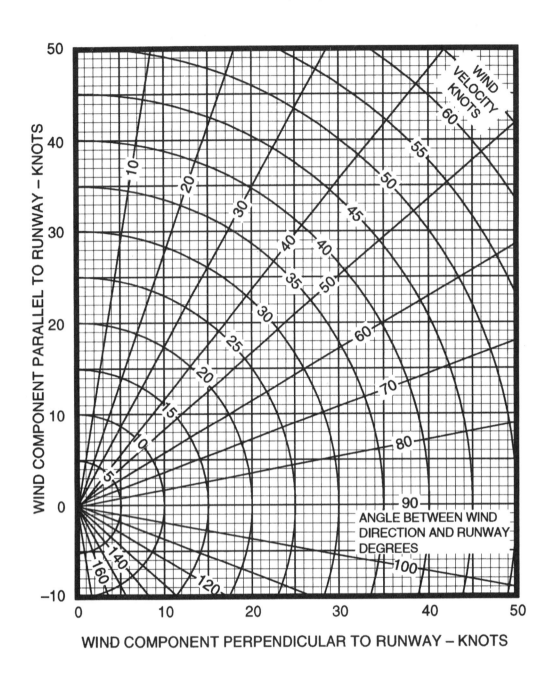

Figure 12-14. Wind Component Chart.

12-92   PLT013
(Refer to figure 12-14 on page 12-42.)
If the tower-reported surface wind is 010° at 18 knots, what is the crosswind component for a Rwy 08 landing?

A– 7 knots.
B– 15 knots.
C– 17 knots.

12-92. Answer C. GFDICM 12B, PHB
See explanation for Question 12-91. The angle between the wind and the runway is 70° (80° - 10° = 70°). Enter the chart on the 70° diagonal line and find the wind speed of 18 knots near the 20 knot arc. Drop straight down from there to find the crosswind component of 17 knots.

12-93   PLT013
(Refer to figure 12-14 on page 12-42.)
The surface wind is 180° at 25 knots. What is the crosswind component for a RWY 13 landing?

A– 19 knots.
B– 21 knots.
C– 23 knots.

12-93. Answer A. GFDICM 12B, PHB
See explanation for Question 12-92. The answer is 19 knots.

12-94   PLT013
(Refer to figure 12-14 on page 12-42.)
What is the headwind component for a Rwy 13 takeoff if the surface wind is 190° at 15 knots?

A– 7 knots.
B– 13 knots.
C– 15 knots.

12-94. Answer A. GFDICM 12B, PHB
The angle between the wind and the runway is 60° (190° - 130° = 60°). Enter the chart on the 60° diagonal line and go to the intersection of that line and the 15-knot arc. Now, move left to the vertical axis to find the headwind component. The answer is approximately 7 knots.

12-95   PLT085
(Refer to figure 12-15 on page 12-44.)
GIVEN:

Temperature...75°F
Pressure altitude...6,000 ft
Weight...2,900 lb
Headwind...20 kts

To safely take off over a 50-foot obstacle in 1,000 feet, what weight reduction is necessary?

A– 50 pounds.
B– 100 pounds.
C– 300 pounds.

12-95. Answer C. GFDICM 12B, PHB
Enter the bottom, left side of the chart at 75°F and move up to the 6,000-foot pressure altitude line. Move right to the reference line, then move right an equal distance between the curved reference lines to intersect the 2,900 pound line. From this point move right horizontally to the second reference line. Now, move right to the headwind guidelines and parallel them to intersect 20 knots. Move horizontally to the total takeoff distance reference line. The total takeoff distance over a 50-foot obstacle is approximately 1,450 feet. To determine the takeoff weight that would reduce the total takeoff distance to 1,000 feet, enter the chart at 1,000 feet on the right side. Move horizontally to the 20-knot line, then move left with the sloping reference lines to the vertical reference line. Move horizontally until you intersect the 2,600 pound line. This point corresponds with the original mark on reference line number 1 and requires a weight reduction of 300 pounds.

ASSOCIATED CONDITIONS:

POWER	TAKEOFF POWER SET BEFORE BRAKE RELEASE
FLAPS	20*
RUNWAY	PAVED, LEVEL, DRY SURFACE
TAKEOFF SPEED	IAS AS TABULATED

NOTE: GROUND ROLL IS APPROX. 73% OF TOTAL TAKEOFF DISTANCE OVER A 50 FT OBSTACLE

EXAMPLE:

OAT	75 °F
PRESSURE ALTITUDE	4000 FT
TAKEOFF WEIGHT	3100 LB
HEADWIND	20 KNOTS

TOTAL TAKEOFF DISTANCE OVER A 50 FT OBSTACLE	1350 FT
GROUND ROLL (73% OF 1350)	986 FT
IAS TAKEOFF SPEED	
LIFT-OFF	74 MPH
AT 50 FT	74 MPH

| WEIGHT POUNDS | IAS TAKEOFF SPEED (ASSUMES ZERO INSTR. ERROR) | | | |
| | LIFT-OFF | | 50 FEET | |
	MPH	KNOTS	MPH	KNOTS
3400	77	67	77	67
3200	75	65	75	65
3000	72	63	72	63
2800	69	60	69	60
2600	66	57	66	57
2400	63	55	63	55

Figure 12-15. Obstacle Take-off Chart.

12-96   PLT085
(Refer to figure 12-15 on page 12-44.)
GIVEN:

Temperature 50°F
Pressure altitude 2,000 feet
Weight ... 2,700 lb
Wind ... Calm

What is the total takeoff distance over a 50-foot
obstacle?

A– 800 feet.
B– 650 feet.
C– 1050 feet.

12-96. Answer A. GFDICM 12B, PHB
Start at the 50°F position and move upward to where
it intersects the 2,000-foot pressure altitude line. Move
right, an equal distance along the reference lines,
upward to intersect 2,700 pounds. Move horizontally
across to the approximate total takeoff distance of 800
feet.

12-97   PLT085
(Refer to figure 12-15 on page 12-44.)
GIVEN:

Temperature...100°F
Pressure altitude...4,000 ft
Weight...3,200 lb
Wind...Calm.

What is the ground roll required for takeoff over a
50-foot obstacle?

A– 1,180 feet.
B– 1,350 feet.
C– 1,850 feet.

12-97. Answer B. GFDICM 12B, PHB
Start with 100°F, and follow the reference lines in the
same manner described in Question 12-96.To find the
ground roll, multiply the total takeoff distance (1,850
feet) by .73 as indicated in the heading portion of the
chart. The answer is approximately 1,350 feet.

12-98   PLT085
(Refer to figure 12-15 on page 12-44.)
GIVEN:

Temperature...30°F
Pressure altitude...6,000 ft
Weight...3,300 lb
Headwind...20 kts

What is the total takeoff distance over a 50-foot
obstacle?

A– 1,100 feet.
B– 1,300 feet.
C– 1,500 feet.

12-98. Answer C. GFDICM 12B, PHB
Start with 30°F, and follow the reference lines in
the same manner described in Question 12-96. The
answer is approximately 1,500 feet.

12-99   PLT085
(Refer to figure 12-16 on page 12-47.)
GIVEN:

Weight...4,000 lb
Pressure altitude...5,000 ft
Temperature...30°C.

What is the maximum rate of climb under the given conditions?

A–655 ft/min.
B–702 ft/min.
C–774 ft/min.

12-99. Answer B. GFDICM 12B, PHB
Enter the chart from the left at 4,000 pounds. Move right to the pressure altitude column. The pressure altitude of 5,000 feet does not appear on the chart. Since 5,000 feet is 1/4 of the difference between the 4,000-foot and 8,000-foot levels, you will need to interpolate by subtracting 25% of the difference from the climb rate at 4,000 feet. The temperature of 30°C also requires interpolation. The climb rate for 30°C falls directly between the climb rates for 20°C and 40°C. The interpolations are as follows:

Interpolate climb rate for 5,000 feet at 20°C
800 ft/min - 695 ft/min = 105
105 x 25% = 26.25
800 - 26.25 = 773.75 (774) ft/min

Interpolate climb rate for 5,000 feet at 40°C
655 ft/min - 555 ft/min = 100
100 x 25% = 25
655 - 25 = 630 ft/min

Interpolate climb rate for 5,000 feet at 30°C
774 ft/min - 630 ft/min = 144
144 x 50% = 72
774 - 72 = 702 ft/min

CONDITIONS:
Flaps Up
Gear Up
2600 RPM
Cowl Flaps Open

PRESS ALT	MP	PPH
S.L. TO 17,000	35	162
18,000	34	156
20,000	32	144
22,000	30	132
24,000	28	120

WEIGHT LBS	PRESS ALT FT	CLIMB SPEED KIAS	RATE OF CLIMB – FPM			
			-20 ˚C	0 ˚C	20 ˚C	40 ˚C
4000	S.L.	100	1170	1035	895	755
	4000	100	1080	940	800	655
	8000	100	980	840	695	555
	12,000	100	870	730	590	---
	16,000	100	740	605	470	---
	20,000	99	485	355	---	---
	24,000	97	190	70	---	---
3700	S.L.	99	1310	1165	1020	875
	4000	99	1215	1070	925	775
	8000	99	1115	965	815	670
	12,000	99	1000	855	710	---
	16,000	99	865	730	590	---
	20,000	97	600	470	---	---
	24,000	95	295	170	---	---
3400	S.L.	97	1465	1320	1165	1015
	4000	97	1370	1220	1065	910
	8000	97	1265	1110	955	795
	12,000	97	1150	995	845	---
	16,000	97	1010	865	725	---
	20,000	96	730	595	---	---
	24,000	94	405	275	---	---

Figure 12-16. Maximum Rate-of-Climb Chart.

12-100   PLT085

(Refer to figure 12-16 on page 12-47.)

GIVEN:

Weight...3,700 lb

Pressure altitude...22,000 ft

Temperature...-10°C.

What is the maximum rate of climb under the given conditions?

A– 305 ft/min.

B– 320 ft/min.

C– 384 ft/min.

12-100. Answer C. GFDICM 12B, PHB

Enter the chart from the left at 3,700 pounds. Move right to the pressure altitude column. You will need to interpolate because the pressure altitude of 22,000 feet does not appear on the chart. Since the climb rate at 22,000 feet is 50% of the way between the rate at 20,000 and 24,000 feet, you will need to add one half of the difference between the respective rates to the climb rate at 24,000 feet. The temperature of -10°C also requires interpolation. The climb rate for -10°C falls directly between the climb rates for -20°C and 0°C. The interpolations are as follows:

Interpolate climb rate for 22,000 feet at -20°C
600 ft/min - 295 ft/min = 305
305 x 50% = 152.5
295 + 152.5 = 447.5 (448) ft/min

Interpolate climb rate for 22,000 feet at 0°C
470 ft/min - 170 ft/min = 300
300 x 50% = 150
170 + 150 = 320 ft/min

Interpolate climb rate for -10°C
448 ft/min - 320 ft/min = 128
128 x 50% = 64
320 + 64 = 384 ft/min

12-101   PLT012

(Refer to figure 12-17 on page 12-49.)

GIVEN:

Pressure altitude...6,000 ft

Temperature...+3°C

Power - 2200 RPM...22 inches MP

Usable fuel available...465 lb

What is the maximum available flight time under the conditions stated?

A– 6 hours 27 minutes.

B– 6 hours 39 minutes.

C– 6 hours 56 minutes.

12-101. Answer B. GFDICM 12B, PHB

Enter the chart at the given power setting of 2,200 RPM and then go to the MP column and locate 22 in the manifold pressure (MP) column. Move directly across from the 22 to the standard temperature column (3°C) and locate the pounds per hour (PPH) column. These settings result in a fuel flow of 70 PPH. Divide your usable fuel (465 lbs) by 70 PPH to determine your available flight time. The answer is 6 hours 38 minutes and 34 seconds.

PRESSURE ALTITUDE 6,000 FEET

CONDITIONS:
Recommended Lean Mixture
3800 Pounds
Cowl Flaps Closed

RPM	MP	20 °C BELOW STANDARD TEMP -17 °C			STANDARD TEMPERATURE 3 °C			20 °C ABOVE STANDARD TEMP 23 °C		
		% BHP	KTAS	PPH	% BHP	KTAS	PPH	% BHP	KTAS	PPH
2550	24	---	---	---	78	173	97	75	174	94
	23	76	167	96	74	169	92	71	171	89
	22	72	164	90	69	166	87	67	167	84
	21	68	160	85	65	162	82	63	163	80
2500	24	78	169	98	75	171	95	73	172	91
	23	74	166	93	71	167	90	69	169	87
	22	70	162	88	67	164	85	65	165	82
	21	66	158	83	63	160	80	61	160	77
2400	24	73	165	91	70	166	88	68	167	85
	23	69	161	87	67	163	84	64	164	81
	22	65	158	82	63	159	79	61	160	77
	21	61	154	77	59	155	75	57	155	73
2300	24	68	161	86	66	162	83	64	163	80
	23	65	158	82	62	159	79	60	159	76
	22	61	154	77	59	155	75	57	155	72
	21	57	150	73	55	150	71	53	150	68
2200	24	63	156	80	61	157	77	59	158	75
	23	60	152	76	58	153	73	56	154	71
	22	57	149	72	54	149	70	53	149	67
	21	53	144	68	51	144	66	49	143	64
	20	50	139	64	48	138	62	46	137	60
	19	46	133	60	44	132	58	43	131	57

Figure 12-17. Cruise Performance Chart.

12-102   PLT012
(Refer to figure 12-17 on page 12-49.)
GIVEN:
Pressure altitude…6,000 ft
Temperature…-17°C
Power - 2300 RPM…23 inches MP
Usable fuel available...370 lb

What is the maximum available flight time under the conditions stated?

A– 4 hours 20 minutes.
B– 4 hours 30 minutes.
C– 4 hours 50 minutes.

12-102. Answer B. GFDICM 12B, PHB
See explanation for Question 12-101.Your fuel flow is 82 pounds per hour (PPH). To determine your maximum available flight time, divide your usable fuel (370 lbs) by 82 PPH. The answer is 4 hours 30 minutes and 44 seconds.

12-103   PLT012
(Refer to figure 12-17 on page 12-49.)
GIVEN:

Pressure altitude…6,000 ft
Temperature…+13°C
Power - 2500 RPM…23 inches MP
Usable fuel available…460 lb

What is the maximum available flight time under the
conditions stated?

A–4 hours 58 minutes.
B–5 hours 7 minutes.
C–5 hours 12 minutes.

12-104   PLT008
(Refer to figure 12-18 on page 12-51.)
GIVEN:

Temperature...70°F
Pressure altitude...Sea level
Weight...3,400 lb
Headwind...16 kts.

Determine the approximate ground roll.

A–689 feet.
B–716 feet.
C–1,275 feet.

12-103. Answer C. GFDICM 12B, PHB
Enter the table at 2,500 RPM and locate 23 in the
manifold pressure (MP) column. Since there is no
+13°C column, you must interpolate the fuel flow
between 3°C and 23°C columns. The pertinent values
are 90 and 87 pounds per hour (PPH), respectively.
Interpolating for 13°C results in a fuel flow of 88.5
PPH. The maximum available flight time is 5 hours 11
minutes and 51 seconds.

12-104. Answer A. GFDICM 12B, PHB
Enter the chart from the bottom at 70°F and move
vertically to the sea level pressure altitude line. From
there, move right and parallel the reference lines to
intersect 3,400 pounds. Move horizontally across to
the next reference line, the move down the diagonal
headwind guideline to intersect 16 knots. Next,
move to the total landing distance reference line.
The approximate landing distance is 1,300 feet. To
determine the ground roll, multiply the total landing
distance by .53 as indicated in the heading portion of
the chart. The answer is 689 feet.

ASSOCIATED CONDITIONS:

POWER	AS REQUIRED TO MAINTAIN 800 FT/MIN DESCENT ON APPROACH
FLAPS	DOWN
RUNWAY	PAVED, LEVEL, DRY SURFACE
APPROACH SPEED	IAS A TABULATED

NOTE: GROUND ROLL IS APPROX. 53% OF TOTAL LANDING DISTANCE OVER A 50 FT OBSTACLE.

EXAMPLE:

OAT	75 °F
PRESSURE ALTITUDE	4000 FT
LANDING WEIGHT	3200 LB
HEADWIND	10 KNOTS
TOTAL LANDING DISTANCE OVER A 50 FT OBSTACLE	1475 FT
GROUND ROLL (53% OF 1475)	782 FT
IAS APPROACH SPEED	87 MPH IAS

WEIGHT POUNDS	IAS APPROACH SPEED (ASSUMES ZERO INSTR. ERROR)	
	MPH	KNOTS
3400	90	78
3200	87	76
3000	84	73
2800	81	70
2600	78	68
2400	75	65

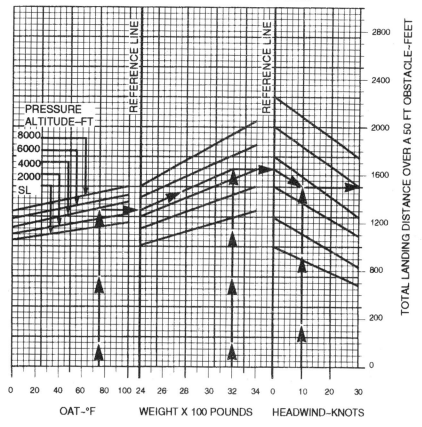

Figure 12-18. Normal Landing Chart.

12-105   PLT008
(Refer to figure 12-18 on page 12-51.)
GIVEN:

Temperature...85°F
Pressure altitude...6,000 ft
Weight...2,800 lb
Headwind...14 kts

Determine the approximate ground roll.

A– 742 feet.
B– 1,280 feet.
C– 1,480 feet.

12-105. Answer A. GFDICM 12B, PHB
Enter the chart at the 85°F and move to the 6,000-foot pressure altitude line. Proceed right and parallel the reference lines to intersect 2,800 pounds. From there move straight across to the next reference line and follow the headwind guideline to intersect 14 knots. Next, proceed to the landing distance reference line. The approximate landing distance is 1,400 feet. To determine the ground roll, multiply the total landing distance by .53 as indicated in the heading portion of the chart. The answer is 742 feet.

12-106   PLT008
(Refer to figure 12-18 on page 12-51.)
GIVEN:

Temperature...50°F
Pressure altitude...Sea level
Weight...3,000 lb
Headwind...10 kts

Determine the approximate ground roll.

A– 425 feet.
B– 636 feet.
C– 836 feet.

12-106. Answer B. GFDICM 12B, PHB
Enter chart at 50°F and follow the reference lines in the same manner described for the previous questions. To find the ground roll, multiply the total landing distance (1,200 feet) by .53 as indicated in the heading portion of the chart. The answer is 636 feet.

12-107   PLT008
(Refer to figure 12-18 on page 12-51.)
GIVEN:

Temperature...80°F
Pressure altitude...4,000 ft
Weight...2,800 lb
Headwind...24 kts

What is the total landing distance over a 50-foot obstacle?

A– 1,125 feet.
B– 1,250 feet.
C– 1,325 feet.

12-107. Answer A. GFDICM 12B, PHB
Enter the chart at the 80°F and follow the reference lines in the same manner described for the previous questions. The approximate landing distance over a 50-foot obstacle is 1,125 feet.

SECTION C - CONTROLLING WEIGHT AND BALANCE

WEIGHT AND BALANCE LIMITATIONS

- For light general aviation airplanes, the maximum weight limit is specified as maximum weight, maximum certificated weight, or maximum gross weight.
- Maximum ramp weight is what the airplane can weigh while on the ramp or during taxi. This is higher than maximum takeoff weight to allow for fuel used during engine start and taxi.
- With the CG located near or in front of the forward CG limit, the tail-down force required to balance the airplane increases. This requires extra lift from the wings, and a higher angle of attack. For this reason, forward loading increases stall speed and reduces cruise performance.
- While an aft CG can increase cruise performance, loading beyond the aft of limits is dangerous. The airplane can become difficult to control and may not be able to recover from a stall or spin.

WEIGHT AND BALANCE DOCUMENTS

- The empty weight of an airplane includes unusable fuel, hydraulic fluid, and undrainable oil, or, in some aircraft, all of the oil.
- When using weight information published in a typical aircraft owner's manual, the empty weight of the actual aircraft may be higher than that shown in the manual because of additional installed equipment. This results in a lower useful load.
- When the reference datum is located at or in front of the nose, all arms and moments will have positive values.

WEIGHT AND BALANCE CALCULATIONS

- A moment is a twisting force calculated by multiplying a weight or other force by its distance from a specific reference.
- To compute the loaded center of gravity (CG) of an aircraft, add up the moments and weights of each item and divide the total moment by the total weight. To determine the moment of an individual item, use a loading graph, or multiply its weight by its arm.
- To determine the effects of fuel consumption on weight and balance, calculate the weight of fuel consumed for the specified period of time. Once the weight has been determined, deduct it from the original fuel weight and recompute the weight and balance for the airplane.
- To perform weight and balance condition checks you can use a loading graph to locate the moment of all useful load items. Once the total weight and total moment are computed, determine if the moment and weight are within allowable limits by using a center of gravity envelope graph.
- The weight shift formula calculates the amount of weight that must be moved a specific distance or determines the distance a specific weight must be moved to bring the CG within limits: Weight Moved ÷ Weight of Airplane = Distance CG Moves ÷ Distance between Arms.

12-108   PLT240

If an airplane is loaded to the rear of its CG range, it will tend to be unstable about its

A— vertical axis.
B— lateral axis.
C— longitudinal axis.

12-108. Answer B. GFDICM 12C, PHB

With an aft CG, the airplane becomes more tail heavy and unstable in pitch, regardless of its speed. Pitch is the movement about the lateral axis.

12-109   PLT395

When computing weight and balance, the basic empty weight includes the weight of the airframe, engine(s), and all installed optional equipment. Basic empty weight also includes

A– all usable fuel and oil, but does not include any radio equipment or instruments that were installed by someone other than the manufacturer.
B– all usable fuel, full oil, hydraulic fluid, but does not include the weight of pilot, passengers, or baggage.
C– the unusable fuel, full operating fluids, and full oil.

12-110   PLT121

If all index units are positive when computing weight and balance, the location of the datum would be at the

A– centerline of the main wheels.
B– nose, or out in front of the airplane.
C– centerline of the nose or tailwheel, depending on the type of airplane.

12-111   PLT121

The CG of an aircraft can be determined by which of the following methods?

A– Dividing total arms by total moments.
B– Multiplying total arms by total weight.
C– Dividing total moments by total weight.

12-112   PLT121

The CG of an aircraft may be determined by

A– dividing total arms by total moments.
B– dividing total moments by total weight.
C– multiplying total weight by total moments.

12-109. Answer C. GFDPPM 12C, PHB

No empty weight definition differentiates between manufacturer-installed equipment and equipment added later, which requires modification of the empty weight and empty weight CG shown in aircraft documents. Empty weight includes unusable, but not usable, fuel.

12-110. Answer B. GFDICM 12C, PHB

In order for all stations to be positive, the reference datum must be located at the nose or out in front of the airplane.

12-111. Answer C. GFDICM 12C, PHB

Most aircraft weight and balance problems can be solved by using the formula: Weight × Arm = Moment. For example, an aircraft's center of gravity (CG) can be determined by arranging the formula to read: Arm (CG) = Moment ÷ Weight.

12-112. Answer B. GFDICM 12C, PHB

See explanation for Question 12-111.

12-113   PLT003
GIVEN:
Weight A - 155 lb at 45 inches aft of datum
Weight B - 165 lb at 145 inches aft of datum
Weight C - 95 lb at 185 inches aft of datum

Based on this information, the CG would be located
how far aft of datum?

A– 86.0 inches.
B– 116.8 inches.
C– 125.0 inches.

12-113. Answer B. GFDICM 12C, PHB
First, fill in the table by multiplying each weight by the
arm to find the moment.

	WEIGHT (lbs)	ARM (in)	MOMENT (lb-in)
Weight A	155	45	6,975
Weight B	165	145	23,925
Weight C	95	185	17,575
Totals	415		48,475

The CG is the total moment divided by the total weight.
The answer is 116.8 inches (48,475 ÷ 415 = 116.8).

12-114   PLT003
GIVEN:
Total weight...4,137 lb
CG location station...67.8
Fuel consumption...13.7 GPH
Fuel CG station...68.0

After 1 hour 30 minutes of flight time, the CG would
be located at station

A– 67.79.
B– 68.79.
C– 70.78.

12-114. Answer A. GFDICM 12C, PHB
Subtract the weight and moment of the fuel burned
from the aircraft's total weight and moment. In 1:30:00,
you will burn 20.55 gallons of fuel (1:30:00 x 13.7 =
20.55), or 123.3 lbs. (20.55 × 6 = 123.3)

	WEIGHT (lbs)	ARM (in)	MOMENT (lb-in/100)
Total	4,137.0	67.8	2,804.88
Fuel 20.55 gal.	– 123.3	68.0	– 83.84
	4,013.7		2,721.04

The CG is the total moment divided by the total weight.
The answer is 67.79 inches (272,104 ÷ 4,013.7 =
67.79).

12-115   PLT003

An aircraft is loaded with a ramp weight of 3,650 pounds and having a CG of 94.0, approximately how much baggage would have to be moved from the rear baggage area at station 180 to the forward baggage area at station 40 in order to move the CG to 92.0?

A– 52.14 pounds.
B– 62.24 pounds.
C– 78.14 pounds.

12-115. Answer A. GFDICM 12C, PHB

To determine how much baggage must be moved, use the weight shift formula:

(Weight of Airplane ÷ Weight Moved) = (Dist. Btwn. Arms ÷ Distance CG Moves)

The weight of the baggage is represented by "X." The distance between arms is 140 inches (180 - 40 = 140), and you want the CG to move 2.0 inches (94.0 - 92.0 =2.0).

(3,650 ÷ X) = (140 ÷ 2.0)

You must move 52.14 pounds of baggage.

12-116   PLT003

GIVEN

Total weight...3,037 lb
CG location...Station 68.8
Fuel consumption...12.7 gal/hr
Fuel CG...Station 68.0

After 1 hour 45 minutes of flight time, the CG would be located at station

A– 68.77.
B– 68.83.
C– 69.77.

12-116. Answer B. GFDICM 12C, PHB

The starting moment is 3,037 lbs x 68.8 inches. The moment of the fuel burned off is 12.7 gals/hr x 1.75 hrs x 6 lbs./gal x 68.0 inches.

	WEIGHT (lbs)	ARM (in)	MOMENT (lb-in/100)
Total	3,037.0	68.8	2,089.45
Fuel 22.22 gal.	133.32	68.0	90.65
	2,903.68		1,998.80

The CG is the total moment divided by the total weight. The answer is 68.83 inches (199,880 ÷ 2,903.68 = 68.83).

12-117   PLT121

(Refer to figure 12-19 on page 12-58.)

GIVEN:

Empty weight (oil is included) in-lb...1,271 lb

Empty weight moment (in-lb/1,000)...102.04

Pilot and copilot...400 lb

Rear seat passenger...140 lb

Cargo...100 lb

Fuel...37 gal

Is the airplane loaded within limits?

A– Yes, the weight and CG is within limits.

B– No, the weight exceeds the maximum allowable.

C– No, the weight is acceptable, but the CG is aft of the aft limit.

12-117. Answer A. GFDICM 12C, PHB

Refer to the figure to convert fuel to pounds. Add up the known weights, for a total of 1,933 pounds. Use the LOADING GRAPH and find the moment for each weight.

	WEIGHT (lbs)	MOMENT (lb-in/100)
Empty wt.	1,271	102.04
Pilot/Co-pilot	400	36.00
Rear seat	140	18.00
Cargo	100	11.50
Fuel	222	20.00
Totals	2,133	187.54

Total the moments and locate the maximum weight on the CENTER OF GRAVITY ENVELOPE graph. The intersection of the loaded weight and moment is in the upper portion of the normal category, but within the envelope.

Figure 12-19. Loading of Graph and Center of Gravity Envelope.

COMMERCIAL FLIGHT CONSIDERATIONS

SECTION A - EMERGENCY PROCEDURES

Chapter 13, Section A of the Instrument/Commercial Manual covers emergency flight procedures for commercial pilots. You may find the following summary a useful review of some important procedures. However, there are no commercial FAA test questions assigned to this section.

EMERGENCY DESCENT

An emergency descent is used to achieve the fastest practical rate of vertical descent to reach a safe altitude or landing during an emergency situation.

EMERGENCY APPROACH AND LANDING

- The best glide airspeed, found in the pilot's operating handbook, will maximize the distance you can glide and increase the number of available emergency landing areas. In some airplanes, the best glide speed may change as gross weight changes.
- Key positions on downwind or base allow you to judge your gliding distance in the same manner you would during a normal traffic pattern.

SYSTEMS AND EQUIPMENT MALFUNCTIONS

- If you experience an in-flight emergency, follow the checklist procedures specified in the POH for your airplane and declare an emergency by radio.
- A cabin or baggage compartment door opening in flight can be a major distraction. Despite the noise and confusion, it is important to maintain control of the airplane, particularly during departure.

SECTION B - COMMERCIAL DECISION MAKING

- The **DECIDE** acronym stands for: **D**etect the fact that a change has occurred. **E**stimate the need to counter or react to the change. **C**hoose a desirable outcome for the success of the flight. **I**dentify actions which could successfully control the change. **D**o the necessary action to adapt to the change. **E**valuate the effect of the action.
- Aeronautical decision making (ADM) is a systematic approach to the mental process used by pilots to consistently determine the best course of action for a given set of circumstances.
- Good cockpit stress management begins with good life stress management. To help you manage cockpit stress, you should avoid situations that degrade your ability to handle cockpit responsibilities.
- Some behavioral traps that experienced pilots fall into are the need to complete a flight as planned, please passengers, meet schedules, and demonstrate the "right stuff." The desire to demonstrate the "right stuff" can generate tendencies that lead to practices that are dangerous, often illegal, and may lead to a mishap. Commercial pilots are also just as prone to peer pressure, get-there-itis, loss of situational awareness, and operating without adequate fuel reserves.
- Identifying hazardous attitudes through an inventory is an early part of the ADM process. There are five hazardous attitudes and corresponding antidotes. The five types of hazardous attitudes and their antidotes are:

    - Anti-authority — "ATC says there are thunderstorm cells reported ahead, but I don't believe those doomsayers."
      ANTIDOTE: ATC is trying to help; they may have information I do not.

    - Invulnerability — "I have weather radar and a lightning detector on board, so I'll be safe."
      ANTIDOTE: These devices have important limitations to consider.

    - Macho — "I'm tough; I can handle a little turbulence."
      ANTIDOTE: There's more than a little turbulence inside a thunderstorm cell.

    - Impulsivity — "I have to try that lighter spot before it closes up."
      ANTIDOTE:Wait a minute — that hole is not big enough to allow me 20 miles of separation.

    - Resignation — "There's nothing I can do to control the aircraft now."
      ANTIDOTE: I can maintain a safe airspeed.

13-1   PLT022
Aeronautical Decision Making (ADM) is a

A– systematic approach to the mental process used by pilots to consistently determine the best course of action for a given set of circumstances.
B– decision making process which relies on good judgment to reduce risks associated with each flight.
C– mental process of analyzing all information in a particular situation and making a timely decision on what action to take.

13-1. Answer A. GFDICM 13B, AC 60-22
All these are good answers, but the FAA defines ADM as a systematic approach to the mental process used by aircraft pilots to consistently determine the best course of action in response to a given set of circumstances.

13-2   PLT103

The Aeronautical Decision Making (ADM) process identifies the steps involved in good decision making. One of these steps includes a pilot

A–making a rational evaluation of the required actions.
B–developing the "right stuff" attitude.
C–identifying personal attitudes hazardous to safe flight.

13-2. Answer C. GFDICM 13B, AC 60-22
These steps are:

1. Identifying personal attitudes hazardous to safe flight.
2. Learning behavior modification techniques.
3. Learning how to recognize and cope with stress.
4. Developing risk assessment skills.
5. Using all resources in a multicrew situation.
6. Evaluating the effectiveness of one's ADM skills.

13-3   PLT103

Examples of classic behavioral traps that experienced pilots may fall into are: trying to

A–assume additional responsibilities and assert PIC authority.
B–promote situational awareness and then necessary changes in behavior.
C–complete a flight as planned, please passengers, meet schedules, and demonstrate the "right stuff."

13-3. Answer C. GFDICM 13B, AC 60-22
Pilots, particularly those with considerable experience, as a rule always try to complete a flight as planned, please passengers, meet schedules, and generally demonstrate that they have the "right stuff." The FAA says that the basic drive to demonstrate the "right stuff" can have an adverse effect on safety and can impose an unrealistic assessment of piloting skills under stressful conditions.

13-4   PLT103

The basic drive for a pilot to demonstrate the "right stuff" can have an adverse effect on safety, by

A–a total disregard for any alternative course of action.
B–generating tendencies that lead to practices that are dangerous, often illegal, and that may lead to a mishap.
C–imposing a realistic assessment of piloting skills under stressful conditions.

13-4. Answer B. GFDICM 13B, AC 60-22
The basic drive to demonstrate the "right stuff" ultimately may lead to practices that are dangerous and often illegal, and may lead to a mishap. All experienced pilots have fallen prey to, or have been tempted by, one or more of these tendencies in their flying careers.

13-5   PLT103

Most pilots have fallen prey to dangerous tendencies or behavior problems at some time. Some of these dangerous tendencies or behavior patterns which must be identified and eliminated include:

A–Deficiencies in instrument skills and knowledge of aircraft systems or limitations.
B–Performance deficiencies from human factors such as, fatigue, illness or emotional problems.
C–Peer pressure, get-there-itis, loss of positional or situation awareness, and operating without adequate fuel reserves.

13-5. Answer C. GFDICM 13B, AC 60-22
The FAA lists the following and identifies them as dangerous tendencies:

1. Peer pressure
2. Mind set
3. Get-there-itis
4. Duck-under syndrome
5. Scud running
6. Continuing visual flight rules (VFR) into instrumentconditions
7. Getting behind the aircraft
8. Loss of positional or situation awareness
9. Operating without adequate fuel reserves
10. Descent below the minimum enroute altitude
11. Flying outside the envelope
12. Neglect of flight planning, preflight inspections, checklists, etc.

13-6   PLT022

An early part of the Aeronautical Decision Making (ADM) process involves

A–taking a self-assessment hazardous attitude inventory test.
B–understanding the drive to have the "right stuff."
C–obtaining proper flight instruction and experience during training.

13-6. Answer A. GFDICM 13B, AC 60-22
The self-assessment hazardous attitude inventory test presents a number of scenarios, each with five answer choices designed to analyze your motivation for making various decisions. Even if none of the answer choices is acceptable to you, the exercise forces you to rank them from the most likely reason to least likely reason for carrying out the action.

13-7   PLT103

Hazardous attitudes which contribute to poor pilot judgment can be effectively counteracted by

A–early recognition of hazardous thoughts.
B–taking meaningful steps to be more assertive with attitudes.
C–redirecting that hazardous attitude so that appropriate action can be taken.

13-7. Answer C. GFDICM 13B, AC 60-22
Hazardous attitudes which contribute to poor pilot judgment can be effectively counteracted by redirecting that hazardous attitude so that appropriate action can be taken. Recognition of hazardous thoughts is the first step in neutralizing them in the ADM process.

13-8   PLT103
What are some of the hazardous attitudes dealt with in Aeronautical Decision Making (ADM)?

A–Antiauthority (don't tell me), impulsivity (do something quickly without thinking), macho (I can do it).
B–Risk management, stress management, and risk elements.
C–Poor decision making, situational awareness, and judgment.

13-8. Answer A. GFDPPM 13B, AC 60-22
The five hazardous attitudes and their antidotes are:

ATTITUDE: Antiauthority: Don't tell me.

ANTIDOTE: Follow the rules. They are usually right.

ATTITUDE: Impulsivity: Do something quickly.

ANTIDOTE: Not so fast. Think first.

ATTITUDE: Invulnerability: It won't happen to me.

ANTIDOTE: It could happen to me.

ATTITUDE: Macho: I can do it.

ANTIDOTE: Taking chances is foolish.

ATTITUDE: Resignation: What's the use?

ANTIDOTE: I'm not helpless. I can make a difference.

13-9   PLT103
When a pilot recognizes a hazardous thought, he or she then should correct it by stating the corresponding antidote. Which of the following is the antidote for MACHO?

A–Follow the rules. They are usually right.
B–Not so fast. Think first.
C–Taking chances is foolish.

13-9. Answer C. GFDPPM 13B, AC 60-22
ATTITUDE: Macho: I can do it.

ANTIDOTE: Taking chances is foolish.

13-10   PLT103
What is the first step in neutralizing a hazardous attitude in the ADM process?

A–Recognition of invulnerability in the situation.
B–Dealing with improper judgment.
C–Recognition of hazardous thoughts.

13-10. Answer C. GFDPPM 13B, AC 60-22
Hazardous attitudes which contribute to poor pilot judgment can be effectively counteracted by redirecting that hazardous attitude so that appropriate action can be taken. Recognition of hazardous thoughts is the first step in neutralizing them in the ADM process.

13-11   PLT103
What should a pilot do when recognizing a thought as hazardous?

A–Avoid developing this hazardous thought.
B–Develop this hazardous thought and follow through with modified action.
C–Label that thought as hazardous, then correct that thought by stating the corresponding learned antidote.

13-11. Answer C. GFDPPM 13B, AC 60-22
When a pilot recognizes a thought as hazardous, the pilot should label that thought as hazardous, then correct that thought by stating the corresponding antidote. Antidotes should be memorized for each of the hazardous attitudes so that they automatically come to mind when needed.

13-12   PLT272
To help manage cockpit stress, pilots must

A– be aware of life stress situations that are similar to those in flying.
B– condition themselves to relax and think rationally when stress appears.
C– avoid situations that will improve their abilities to handle cockpit responsibilities.

13-12. Answer B. GFDICM 13B, AC 60-22
Here are some of the tips the FAA offers for managing cockpit stress:

1. Avoid situations that distract you from flying the aircraft.
2. Reduce your workload to reduce stress levels. This will create a proper environment in which to make good decisions.
3. If an emergency does occur, relax and remain calm. Think for a moment, weigh the alternatives, then act.
4. Maintain proficiency in your aircraft; proficiency builds confidence. Familiarize yourself thoroughly with your aircraft, its systems, and emergency procedures.
5. Know and respect your own personal limits.
6. Do not let little mistakes bother you because they can build into a big thing. Wait until after you land, then "debrief" and analyze past actions.
7. If flying is adding to your stress, either stop flying or seek professional help to manage your stress within acceptable limits.

13-13   PLT272
What does good cockpit stress management begin with?

A– Knowing what causes stress.
B– Eliminating life and cockpit stress issues.
C– Good life stress management.

13-13. Answer C. GFDPPM 13B, AC 60-22
Good cockpit stress management begins with good life stress management.

13-14   PLT103
The passengers for a charter flight have arrived almost an hour late for a flight that requires a reservation. Which of the following alternatives best illustrates the ANTI-AUTHORITY reaction?

A– Those reservation rules do not apply to this flight.
B– If the pilot hurries, he or she may still make it on time.
C– The pilot can't help it that the passengers are late.

13-14. Answer A. GFDPPM 13B, AC 60-22
The Anti-authority attitude is demonstrated by a lack of respect for the regulations and/or rules applicable to the flight.

13-15   PLT103

While conducting an operational check of the cabin pressurization system, the pilot discovers that the rate control feature is inoperative. He knows that he can manually control the cabin pressure, so he elects to disregard the discrepancy. Which of the following alternatives best illustrates the INVULNERABILITY reaction?

A– What is the worst that could happen.
B– He can handle a little problem like this.
C– It's too late to fix it now.

13-15. Answer A. GFDPPM 13B, AC 60-22
The invulnerability attitude is that bad things cannot happen to you.

13-16   PLT103

The pilot and passengers are anxious to get to their destination for a business presentation. Level IV thunderstorms are reported to be in a line across their intended route of flight. Which of the following alternatives best illustrates the IMPULSIVITY reaction?

A– They want to hurry and get going, before things get worse.
B– A thunderstorm won't stop them.
C– They can't change the weather, so they might as well go.

13-16. Answer A. GFDPPM 13B, AC 60-22
Impulsivity is the need to make a quick decision without fully weighing the consequences.

13-17   PLT103

While on an IFR flight, a pilot emerges from a cloud to find himself within 300 feet of a helicopter. Which of the following alternatives best illustrates the MACHO reaction?

A– He is not too concerned; everything will be alright.
B– He flies a little closer, just to show him.
C– He quickly turns away and dives, to avoid collision.

13-17. Answer B. GFDPPM 13B, AC 60-22
Part of the macho attitude is the predisposition to take chances.

13-18   PLT103

When a pilot recognizes a hazardous thought, he or she then should correct it by applying the corresponding antidote. Which of the following is the antidote for ANTI-AUTHORITY/DON'T TELL ME hazardous attitude

A– Not so fast. Think first.
B– It won't happen to me. It could happen to me.
C– Follow the rules. They are usually right.

13-18. Answer C. GFDPPM 13B, AC 60-22
This is a statement of the attitude (don't tell me) and the antidote (follow the rules; they are usually right).

13-19   PLT103
A pilot and friends are going to fly to an out-of-town football game. When the passengers arrive, the pilot determines that they will be over the maximum gross weight for takeoff with the existing fuel load. Which of the following alternatives best illustrates the RESIGNATION reaction?

A– Well, nobody told him about the extra weight.
B– Weight and balance is a formality forced on pilots by the FAA.
C– He can't wait around to de-fuel, they have to get there on time.

13-19. Answer A. GFDPPM 13B, AC 60-22
Resignation occurs when a pilot proceeds with an inappropriate course of action with the attitude that it is not his/her responsibility, or that nothing can be done about the situation.

13-20   PLT022
Which of the following is the final step of the Decide Model for effective risk management and Aeronautical Decision Making?

A– Estimate.
B– Evaluate.
C– Eliminate.

13-20. Answer B. GFDPPM 13B, AC 60-22
There are six steps:

1. Detect. The decision maker detects the fact that change has occurred.
2. Estimate. The decision maker estimates the need to counter or react to the change.
3. Choose. The decision maker chooses a desirable outcome (in terms of success) for the flight.
4. Identify. The decision maker identifies actions which could successfully control the change.
5. Do. The decision maker takes the necessary action.
6. Evaluate. The decision maker evaluates the effect(s) of his action countering the change.

13-21   PLT022
Which of the following is the first step of the Decide Model for effective risk management and Aeronautical Decision Making?

A– Detect.
B– Identify.
C– Evaluate.

13-21. Answer A. GFDPPM 13B, AC 60-22
There are six steps:

1. Detect. The decision maker detects the fact that change has occurred.
2. Estimate. The decision maker estimates the need to counter or react to the change.
3. Choose. The decision maker chooses a desirable outcome (in terms of success) for the flight.
4. Identify. The decision maker identifies actions which could successfully control the change.
5. Do. The decision maker takes the necessary action.
6. Evaluate. The decision maker evaluates the effect(s) of his action countering the change.

13-22   PLT022

The Decide Model is comprised of a 6-step process to provide a pilot a logical way of approaching Aeronautical Decision Making. These steps are:

A– Detect, estimate, choose, identify, do, and evaluate.
B– Determine, evaluate, choose, identify, do, and eliminate.
C– Determine, eliminate, choose, identify, detect, and evaluate.

13-22. Answer A. GFDPPM 13B, AC 60-22
Explanation of the six steps:

1. Detect. The decision maker detects the fact that change has occurred.
2. Estimate. The decision maker estimates the need to counter or react to the change.
3. Choose. The decision maker chooses a desirable outcome (in terms of success) for the flight.
4. Identify. The decision maker identifies actions which could successfully control the change.
5. Do. The decision maker takes the necessary action.
6. Evaluate. The decision maker evaluates the effect(s) of his action countering the change.

COMMERCIAL MANEUVERS

COMMERCIAL MANEUVERS

Chapter 14 covers the performance maneuvers required for the commercial pilot airplane practical test. There are two commercial FAA test questions assigned.

- During a crosswind takeoff, use the rudder to maintain directional control, turn the ailerons into the wind, and lift off at a slightly higher-than-normal speed.
- During a crosswind takeoff, use the rudder to maintain directional control, turn the ailerons into the wind, and lift off at a slightly higher-than-normal speed.

14-1 PLT486

With regard to the technique required for a crosswind correction on takeoff, a pilot should use

A– aileron pressure into the wind and initiate the lift-off at a normal airspeed in both tailwheel-and nosewheel-type airplanes.

B– right rudder pressure, aileron pressure into the wind, and higher than normal lift-off airspeed in both tricycle- and conventional-gear airplanes.

C– rudder as required to maintain directional control, aileron pressure into the wind, and higher than normal lift-off airspeed in both conventional- and nosewheel-type airplanes.

14-1. Answer C. GFDPMM M11, AFH

During a crosswind takeoff, the rudder should be used to maintain directional control, the ailerons positioned into the wind, and lift off should be initiated at a slightly higher-than-normal speed.

14-2 PLT170

A proper crosswind landing on a runway requires that, at the moment of touchdown, the

A– direction of motion of the airplane and its lateral axis be perpendicular to the runway.

B– direction of motion of the airplane and its longitudinal axis be parallel to the runway.

C– downwind wing be lowered sufficiently to eliminate the tendency for the airplane to drift.

14-2. Answer B. GFDPMM M11, AFH

With either the crab or wing-low method of drift correction, the flight path and the aircraft's longitudinal axis must be parallel to the runway at touchdown.

FEDERAL AVIATION REGULATIONS

CHAPTER 15

SECTION A - 14 CFR PART 1 - DEFINITIONS AND ABBREVIATIONS

- A "commercial operator" is a person who, for compensation or hire, engages in air commerce through the carriage of persons or property by aircraft, other than as an air carrier. To determine if an operation is for compensation or hire you must determine whether the flight is incidental to other business being conducted or whether it is, in itself, an enterprise for profit or benefit.
- The term "operate", as referred to by the FARs, is defined as the use or approval of the use of an aircraft for the purpose of air navigation, with or without the right of legal control.
- "Operational control" differs from "operate" in that the person initiating, conducting, or terminating the flight has the authority to do so.

15-1   PLT389
Regulations which refer to "commercial operators" relate to that person who

A– is the owner of a small scheduled airline.
B– for compensation or hire, engages in the carriage by aircraft in air commerce of persons or property, as an air carrier.
C– for compensation or hire, engages in the carriage by aircraft in air commerce of persons or property, other than as an air carrier.

15-1. Answer C. FAR 1.1
"Commercial operator," means a person who, for compensation or hire, engages in the carriage by aircraft in air commerce of persons or property, other than as an air carrier or foreign air carrier.

15-2   PLT374
Regulations which refer to "operate" relate to that person who

A– acts as pilot in command of the aircraft.
B– is the sole manipulator of the aircraft controls.
C– causes the aircraft to be used or authorizes its use.

15-2. Answer C. FAR 1.1
"Operate," with respect to aircraft, means use, cause to use, or authorize to use aircraft, for the purpose of air navigation including the piloting of aircraft, with or without the right of legal control (as owner, lessee, or otherwise).

15-3   PLT432
Regulations which refer to the "operational control" of a flight are in relation to

A– the specific duties of any required crewmember.
B– acting as the sole manipulator of the aircraft controls.
C– exercising authority over initiating, conducting, or terminating a flight.

15-3. Answer C. FAR 1.1
"Operational control," with respect to a flight, means the exercise of authority over initiating, conducting, or terminating a flight.

15-4   PLT371
If an airplane category is listed as utility, it would mean that this airplane could be operated in which of the following maneuvers?

A– Any maneuver except acrobatics or spins.
B– Limited acrobatics, including spins (if approved).
C– Limited acrobatics, excluding spins.

15-4. Answer B. FAR 23.3
An airplane in the utility category can conduct limited acrobatics, including spins.

SECTION B - 14 CFR PART 61 - CERTIFICATION: PILOTS AND FLIGHT INSTRUCTORS
COMMERCIAL PILOT REQUIREMENTS AND LIMITATIONS

- A commercial pilot, like any pilot, is required to have the appropriate certificate in his/her possession when acting as pilot in command or as a required crewmember.

- A second-class medical is required to exercise commercial privileges and allows you to exercise these privileges for 12 calendar months from the month of issue.

- When an action has been taken against a pilot for violating any Federal or State statutes relating to the operation of a motor vehicle while intoxicated, impaired, or under the influence of alcohol or a drug, then the pilot must submit a written report to the FAA, Civil Aviation Security Division (AFC-700), within 60 days of the action. If a pilot commits the act of operating an aircraft while intoxicated, impaired, or under the influence of alcohol or a drug, then any of the pilot's certificates, ratings, or authorizations may be suspended or revoked. In addition, committing the act is grounds for denial of an application for a certificate, rating, or authorization issued under Part 61 for a period of up to 1 year after the date of that act.

- A type rating is required to act as PIC of any aircraft having a maximum certificated takeoff weight of more than 12,500 pounds.

- A complex airplane has retractable landing gear, flaps, and a controllable-pitch propeller. In order to act as pilot-in-command of a complex airplane, you are required to have received and logged ground and flight training, and received a logbook endorsement of competency. A high performance airplane has an engine with more than 200 horsepower. To act as pilot-in-command of a high-performance airplane, you must also obtain training and a logbook endorsement stating that you are proficient to operate such an airplane.

COMMERCIAL CURRENCY

- To act as pilot in command of an aircraft carrying passengers, you must have made at least three takeoffs and three landings in an aircraft of the same category and class, and if a type rating is required, of the same type, within the preceding 90 days.

- To act as pilot in command of an aircraft carrying passengers, you must have made at least three takeoffs and three landings in an aircraft of the same category and class, and if a type rating is required, of the same type, within the preceding 90 days.

- To act as pilot in command of an aircraft, you must show, by logbook endorsement, the satisfactory completion of a flight review or completion of a pilot proficiency check within the preceding 24 calendar months.

15-5 PLT444
Commercial pilots are required to have a valid and appropriate pilot certificate in their physical possession or readily accessible in the aircraft when

A– acting as pilot in command.
B– carrying passengers only.
C– piloting for hire only.

15-5. Answer A. FAR 61.3
You must have a current pilot certificate and medical certificate readily available and in your physical possession or readily accessible in the aircraft any time you act as pilot in command (PIC). It makes no difference whether you are carrying passengers or flying for hire.

15-6   PLT371
Which of the following are considered aircraft class ratings?

A– Transport, normal, utility, and acrobatic.
B– Airplane, rotorcraft, glider, and lighter-than-air.
C– Single-engine land, multiengine land, single-engine sea, and multiengine sea.

15-6. Answer C. FAR 61.5
Single-engine land, multi-engine land, single-engine sea, and multi-engine sea are airplane class ratings placed on a pilot certificate.

15-7   PLT386
Does a commercial pilot certificate have a specific expiration date?

A– No, it is issued without a specific expiration date.
B– Yes, it expires at the end of the 24th month after the month in which it was issued.
C– No, but commercial privileges expire if a flight review is not satisfactorily completed each 12 months.

15-7. Answer A. FAR 61.19
Any pilot certificate (other than a student pilot certificate) issued under FAR Part 61 is issued without a specific expiration date.

15-8   PLT427
A second-class medical certificate issued to a commercial pilot on April 10, this year, permits the pilot to exercise which of the following privileges?

A– Commercial pilot privileges through April 30, next year.
B– Commercial pilot privileges through April 10, 2 years later.
C– Private pilot privileges through, but not after, March 31, next year.

15-8. Answer A. FAR 61.23
To exercise the privileges of a commercial pilot, that person also must hold at least a second-class medical certificate that was issued within the past 12 calendar months.

15-9   PLT444
When is the pilot in command required to hold a category and class rating appropriate to the aircraft being flown?

A– On flights when carrying another person.
B– On practical tests given by an examiner or FAA Inspector.
C– All solo flights.

15-9. Answer A. FAR 61.31
To act as pilot in command (other than authorized student pilot solo activity), you must hold a pilot certificate with the appropriate category, class, and type rating (if a class and type rating is required) that applies to the aircraft.

15-10   PLT451

Unless otherwise authorized, the pilot in command is required to hold a type rating when operating any

A— aircraft that is certificated for more than one pilot.

B— multiengine airplane having a gross weight of more than 12,000 pounds.

C— aircraft of more than 12,500 pounds maximum certificated takeoff weight.

15-10. Answer C. FAR 61.31

According to FAR 61.31, a person may not act as pilot in command of a large aircraft unless he or she hold a type rating for that aircraft. According to FAR Part 1, "Large Aircraft" means an aircraft of more than 12,500 pounds, maximum certificated takeoff weight.

15-11   PLT442

To act as pilot in command of an airplane that is equipped with retractable landing gear, flaps, and controllable-pitch propeller, a person is required to

A— make at least six takeoffs and landings in such an airplane within the preceding 6 months.

B— receive and log ground and flight training in such an airplane, and obtain a logbook endorsement certifying proficiency.

C— hold a multiengine airplane class rating.

15-11. Answer B. FAR 61.31

No person may act as pilot in command of a complex airplane (an airplane that has retractable landing gear, flaps, and a controllable pitch propeller) unless that person has received and logged ground and flight training from an authorized instructor in a complex airplane, or flight simulator that is representative of a complex airplane, and has received a one-time endorsement in the logbook from the instructor who certifies that the person is proficient to operate a complex airplane.

15-12   PLT443

What flight time may a pilot log as second in command?

A— Only that flight time during which the second in command is the sole manipulator of the controls.

B— All flight time while acting as second in command in aircraft configured for more than one pilot.

C— All flight time when qualified and occupying a crewmember station in an aircraft that requires more than one pilot.

15-12. Answer C. FAR 61.51

A pilot may log second in command time if qualified in accordance with the second-in-command requirements of FAR 61.55, and occupies a crewmember station in an aircraft that requires more than one pilot by the aircraft's type certificate, or if he/she holds the appropriate category, class, and instrument rating (if an instrument rating is required for the flight) for the aircraft being flown, and more than one pilot is required under the type certification of the aircraft or the regulations under which the flight is being conducted.

15-13   PLT443

What flight time must be documented and recorded by a pilot exercising the privileges of a commercial certificate?

A— Flight time showing training and aeronautical experience to meet requirements for a certificate, rating or flight review.

B— Only flight time for compensation or hire with passengers aboard which is necessary to meet the recent flight experience requirements.

C— All flight time flown for compensation or hire.

15-13. Answer A. FAR 61.51

According to the regulation, "Each person must document and record the following flight time in a manner acceptable to the Administrator. This includes any time that is training and aeronautical experience used to meet the requirements for a certificate, rating, or flight review and aeronautical experience required for meeting the recent flight experience requirements."

15-14   PLT442

If a pilot does not meet the recency of experience requirements for night flight and official sunset is 1900 CST, the latest time passengers should be carried is

A– 1959 CST.
B– 1900 CST.
C– 1800 CST.

15-14. Answer A. FAR 61.57b

No person may act as pilot in command of an aircraft carrying passengers during the period beginning 1 hour after sunset and ending 1 hour before sunrise (as published in the American Air Almanac), unless that person meets night experience requirements.

15-15   PLT442

Prior to carrying passengers at night, the pilot in command must have accomplished the required takeoffs and landings in

A– the same category, class, and type of aircraft (if a type rating is required).
B– any category aircraft.
C– the same category and class of aircraft to be used.

15-15. Answer A. FAR 61.57

No person may act as pilot in command of an aircraft carrying passengers unless that person has made at least three takeoffs and three landings within the preceding 90 days, and the required takeoffs and landings were performed in an aircraft of the same category, class, and type (if a type rating is required).

15-16   PLT442

No pilot may act as pilot in command of an aircraft under IFR or in weather conditions less than the minimums prescribed for VFR unless that pilot has, within the past 6 months, performed and logged under actual or simulated instrument conditions, at least

A– six instrument approaches, holding procedures, intercepting and tracking courses, or passed an instrument proficiency check in an aircraft that is appropriate to the aircraft category.
B– three instrument approaches and logged 3 hours of instruments.
C– six instrument flights and six approaches.

15-16. Answer A. FAR 61.57

Six instrument approaches are required, as well as holding procedures, intercepting and tracking courses, or passing an instrument competency check in an aircraft that is appropriate to the aircraft category. There is no minimum instrument time required.

15-17   PLT449

To act as pilot in command of an aircraft operated under 14 CFR part 91, a commercial pilot must have satisfactorily accomplished a flight review or completed a proficiency check within the preceding

A– 6 calendar months.
B– 12 calendar months.
C– 24 calendar months.

15-17. Answer C. FAR 61.56

No person (not just a commercial pilot) may act as pilot in command of an aircraft unless, within the preceding 24 calendar months, they have satisfactorily completed a flight review, a pilot proficiency check, or one or more phases of an FAA-sponsored pilot proficiency award program.

15-18   PLT387
Pilots who change their permanent mailing address and fail to notify the FAA Airmen Certification Branch of this change are entitled to exercise the privileges of their pilot certificate for a period of

A– 30 days.
B– 60 days.
C– 90 days.

15-18. Answer A. FAR 61.60
After changing your permanent mailing address, you may not exercise the privileges of a pilot or flight instructor certificate after 30 days unless the FAA Airman Certification Branch has been notified in writing.

15-19   PLT444
To act as pilot in command of an airplane towing a glider, the tow pilot is required to have

A– a logbook endorsement from an authorized glider instructor certifying receipt of ground and flight training in gliders, and be proficient with techniques and procedures for safe towing of gliders.
B– at least a private pilot certificate with a category rating for powered aircraft, and made and logged at least three flights as pilot or observer in a glider being towed by an airplane.
C– a logbook record of having made at least three flights as sole manipulator of the controls of a glider being towed by an airplane.

15-19. Answer A. FAR 61.69
No person may act as pilot in command of an aircraft towing a glider unless he or she has an endorsement in his or her pilot logbook from a person authorized to give flight instruction in gliders, certifying that the pilot has received ground and flight instruction in gliders and is familiar with the techniques and procedures essential to the safe towing of gliders.

15-20   PLT442
To act as pilot in command of an airplane towing a glider, a pilot must have accomplished, within the preceeding 12 months, at least

A– three actual glider tows under the supervision of a qualified tow pilot.
B– three actual or simulated glider tows while accompanied by a qualified tow pilot.
C– ten flights as pilot in command of an aircraft while towing a glider.

15-20. Answer B. FAR 61.69
Three actual or simulated glider tows while accompanied by a qualified pilot are required within the previous 12 months, or at least three flights as pilot in command of a glider towed by an aircraft.

15-21   PLT448
What limitation is imposed on a newly certificated commercial pilot - airplane, if that person does not hold an instrument rating? The carriage of passengers

A– for hire on cross-country flights is limited to 50 NM for night flights, but not limited for day flights.
B– or property for hire on cross-country flights at night is limited to a radius of 50 NM.
C– for hire on cross-country flights in excess of 50 NM, or for hire at night is prohibited.

15-21. Answer C. FAR 61.133b
Commercial night operations and flights of more than 50 NM require an instrument rating.

15-22   PLT444

To act as pilot-in-command of an airplane with more than 200 horsepower, a person is required to

A– receive and log ground and flight training from a qualified pilot in such an airplane.

B– obtain an endorsement from a qualified pilot stating that the person is proficient to operate such an airplane.

C– receive and log ground and flight training from an authorized instructor in such an airplane.

15-22. Answer C. GFDPPM 1B, FAR 61.31f

No person may act as PIC of a high-performance airplane unless the person has received and logged ground and flight training from an authorized instructor in a high-performance airplane and has been found proficient in the operation and systems of the airplane. Additionally, you must have a high-performance endorsement in your logbook from an authorized instructor.

15-23   PLT449

To serve as pilot in command of an airplane that is certified for more than one pilot crewmember, and operated under part 91, a person must

A– complete a flight review within the preceding 24 calendar months.

B– receive and log ground and flight training from an authorized flight instructor.

C– complete a pilot-in-command proficiency check within the preceding 12 calendar months in an airplane that is type certificated for more than one pilot.

15-23. Answer C. FAR 61.58

A PIC proficiency check in any airplane requiring more than one pilot is required within the preceding 12 calendar months, and a check in the same type of aircraft is required within the preceding 24 months.

15-24   PLT442

To serve as second in command of an airplane that is certified for more than one pilot crewmember, and operated under part 91, a person must

A– receive and log flight training from an authorized flight instructor in the type of airplane for which privileges are requested.

B– hold at least a commercial pilot certificate with an airplane category rating.

C– within the last 12 months become familiar with the required information, and perform and log pilot time in the type of airplane for which privileges are requested.

15-24. Answer C. FAR 61.55

A private pilot certificate is the minimum required, with an instrument rating for IFR operations. Three takeoffs and landings are required within the previous 12 months, plus engine-out and other procedures.

15-25   PLT444

A person with a Commercial Pilot certificate may act as pilot in command of an aircraft for compensation or hire, if that person

A– is qualified in accordance with 14 CFR part 61 and with the applicable parts that apply to the operation.

B– is qualified in accordance with 14 CFR part 61 and has passed a pilot competency check given by an authorized check pilot.

C– holds appropriate category, class ratings, and meets the recent flight experience requirements of 14 CFR part 61.

15-25. Answer A. FAR 61.133

The person must be qualified under part 61 and under part 91, 119, 121, 135, or other applicable FARs.

15-26   PLT444

A person with a commercial pilot certificate may act as pilot in command of an aircraft carrying persons or property for compensation or hire, if that person

A– holds appropriate category, class ratings, and meets the recent flight experience requirements of 14 CFR part 61

B– is qualified in accordance with 14 CFR part 61 and with the applicable parts that apply to the operation.

C– is qualified in accordance with 14 CFR part 61 and has passed a pilot competency check given by an authorized check pilot.

15-26. Answer B. FAR 61.133

The person must be qualified under part 61 and under part 91, 119, 121, 135, or other applicable FARs.

15-27   PLT443

To act as pilot in command of a tailwheel airplane, without prior experience, a pilot must

A– log ground and flight training from an authorized instructor.

B– pass a competency check and receive an endorsement from an authorized instructor.

C– receive and log flight training from an authorized instructor as well as receive a logbook endorsement from an authorized instructor who finds the person proficient in a tailwheel airplane.

15-27. Answer C. FAR 61.31

A pilot must receive flight training and a one-time instructor endorsement from an authorized instructor who found the person proficient in the operation of a tailwheel airplane.

15-28   PLT463

A pilot convicted of operating a motor vehicle while either intoxicated by, impaired by, or under the influence of alcohol or a drug is required to provide a

A– written report to the FAA Civil Aeromedical Institute (CAMI) within 60 days after the motor vehicle action.

B– written report to the FAA Civil Aviation Security Division (AMC-700) not later than 60 days after the conviction.

C– notification of the conviction to an FAA Aviation Medical Examiner (AME) not later than 60 days after the motor vehicle action.

15-28. Answer B. FAR 61.15

When a pilot is convicted of operating a motor vehicle while either intoxicated or impaired by alcohol or a drug, the pilot must notify the FAA Civil Aviation Security Division, in writing, not later than 60 days after the conviction.

15-29   PLT463

A pilot convicted of a motor vehicle offense involving alcohol or drugs is required to provide a written report to the

A– FAA Civil Aeromedical Institute (CAMI) within 60 days after the conviction.

B– FAA Civil Aviation Security Division (AMC-700) within 60 days after the conviction.

C– nearest FAA Flight Standards District Office (FSDO) within 60 days after such action.

15-29. Answer B. FAR 61.15

When a pilot is convicted of operating a motor vehicle while either intoxicated or impaired by alcohol or a drug, the pilot must notify the FAA Civil Aviation Security Division, in writing, not later than 60 days after the conviction.

SECTION C - 14 CFR PART 91 - GENERAL OPERATING AND FLIGHT RULES

PILOT-IN-COMMAND RESPONSIBILITY

The pilot in command is the final authority as to the operation of an aircraft. If an in-flight emergency requires immediate action, the pilot in command may deviate from the FARs to the extent required to meet that emergency. A written report is not required unless requested by the FAA.

AIRCRAFT DOCUMENTS

In addition to a valid airworthiness certificate, operating limitations and the registration certificate must also be on board an aircraft during flight.

DROPPING OBJECTS

Objects may be dropped from an aircraft if precautions are taken to avoid injury or damage to persons or property on the surface.

PREFLIGHT PLANNING

FAR 91.103 requires that a pilot in command, before beginning a flight, become familiar with all available information concerning that flight. For a flight under IFR or a flight not in the vicinity of an airport, this information must specifically include weather reports and forecasts, fuel requirements, alternatives available if the planned flight cannot be completed, and any known traffic delays of which the pilot in command has been advised by ATC. For any flight, the PIC must determine the runway lengths at airports of intended use, and takeoff and landing distance information for the aircraft.

AIRCRAFT EQUIPMENT

- Flight crewmembers are required to keep their safety belts and shoulder harnesses fastened during takeoffs and landings. Safety belts must stay fastened while enroute.
- The pilot in command must brief the passengers on the use of safety belts and notify them to fasten their safety belts during taxi, takeoff and landing. Passengers must have their safety belts fastened during taxi, takeoffs and landings.
- When the ELT has been in use for more than 1 cumulative hour, or if 50 percent of the useful life of the batteries expires, the batteries must be replaced or recharged.
- An ATC transponder must be inspected, tested, and found to comply with FAA standards every 24 calendar months.
- All operations within Class C airspace must be in an aircraft equipped with a 4096-code transponder with Mode C encoding capability.
- During the period from sunset to sunrise, except in Alaska, lighted position lights must be displayed on an aircraft.

SUPPLEMENTAL OXYGEN

- Supplemental oxygen must be used by required crewmembers when operating an aircraft at cabin pressure altitudes above 12,500 feet MSL up to and including 14,000 feet MSL, for flight time at those altitudes that exceeds 30 minutes. Above 14,000 feet MSL, required crewmembers must use oxygen continuously.
- Above cabin pressure altitudes of 15,000 feet MSL each person on board the aircraft must be provided with supplemental oxygen.

AIRCRAFT CATEGORIES

Unless specifically authorized, no person may operate a restricted category aircraft or an aircraft that has an experimental certificate over a densely populated area or in a congested airway.

SPECIAL FLIGHT RULES

- No person may operate an aircraft in formation flight except by prior arrangement with the pilot in command of each aircraft.
- No person may operate an aircraft in acrobatic flight when over any congested area of a city, town or settlement, in Class D airspace, or Class E airspace designated for Federal Airways. Acrobatic flight is also prohibited below 1,500 feet AGL, or when flight visibility is less than 3 statute miles.
- With certain exceptions, each occupant must wear an approved parachute when intentionally pitching the nose of the aircraft up or down more than 30° or when exceeding 60° of bank. A chair-type parachute must have been packed by a certificated and appropriately rated parachute rigger within the preceding 120 days.

AIRSPEED

- Unless otherwise authorized, the maximum indicated airspeed at which you may operate an aircraft below 10,000 feet MSL is 250 knots. This is also the maximum indicated airspeed within Class B airspace.
- Under Class B airspace, or in a VFR corridor through a Class B area, you may not operate at an indicated airspeed of more than 200 knots.

ATC CLEARANCES

- When an ATC clearance has been obtained, you may not deviate from that clearance, unless you obtain an amended clearance. The exception to this regulation is in an emergency.
- If given priority by ATC because of an emergency, you must submit a detailed report of that emergency within 48 hours to the manager of the ATC facility, if requested to do so.

MAINTENANCE

- The responsibility for ensuring that maintenance personnel make the appropriate entries in the aircraft maintenance records, indicating the aircraft has been approved for return to service, lies with the owner or operator.
- Completion of an annual inspection and the return of the aircraft to service should always be indicated by an appropriate notation in the aircraft maintenance records.
- If an alteration or repair substantially affects an aircraft's operation in flight, that aircraft must be flown by an appropriately rated private pilot and approved for return to service before being operated with passengers aboard.
- No person may operate an aircraft unless, within the preceding 12 calendar months, it has had an annual inspection.
- To determine the expiration date of the last annual inspection, a person should refer to the aircraft maintenance records.
- You may not operate an aircraft carrying any person for hire, or give flight instruction for hire in an aircraft you provide, unless, within the preceding 100 hours of time in service, the aircraft has received an annual or 100-hour inspection. The aircraft may be flown beyond the 100 hours if it is being transported to a place where service can be completed. However, the next 100 hour inspection must be completed within 100 hours of the original expiration time.
- The owner or operator of an aircraft must keep a record of current status of applicable airworthiness directives in the aircraft maintenance records.

15-30 PLT444
What action must be taken when a pilot in command deviates from any rule in 14 CFR part 91?

A– Upon landing, report the deviation to the nearest FAA Flight Standards District Office.
B– Advise ATC of the pilot in command's intentions.
C– Upon the request of the Administrator, send a written report of that deviation to the Administrator.

15-30. Answer C. FAR 91.3
The pilot in command (PIC) of an aircraft is directly responsible for, and is the final authority as to, the operation of the aircraft. This regulation gives the PIC authority to deviate from any rule in order to meet the requirements of an emergency. However, the pilot in command is required to submit a written report of the deviation, upon request of the Administrator.

15-31 PLT444
Who is responsible for determining if an aircraft is in condition for safe flight?

A– A certificated aircraft mechanic.
B– The pilot in command.
C– The owner or operator.

15-31. Answer B. FAR 91.7
According to FAR Part 91.7, no person may operate an aircraft unless it is in an airworthy condition. The pilot in command of a civil aircraft is responsible for determining whether that aircraft is in condition for safe flight. The pilot in command shall discontinue the flight when unairworthy mechanical, electrical, or structural conditions occur.

15-32 PLT400
When operating a U.S.-registered civil aircraft, which document is required by regulation to be available in the aircraft?

A– A manufacturer's Operations Manual.
B– A current, approved Airplane Flight Manual.
C– An Owner's Manual.

15-32. Answer B. FAR 91.9
No person may operate a civil aircraft without complying with the operating limitations specified in the approved Airplane or Rotorcraft Flight Manual, markings, and placards, or as otherwise prescribed by the certifying authority of the country of registry.

15-33 PLT401
A pilot in command (PIC) of a civil aircraft may not allow any object to be dropped from that aircraft in flight

A– unless the PIC has permission to drop any object over private property.
B– if it creates a hazard to persons and property.
C– unless reasonable precautions are taken to avoid injury to property.

15-33. Answer B. FAR 91.15
According to FAR 91.15, no pilot in command of a civil aircraft may allow any object to be dropped in flight that creates a hazard to persons or property. The regulation provides an exception, that an object may be dropped if reasonable precautions are taken to avoid injury or damage to persons or property.

15-34 PLT445
When is preflight action required, relative to alternatives available, if the planned flight cannot be completed?

A– IFR flights only.
B– any flight not in the vicinity of an airport.
C– any flight conducted for compensation or hire.

15-34. Answer B. FAR 91.103
Each pilot in command shall, before beginning a flight, become familiar with all available information concerning that flight. For a flight under IFR or not in the vicinity of an airport, this information must include weather reports and forecasts, fuel requirements, alternatives available if the planned flight cannot be completed, and any known traffic delays of which the pilot in command has been advised by ATC.

15-35   PLT445
The required preflight action relative to weather reports and fuel requirements is applicable to

A– IFR flights only.
B– any flight conducted for compensation or hire.
C– any flight not in the vicinity of an airport.

15-35. Answer C. FAR 91.103
Each pilot in command shall, before beginning a flight, become familiar with all available information concerning that flight. For a flight under IFR or not in the vicinity of an airport, this information must include weather reports and forecasts, fuel requirements, alternatives available if the planned flight cannot be completed, and any known traffic delays of which the pilot in command has been advised by ATC.

15-36   PLT456
Before beginning any flight under IFR, the pilot in command must become familiar with all available information concerning that flight. In addition, the pilot must

A– be familiar with all instrument approaches at the destination airport.
B– list an alternate airport on the flight plan, and confirm adequate takeoff and landing performance at the destination airport.
C– be familiar with the runway lengths at airports of intended use, and the alternatives available, if the flight cannot be completed.

15-36. Answer C. FAR 91.109
Each pilot in command shall, before beginning a flight, become familiar with all available information concerning that flight. This includes flights under IFR, and alternatives available if the planned flight cannot be completed. In addition, for any flight, the pilot must be familiar with runway lengths at airports of intended use, as well as takeoff and landing distance information.

15-37   PLT456
Before beginning any flight under IFR, the pilot in command must become familiar with all available information concerning that flight. In addition, the pilot must

A– be familiar with the runway lengths at airports of intended use, weather reports, fuel requirements, and alternatives available, if the planned flight cannot be completed.
B– list an alternate airport on the flight plan, and confirm adequate takeoff and landing performance at the destination airport.
C– be familiar with all instrument approaches at the destination airport.

15-37. Answer A. FAR 91.103
Regulations specifically require the pilots know runway lengths at airports of intended use for ALL flights.

15-38   PLT464
Required flight crewmembers' safety belts must be fastened

A– only during takeoff and landing.
B– while the crewmembers are at their stations.
C– only during takeoff and landing when passengers are aboard the aircraft.

15-38. Answer B. FAR 91.105
During takeoffs and landings, and while enroute, each required flight crewmember shall keep their safety belt fastened while at the crewmember station.

15-39   PLT464

Each required flight crewmember is required to keep his or her shoulder harness fastened

A–during takeoff and landing only when passengers are aboard the aircraft.
B–during takeoff and landing, unless he or she is unable to perform required duties.
C–while the crewmembers are at their stations, unless he or she is unable to perform required duties.

15-39. Answer C. FAR 91.105

Each required flight crewmember of a U.S.-registered civil aircraft shall, during takeoff and landing, keep his or her shoulder harness fastened while at his or her assigned duty station, unless the crewmember would be unable to perform required duties with the shoulder harness fastened.

15-40   PLT464

With U.S.-registered civil airplanes, the use of safety belts is required during movement on the surface, takeoffs, and landings for

A–safe operating practice, but not required by regulations.
B–each person over 2 years of age on board.
C–commercial passenger operations only.

15-40. Answer B. FAR 91.107, FAR 91.105

In addition to the required use of seat belts and shoulder harnesses for crewmembers, no pilot may cause to be moved on the surface, takeoff, or land a U.S.-registered civil aircraft unless the pilot in command of that aircraft ensures that each person on board has been notified to fasten his or her safety belt and, if installed, shoulder harness. In addition, the safety belt and shoulder harness must be properly secured about each person more than 2 years of age.

15-41   PLT401

Which is required to operate an aircraft towing an advertising banner?

A–Approval from ATC to operate in Class E airspace.
B–A certificate of waiver issued by the Administrator.
C–A safety link at each end of the towline which has a breaking strength not less than 80 percent of the aircraft's gross weight.

15-41. Answer B. FAR 91.311

According to FAR 91.311, no pilot of a civil aircraft may tow anything with that aircraft (other than gliders), except in accordance with the terms of a certificate of waiver issued by the Administrator.

15-42   PLT421

Portable electronic devices which may cause interference with the navigation or communication system may not be operated on a U.S.-registered civil aircraft being flown

A–in air carrier operations.
B–along Federal airways.
C–within the U.S.

15-42. Answer A. FAR 91.21

No person may operate or allow the operation of, any portable electronic device on U.S.-registered civil aircraft which is operated by a holder of an air carrier operating certificate, or any other aircraft while it is operated under IFR.

15-43   PLT421
Portable electronic devices which may cause interference with the navigation or communication system may not be operated on U.S.-registered civil aircraft being operated

A– under IFR.
B– along Federal airways.
C– in passenger carrying operations.

15-43. Answer A. FAR 91.21
No person may operate or allow the operation of, any portable electronic device on U.S.-registered civil aircraft which is operated by a holder of an air carrier operating certificate, or any other aircraft while it is operated under IFR.

15-44   PLT413
If weather conditions are such that it is required to designate an alternate airport on your IFR flight plan, you should plan to carry enough fuel to arrive at the first airport of intended landing, fly from that airport to the alternate airport, and fly thereafter for

A– 30 minutes at slow cruising speed.
B– 45 minutes at normal cruising speed.
C– 1 hour at normal cruising speed.

15-44. Answer B. FAR 91.167
If an alternate airport is required on your IFR flight plan, you may not operate a civil aircraft in IFR conditions unless it carries enough fuel to fly to the first airport of intended landing, fly from that airport to the alternate airport, and fly thereafter for 45 minutes at normal cruising speed (30 minutes for helicopters).

15-45   PLT438
In accordance with 14 CFR part 91, supplemental oxygen must be used by the required minimum flightcrew for that time exceeding 30 minutes while at cabin pressure altitudes of

A– 10,500 feet MSL up to and including 12,500 feet MSL.
B– 12,000 feet MSL up to and including 18,000 feet MSL.
C– 12,500 feet MSL up to and including 14,000 feet MSL.

15-45. Answer C. FAR 91.211
No person may operate a civil aircraft of U.S. registry at cabin pressure altitudes above 12,500 feet MSL up to and including 14,000 feet MSL, unless the required minimum flight crew is provided with, and uses, supplemental oxygen for that part of the flight at those altitudes that is more than 30 minutes in duration.

15-46   PLT438
What are the oxygen requirements when operating at cabin pressure altitudes above 15,000 feet MSL?

A– Oxygen must be available for the flightcrew.
B– Oxygen is not required at any altitude in a balloon.
C– The flightcrew and passengers must be provided with supplemental oxygen.

15-46. Answer C. FAR 91.211
No person may operate a civil aircraft of U.S. registry at cabin pressure altitudes above 14,000 feet MSL unless the required minimum flight crew uses supplemental oxygen. Above 15,000 each occupant must be provided with supplemental oxygen.

15-47   PLT405

Which is required equipment for powered aircraft during VFR night flights?

A– Anticollision light system.
B– Gyroscopic direction indicator.
C– Gyroscopic bank-and-pitch indicator.

15-47. Answer A. FAR 91.205

In addition to the instrument and equipment required for day VFR, night VFR also requires position lights, anticollision lights, landing light (only during operations for hire), an adequate source of electrical energy, and a spare set of fuses when applicable.

15-48   PLT405

Which is required equipment for powered aircraft during VFR night flights?

A– Sensitive altimeter adjustable for barometric pressure.
B– An electric landing light, if the flight is for hire.
C– Flashlight with red lens, if the flight is for hire.

15-48. Answer B. FAR 91.205

In addition to the instrument and equipment required for day VFR, night VFR also requires position lights, anticollision lights, an electric landing light when the flight is operated for hire, an adequate source of electrical energy, and a spare set of fuses when applicable.

15-49   PLT437

Approved flotation gear, readily available to each occupant, is required on each airplane if it is being flown for hire over water,

A– beyond power-off gliding distance from shore.
B– more than 50 statute miles from shore.
C– in amphibious aircraft beyond 50 NM from shore.

15-49. Answer A. FAR 91.205b

If the aircraft is operated for hire over water and beyond power-off gliding distance from shore, approved flotation gear must be readily available to each occupant, and the aircraft must have at least one pyrotechnic signaling device on board.

15-50   PLT371

Which is true with respect to operating limitations of a "restricted" category airplane?

A– No person may operate a "restricted" category airplane carrying passengers or property for compensation or hire.
B– A pilot of a "restricted" category airplane is required to hold a commercial pilot certificate.
C– A "restricted" category airplane is limited to an operating radius of 25 miles from its home base.

15-50. Answer A. FAR 91.313

No person may operate a restricted category civil aircraft carrying persons or property for compensation or hire.

15-51   PLT373

Which is true with respect to operating limitations of a "primary" category airplane?

A– No person may operate a "primary" category airplane carrying passengers or property for compensation or hire.

B– A "primary" category airplane is limited to a specified operating radius from its home base.

C– A pilot of a "primary" category airplane must hold a commercial pilot certificate when carrying passengers for compensation or hire.

15-51. Answer A. FAR 91.325

No person may operate a primary category civil aircraft carrying persons or property for compensation or hire.

15-52   PLT371

The carriage of passengers for hire by a commercial pilot is

A– not authorized in a "utility" category aircraft.

B– authorized in "restricted" category aircraft.

C– not authorized in a "limited" category aircraft.

15-52. Answer C. FAR 91.315, FAR 91.313

FAR 91.315 simply states that no person may operate a limited category civil aircraft carrying persons or property for compensation or hire. There are no exceptions mentioned.

15-53   PLT402

The maximum cumulative time that an emergency locator transmitter may be operated before the rechargeable battery must be recharged is

A– 30 minutes.

B– 45 minutes.

C– 60 minutes.

15-53. Answer C. FAR 91.207

Batteries used in the emergency locator transmitter must be replaced or recharged (if appropriate) when the transmitter has been in use more than 1 cumulative hour.

15-54   PLT389

No person may operate a large civil aircraft of U.S. registry which is subject to a lease, unless the lessee has mailed a copy of the lease to the FAA Aircraft Registration Branch, Technical Section, Oklahoma City, OK, within how many hours of its execution?

A– 24

B– 48

C– 72

15-54. Answer A. FAR 91.23

A copy of the lease or contract that complies with the requirements involving a U.S. registered large civil aircraft must be mailed within 24 hours.

15-55 PLT431

Which is true with respect to formation flights?
Formation flights are

A– authorized when carrying passengers for hire, with prior arrangement with the pilot in command of each aircraft in the formation.
B– not authorized when visibilities are less than 3 SM.
C– not authorized when carrying passengers for hire.

15-55. Answer C. FAR 91.111
No person may operate an aircraft, carrying passengers for hire, in formation flight.

15-56 PLT431

Which is true with respect to operating near other aircraft in flight? They are

A– not authorized, when operated so close to another aircraft they can create a collision hazard.
B– not authorized, unless the pilot in command of each aircraft is trained and found competent in formation.
C– authorized when carrying passengers for hire, with prior arrangement with the pilot in command of each aircraft in the formation.

15-56. Answer A. FAR 91.111
Regulations on formation flight specifically prohibit operation so close to another aircraft as to create a collision hazard.

15-57 PLT431

Which is true with respect to formation flights?
Formation flights are

A– not authorized, except by arrangement with the pilot in command of each aircraft.
B– authorized when carrying passengers for hire, with prior arrangement with the pilot in command of each aircraft in the formation.
C– not authorized, unless the pilot in command of each aircraft is trained and found competent in formation.

15-57. Answer A. FAR 91.111
Pilots must make prior arrangements with each other to fly formation. No person may operate an aircraft, carrying passengers for hire, in formation flight.

15-58 PLT414

While in flight a helicopter and an airplane are converging at a 90° angle, and the helicopter is located to the right of the airplane. Which aircraft has the right-of-way, and why?

A– The helicopter, because it is to the right of the airplane.
B– The helicopter, because helicopters have the right-of-way over airplanes.
C– The airplane, because airplanes have the right-of-way over helicopters.

15-58. Answer A. FAR 91.113
Because helicopters and airplanes are considered to have the same maneuverability, neither one has the right of way over the other. When two aircraft with the same maneuverability are converging at approximately the same altitude (except head-on, or nearly so) the aircraft to the other's right has the right-of-way. In this case, it is the helicopter that has the right of way because it is on the right. Answers (B) and (C) are incorrect because in terms of the right-of-way rules, airplane and rotorcraft are given the same status for giving way to less maneuverable categories of aircraft.

15-59   PLT414

Two aircraft of the same category are approaching an airport for the purpose of landing. The right-of-way belongs to the aircraft

A–at the higher altitude.

B–at the lower altitude, but the pilot shall not take advantage of this rule to cut in front of or to overtake the other aircraft.

C–that is more maneuverable, and that aircraft may, with caution, move in front of or overtake the other aircraft.

15-59. Answer B. FAR 91.113

When two or more aircraft are approaching an airport for the purpose of landing, the aircraft at the lower altitude has the right-of-way, but it shall not take advantage of this rule to cut in front of another aircraft on final approach, or to overtake that aircraft.

15-60   PLT414

During a night operation, the pilot of aircraft #1 sees only the green light of aircraft #2. If the aircraft are converging, which pilot has the right-of-way? The pilot of aircraft

A–#2; aircraft #2 is to the left of aircraft #1.

B–#2; aircraft #2 is to the right of aircraft #1.

C–#1; aircraft #1 is to the right of aircraft #2.

15-60. Answer C. FAR 91.113

If aircraft #1 sees only the green light of aircraft #2, it would be looking at the right wingtip. Aircraft #1 has the right-of-way, since it is to the right of aircraft #2.

15-61   PLT414

A pilot flying a single-engine airplane observes a multiengine airplane approaching from the left. Which pilot should give way?

A–The pilot of the multiengine airplane should give way; the single-engine airplane is to its right.

B–The pilot of the single-engine airplane should give way; the other airplane is to the left.

C–Each pilot should alter course to the right.

15-61. Answer A. FAR 91.113

When two aircraft of the same category are converging, that is, on intersecting courses, the aircraft to the right has the right of way.

15-62   PLT414

Airplane A is overtaking airplane B. Which airplane has the right-of-way?

A–Airplane A; the pilot should alter course to the right to pass.

B–Airplane B; the pilot should expect to be passed on the right.

C–Airplane B; the pilot should expect to be passed on the left.

15-62. Answer B. FAR 91.113f

When one aircraft is overtaking another, regardless of the categories of each aircraft, the aircraft being overtaken has the right of way over the aircraft that is passing.

15-63   PLT414

An airplane is overtaking a helicopter. Which aircraft has the right-of-way?

A– Airplane; the airplane pilot should alter course to the left to pass.

B– Helicopter; the pilot should expect to be passed on the right.

C– Helicopter; the pilot should expect to be passed on the left.

15-63. Answer B. FAR 91.113

When one aircraft is overtaking another, regardless of the categories of each aircraft, the aircraft being overtaken has the right of way over the aircraft that is passing. The faster aircraft should pass on the right.

15-64   PLT430

What is the minimum altitude and flight visibility required for acrobatic flight?

A– 1,500 feet AGL and 3 miles.

B– 2,000 feet MSL and 2 miles.

C– 3,000 feet AGL and 1 mile.

15-64. Answer A. FAR 91.303

No person may operate an aircraft in acrobatic flight below an altitude of 1,500 feet above the surface, or when flight visibility is less than three statute miles.

15-65   PLT461

If not equipped with required position lights, an aircraft must terminate flight

A– at sunset.

B– 30 minutes after sunset.

C– 1 hour after sunset.

15-65. Answer A. FAR 91.209

No person may, during the period from sunset to sunrise operate an aircraft unless it has lighted position lights.

15-66   PLT461

If an aircraft is not equipped with an electrical or anticollision light system, no person may operate that aircraft

A– after sunset to sunrise.

B– 1 hour after sunset.

C– after dark.

15-66. Answer A. FAR 91.209, FAR 91.205

If an aircraft does not have approved position lights, it may not be operated after sunset. The regulation is clear that anticollision lights are required starting at sunset.

15-67   PLT163

The minimum flight visibility for VFR flight increases to 5 statute miles beginning at an altitude of

A– 14,500 feet MSL.

B– 10,000 feet MSL if above 1,200 feet AGL.

C– 10,000 feet MSL regardless of height above ground.

15-67. Answer B. FAR 91.155

When in airspace above 10,000 feet MSL and more than 1,200 feet above the surface, the visibility is 5 statute miles, regardless of the type of airspace.

15-68   PLT163
What is the minimum flight visibility and proximity to cloud requirements for VFR flight, at 6,500 feet MSL, in Class C, D, and E airspace?

A– 1 mile visibility; clear of clouds.
B– 3 miles visibility; 1,000 feet above and 500 feet below.
C– 5 miles visibility; 1,000 feet above and 1,000 feet below.

15-68. Answer B. FAR 91.155
When flying in Class C, Class D, or Class E airspace below 10,000 feet MSL, visibility must be at least 3 statute miles and the aircraft must maintain at least 1,000 feet above, 500 feet below, and 2,000 feet horizontal cloud separation.

15-69   PLT430
VFR cruising altitudes are required to be maintained when flying

A– at 3,000 feet or more AGL, based on true course.
B– more than 3,000 feet AGL, based on magnetic course.
C– at 3,000 feet or more above MSL, based on magnetic heading.

15-69. Answer B. FAR 91.159
Anytime you fly in level cruising flight above 3,000 feet AGL, you must follow the VFR east/ west cruising altitudes. The VFR cruising altitudes are based on magnetic course.

15-70   PLT421
Except when necessary for takeoff or landing or unless otherwise authorized by the Administrator, the minimum altitude for IFR flight is

A– 2,000 feet over all terrain.
B– 2,000 feet above the highest obstacle over designated mountainous terrain; 1,000 feet above the highest obstacle over terrain elsewhere.
C– 3,000 feet over designated mountainous terrain; 2,000 feet over terrain elsewhere.

15-70. Answer B. FAR 91.177
Except when necessary for takeoff or landing, no person may operate an aircraft under IFR below an altitude of 2,000 feet above the highest obstacle within a horizontal distance of 4 nautical miles from the course to be flown in mountainous areas, or in other than mountainous areas, 1,000 feet above the highest obstacle within a horizontal distance of 4 nautical miles from the course to be flown.

15-71   PLT374
Who is primarily responsible for maintaining an aircraft in an airworthy condition?

A– The lead mechanic responsible for that aircraft.
B– Pilot in command or operator.
C– Owner or operator of the aircraft.

15-71. Answer C. FAR 91.403
The owner or operator is responsible for maintaining the aircraft in an airworthy condition. The pilot in command is responsible for making sure the airplane is airworthy before flying it.

15-72   PLT374
Assuring compliance with an Airworthiness Directive is the responsibility of the

A– owner or operator of that aircraft.
B– pilot in command of that aircraft.
C– pilot in command and the FAA certificated mechanic assigned to that aircraft.

15-72. Answer A. FAR 91.403
Compliance with Airworthiness Directives (FAR Part 39) is a function of maintaining an aircraft in an airworthy condition. Therefore, it is the owner or operator of an aircraft who is primarily responsible for maintaining the aircraft in an airworthy condition.

15-73   PLT375
After an annual inspection has been completed and the aircraft has been returned to service, an appropriate notation should be made

A– on the airworthiness certificate.
B– in the aircraft maintenance records.
C– in the FAA-approved flight manual.

15-73. Answer B. FAR 91.407, FAR 91.409
According to FAR 91.409 no person may operate an aircraft unless, within the preceding 12 calendar months, it has had an annual inspection in accordance with FAR Part 43. FAR 91.407 states that no person may operate any aircraft following maintenance unless it has been returned to service by an authorized mechanic. FAR Part 43.9 states that each person who maintains, performs preventive maintenance, rebuilds, or alters an aircraft, airframe, aircraft engine, propeller, appliance, or component part shall make an entry in the maintenance record. Since an annual inspection is one of the requirements for maintaining an aircraft, an aircraft maintenance logbook entry is required.

15-74   PLT377
A standard airworthiness certificate remains in effect as long as the aircraft receives

A– required maintenance and inspections.
B– an annual inspection.
C– an annual inspection and a 100-hour inspection prior to their expiration dates.

15-74. Answer A. FAR 91.407
Airworthiness certificates are effective as long as the maintenance, preventive maintenance, and alterations are performed in accordance with Parts 43 and 91. Part 43 requires that an appropriate return to service statement entry is recorded in aircraft maintenance records.

15-75   PLT375
If an aircraft's operation in flight was substantially affected by an alteration or repair, the aircraft documents must show that it was test flown and approved for return to service by an appropriately-rated pilot prior to being operated

A– under VFR or IFR rules.
B– with passengers aboard.
C– for compensation or hire.

15-75. Answer B. FAR 91.407
No person may carry any person in an aircraft that has been maintained, rebuilt, or altered in a manner that may have appreciable changed its flight characteristics or substantially affect its operation in flight until an appropriately rated pilot with at least a private pilot certificate flies the aircraft to make an operational check and logs the flight in the aircraft records.

15-76   PLT446

Which is correct concerning preventive maintenance, when accomplished by a pilot?

A– A record of preventive maintenance is not required.

B– A record of preventive maintenance must be entered in the maintenance records.

C– Records of preventive maintenance must be entered in the FAA-approved flight manual.

15-76. Answer B. FAR 43.9

FAR Part 43.9 states that each person who maintains, performs preventive maintenance, rebuilds, or alters and aircraft part shall make an entry in the maintenance record. This includes the pilot if he or she performs preventative maintenance.

15-77   PLT426

An aircraft carrying passengers for hire has been on a schedule of inspection every 100 hours of time in service. Under which condition, if any, may that aircraft be operated beyond 100 hours out a new inspection?

A– The aircraft may be flown for any flight as long as the time in service has not exceeded 110 hours.

B– The aircraft may be dispatched for a flight of any duration as long as 100 hours has not been exceeded at the time it departs.

C– The 100-hour limitation may be exceeded by not more than 10 hours if necessary to reach a place at which the inspection can be done.

15-77. Answer C. FAR 91.409

The 100-hour limitation may be exceeded by not more than 10 hours while enroute to reach a place where the inspection can be done. The excess time used to reach a place where the inspection can be performed must be included in computing the next 100 hours of time in service.

15-78   PLT426

Which is true concerning required maintenance inspections?

A– A 100-hour inspection may be substituted for an annual inspection.

B– An annual inspection may be substituted for a 100-hour inspection.

C– An annual inspection is required even if a progressive inspection system has been approved.

15-78. Answer B. FAR 91.409

No person may operate an aircraft carrying any person (other than required crewmembers) for hire, and no person may give flight instruction for hire in an aircraft which that person provides, unless within the preceding 100 hours of time in service the aircraft has received an annual or 100-hour inspection, and the aircraft has been approved for return to service in accordance with FAR Part 43.

15-79   PLT405

An ATC transponder is not to be used unless it has been tested, inspected, and found to comply with regulations within the preceding

A– 30 days.

B– 12 calendar months.

C– 24 calendar months.

15-79. Answer C. FAR 91.413

No person may use an ATC transponder unless within the preceding 24 calendar months, that ATC transponder has been tested and inspected.

15-80   PLT425

Aircraft maintenance records must include the current status of the

A– applicable airworthiness certificate.
B– life-limited parts of only the engine and airframe.
C– life-limited parts of each airframe, engine, propeller, rotor, and appliance.

15-80. Answer C. FAR 91.417
Aircraft maintenance records must contain the current status of life-limited parts of each airframe, engine, propeller, rotor, and appliance.

15-81   PLT378

Which is true relating to Airworthiness Directives (ADs) ?

A– ADs are advisory in nature and are, generally, not addressed immediately.
B– Noncompliance with ADs renders an aircraft unairworthy.
C– Compliance with ADs is the responsibility of maintenance personnel.

15-81. Answer B. FAR 91.403, FAR 91.417
FAR Part 91.403 states that the owner or operator of an aircraft is primarily responsible for maintaining that aircraft in an airworthy condition and in compliance with Part 39, Airworthiness Directives.

15-82   PLT425

A new maintenance record being used for an aircraft engine rebuilt by the manufacturer must include previous

A– operating hours of the engine.
B– annual inspections performed on the engine.
C– changes as required by Airworthiness Directives.

15-82. Answer C. FAR 91.421
Each manufacturer or agency that rebuilds an engine and grants zero time to an engine, shall enter in the new record, each change made as required by airworthiness directives.

15-83   PLT497

If an ATC transponder installed in an aircraft has not been tested, inspected, and found to comply with regulations within a specified period, what is the limitation on its use?

A– Its use is not permitted.
B– It may be used when in Class G airspace.
C– It may be used for VFR flight only.

15-83. Answer A. FAR 91.413
No person may use an ATC transponder unless it has been tested and inspected within the preceding 24 months.

15-84   PLT444

What person is directly responsible for the final authority as to the operation of the airplane?

A– Certificate holder.
B– Pilot in command.
C– Airplane owner/operator.

15-84. Answer B. FAR 91.3
The pilot in command of an aircraft is directly responsible for, and is the final authority as to, the operation of that aircraft.

15-85   PLT465
Operating regulations for U.S.-registered civil airplanes require that during movement on the surface, takeoffs, and landings, a seat belt and shoulder harness (if installed) must be properly secured about each

A–flight crewmember only.
B–person on board.
C–flight and cabin crewmembers.

15-85. Answer B. FAR 91.107, FAR 91.105
Each person must occupy an approved seat or berth with a safety belt and, if installed, shoulder harness, properly secured about him or her during movement on the surface, takeoff, and landing. There are exceptions for children under 2 years of age, and flight crewmembers do not have to wear shoulder harnesses if those harnesses prevent the crew from performing their duties.

15-86   PLT443
No person may operate an aircraft in simulated instrument flight conditions unless the

A–other control seat is occupied by a safety pilot, who holds at least a private pilot certificate and is appropriately rated.
B–pilot has filed an IFR flight plan and received an IFR clearance.
C–other control seat is occupied by at least an appropriately rated commercial pilot.

15-86. Answer A. FAR 91.109
No person may operate a civil aircraft in simulated instrument flight unless the other control seat is occupied by a safety pilot who possesses at least a private pilot certificate with category and class ratings appropriate to the aircraft being flown. The safety pilot must have adequate vision forward and to each side of the aircraft, or a competent observer in the aircraft that adequately supplements the vision of the safety pilot.

15-87   PLT373
If the minimum safe speed for any particular operation is greater than the maximum speed prescribed in 14 CFR part 91, the

A–operator must have a Memorandum of Agreement (MOA) with the controlling agency.
B–operator must have a Letter of Agreement with ATC.
C–aircraft may be operated at that speed.

15-87. Answer C. FAR 91.117
The speed limit is 200 KIAS in most Class C and D airspace, under Class B airspace and in VFR corridors through Class B airspace. It is 250 KIAS elsewhere below 10,000 feet MSL. If the minimum safe speed for your aircraft is higher, then use that speed.

15-88   PLT370
After an ATC clearance has been obtained, a pilot may not deviate from that clearance, unless the pilot

A–requests an amended clearance.
B–is operating VFR on top.
C–receives an amended clearance or has an emergency.

15-88. Answer C. FAR 91.123
Even when operating VFR-on-top, you can deviate from a clearance only if you request AND RECEIVE an amended clearance. Exceptions are emergencies and TCAS alerts requiring immediate action.

15-89   PLT435

When approaching to land at an airport, without an operating control tower, in Class G airspace, the pilot should

A– fly a left-hand traffic pattern at 800 feet AGL.
B– enter and fly a traffic pattern at 800 feet AGL.
C– make all turns to the left, unless otherwise indicated.

15-89. Answer C. FAR 91.126
Airplane pilots must make all turns to the left unless the airport displays approved light signals or visual markings indicating that turns should be made to the right, in which case right turns are mandatory.

15-90   PLT430

When weather information indicates that abnormally high barometric pressure exists, or will be above _____ inches of mercury, flight operations will not be authorized contrary to the requirements published in NOTAMs.

A– 31.00
B– 32.00
C– 30.50

15-90. Answer A. FAR 91.144
When any information indicates that the barometric pressure on the route of flight currently exceeds or will exceed 31 inches of mercury, no one may operate an aircraft or initiate a flight contrary to any NOTAM published under this section or in violation of requirements established by the Administrator.

15-91   PLT379

For an airport with an approved instrument approach procedure to be listed as an alternate airport on an IFR flight plan, the forecasted weather conditions at the time of arrival must be at or above the following weather minimums.

A– Ceiling 600 feet and visibility 2 NM for precision.
B– Ceiling 800 feet and visibility 2 SM for nonprecision.
C– Ceiling 800 feet and visibility 2 NM for nonprecision.

15-91. Answer B. FAR 91.169
The requirement is 600-2 if a precision approach is available, 800-2 for nonprecision approaches, and basic VFR below the MEA if no approaches are available.

15-92   PLT379

For an airport without an approved instrument approach procedure to be listed as an alternate airport on an IFR flight plan, the forecasted weather conditions at the time of arrival must have at least a

A– ceiling and visibility that allows for a descent, approach, and landing under basic VFR.
B– ceiling of 2,000 feet and visibility 3 SM.
C– ceiling of 1,000 feet and visibility 3 NM.

15-92. Answer A. FAR 91.169
The requirement is 600-2 if a precision approach is available, 800-2 for nonprecision approaches, and basic VFR below the MEA if no approaches are available.

15-93   PLT382

Pilots are not authorized to land an aircraft from an instrument approach unless the

A– flight visiblity is at, or exceeds the visibility prescribed in the approach procedure being used.

B– flight visibility and ceiling are at, or exceeds the minimums prescribed in the approach being used

C– visual approach slope indicator and runway references are distinctly visible to the pilot

15-93. Answer A. FAR 91.175

You must have the required flight visibility, and be able to identify approach lights, runway lights, or one of the other references listed in FAR 91.175. Plus, you must be able to make a normal descent to a landing.

15-94   PLT420

On an instrument approach where a DH or MDA is applicable, the pilot may not operate below, or continue the approach unless the

A– aircraft is continuously in a position from which a descent to a normal landing, on the intended runway, can be made.

B– approach and runway lights are distinctly visible to the pilot.

C– flight visibility and ceiling are at, or above, the published minimums for that approach.

15-94. Answer A. FAR 91.175

You must have the required flight visibility, and be able to identify approach lights, runway lights, or one of the other references listed in FAR 91.175. Plus, you must be able to make a normal descent to a landing.

15-95   PLT420

A pilot performing a published instrument approach is not authorized to perform a procedure turn when

A– receiving a radar vector to a final approach course or fix.

B– maneuvering at minimum safe altitudes.

C– maneuvering at radar vectoring altitudes.

15-95. Answer A. FAR 91.175

With radar vectors to a final approach course or fix, a timed approach from a holding fix, or an approach procedure which specifies "NoPT," you may not make a procedure turn unless it is cleared by ATC.

15-96   PLT390

The pilot in command of an aircraft operated under IFR, in controlled airspace, not in radar contact, shall report by radio as soon as possible when

A– passing FL 180.

B– passing each designated reporting point, to include time and altitude.

C– changing control facilities.

15-96. Answer B. FAR 91.183

IFR flights in controlled airspace must continuously monitor the appropriate frequency and, when not in radar contact, report the time and altitude of passing each designated reporting point. In addition, pilots are obligated to report any unforecast weather conditions encountered and any other information relating to the safety of flight.

15-97   PLT390

The pilot in command of an aircraft operated under IFR, in controlled airspace, shall report as soon as practical to ATC when

A– climbing or descending to assigned altitudes.
B– experiencing any malfunctions of navigational, approach, or communications equipment, occurring in flight.
C– requested to contact a new controlling facility.

15-97. Answer B. FAR 91.187

The pilot in command of each aircraft operated in controlled airspace under IFR shall report as soon as practical to ATC any malfunctions of navigational, approach, or communication equipment occurring in flight. This report shall include the

1. Aircraft identification;
2. Equipment affected;
3. Degree to which the capability of the pilot to operate under IFR in the ATC system is impaired; and
4. Nature and extent of assistance desired from ATC.

15-98   PLT378

No person may operate an aircraft that has an experimental airworthiness certificate

A– under instrument flight rules (IFR).
B– when carrying property for hire.
C– when carrying persons or property for hire.

15-98. Answer C. FAR 91.319

No person may carry passengers or property for hire in an experimental aircraft.

15-99   PLT224

For IFR operations off established airways, ROUTE OF FLIGHT portion of an IFR flight plan should list VOR navigational aids which are no more than

A– 40 miles apart.
B– 70 miles apart.
C– 80 miles apart.

15-99. Answer C. AIM

An operational service volume has been established for each class in which adequate signal coverage and frequency protection can be assured. To facilitate use of VOR, VORTAC, or TACAN aids, consistent with their operational service volume limits, pilot use of such aids for defining a direct route of flight in controlled airspace should not exceed the 80 NM apart when operating off established airways below 18,000 feel MSL.

15-100   PLT444

In what type of operation, not regulated by 14 CFR part 119, may a commercial pilot act as pilot in command and receive compensation for services?

A– Part-time contract pilot.
B– Nonstop flights within a 25 SM radius of an airport to carry persons for intentional parachute jumps.
C– Nonstop flights within a 25 SM radius of an airport to carry cargo only.

15-100. Answer B. FAR 119.1

FAR Part 119 applies to civil aircraft operating as an air carrier and/or commercial operator, or for aircraft with a passenger seat configuration of 20 or more. Additionally, 119 applies to aircraft with a payload of 6,000 lbs. or more even if it is not used in common carriage. It does not apply to nonstop flights carrying parachutists conducted within 25 statute miles of the airport of takeoff.

15-101   PLT444

In what type of operation, not regulated by 14 CFR part 119, may a commercial pilot act as pilot in command and receive compensation for services?

A–Crop dusting, spraying, and bird chasing.
B–On-demand, nine or less passenger, charter flights.
C–On-demand cargo flights.

15-101. Answer A. FAR 119.1
FAR Part 119 does not apply to aerial work operations, including crop dusting, seeding, spraying, and bird chasing.

SECTION D - NTSB 830 - AIRCRAFT ACCIDENT AND INCIDENT REPORTING

ACCIDENTS

- If an aircraft is involved in an accident which results in substantial damage to the aircraft, the nearest NTSB field office must be notified immediately.
- Aircraft wreckage may be moved prior to the time the NTSB takes custody only to protect the wreckage from further damage.
- The operator of an aircraft that has been involved in an accident is required to file an accident report within 10 days or after 7 days if an overdue aircraft is still missing.

INCIDENTS REQUIRING IMMEDIATE NOTIFICATION:

- In-flight fire
- Aircraft collide in flight
- Flight control system malfunction or failure
- Inability of any required flight crewmember to perform normal flight duties as a result of injury or illness
- Failure of structural components of a turbine engine excluding compressor and turbine blades and vanes
- Damage to property, other than the aircraft, estimated to exceed $25,000 for repair (including materials and labor) or fair market value in the event of total loss, whichever is less
- An overdue aircraft that is believed to be involved in an accident

NOTIFICATION

The operator of an aircraft that has been involved in an incident is required to submit a report to the nearest NTSB field office when requested.

15-102   PLT366
Notification to the NTSB is required when there has been substantial damage

A– which requires repairs to landing gear.
B– to an engine caused by engine failure in flight.
C– which adversely affects structural strength or flight characteristics.

15-102. Answer C. NTSB 830.2
"Substantial damage," means damage or failure which adversely affects the structural strength, performance, or flight characteristics of the aircraft, and which would normally require major repair or replacement of the affected component. The definition specifically states that, among other things, engine failure and damage limited to one engine (answer B) or damage to landing gear (answer A) are not considered substantial damage.

15-103   PLT366
NTSB Part 830 requires an immediate notification as a result of which incident?

A– Engine failure for any reason during flight.
B– Damage to the landing gear as a result of a hard landing.
C– Any required flight crewmember being unable to perform flight duties because of illness.

15-103. Answer C. NTSB 830.5
The operator of an aircraft shall immediately, and by the most expeditious means available, notify the nearest National Transportation Safety Board field office when any required flight crewmember is unable to perform flight duties because of illness.

15-104   PLT366
Which incident would require that the nearest NTSB field office be notified immediately?

A–In-flight fire.
B–Ground fire resulting in fire equipment dispatch.
C–Fire of the primary aircraft while in a hanger which results in damage to other property of more than $25,000.

15-104. Answer A. NTSB 830
The operator of an aircraft shall immediately, and by the most expeditious means available, notify the nearest National Transportation Safety Board field office when an in-flight fire occurs.

15-105   PLT366
Which airborne incident would require that the nearest NTSB field office be notified immediately?

A–Flight control system malfunction or failure.
B–Cabin door opened in-flight.
C–Cargo compartment door malfunction or failure.

15-105. Answer A. NTSB 830
The operator of an aircraft shall immediately, and by the most expeditious means available, notify the nearest National Transportation Safety Board field office when there is a flight control system malfunction or failure.

15-106   PLT366
During flight, a fire, which was extinguished, burned the insulation from a transceiver wire. What action is required by regulations?

A–No notification or report is required.
B–A report must be filed with the avionics inspector at the nearest FAA Flight Standards District Office within 48 hours.
C–An immediate notification by the operator of the aircraft to the nearest NTSB field office.

15-106. Answer C. NTSB 830.5
Immediate notification to the nearest NTSB field office is required when a fire in flight occurs.

15-107   PLT366
When should notification of an aircraft accident be made to the NTSB if there was substantial damage and no injuries?

A–Immediately.
B–Within 10 days.
C–Within 30 days.

15-107. Answer A. NTSB 830.5, NTSB 830.2
NTSB 830.5 specifies that immediate notification is required when an accident occurs. "Aircraft Accident" means an occurrence associated with the operation of an aircraft which takes place between the time any person boards the aircraft with the intention of flight and all such persons have disembarked, and in which the aircraft receives substantial damage.

15-108   PLT366
The operator of an aircraft that has been involved in an incident is required to submit a report to the nearest field office of the NTSB

A–within 7 days.
B–within 10 days.
C–only if requested to do so.

15-108. Answer C. NTSB 830.15
A report on an incident for which immediate notification is required shall be filed only if requested by an authorized representative of the board.

15-109   PLT366

How many days after an accident is a report required to be filed with the nearest NTSB field office?

A– 2.
B– 7.
C– 10.

15-109. Answer C. NTSB 830.15

The operator of an aircraft shall file a report within 10 days after an accident.

15-110   PLT366

What period of time must a person be hospitalized before an injury may be defined by the NTSB as a "serious injury"?

A– 10 days, with no other extenuating circumstances.
B– 48 hours; commencing within 7 days after date of the injury.
C– 72 hours; commencing within 10 days after date of the injury.

15-110. Answer B. NTSB 830.2

"Serious injury" is defined as any injury which:(1) requires hospitalization for more than 48 hours, commencing within 7 days from the date the injury was received; (2) results in a fracture of any bone (except simple fractures of fingers, toes, or nose); (3) causes severe hemorrhages, nerve, muscle, or tendon damage; (4) involves any internal organ; or (5) involves second- or third-degree burns, or any burns affecting more than 5 percent of the body surface.

LEARNING STATEMENT CODES AND LEARNING STATEMENTS

To determine the knowledge area in which a particular question was incorrectly answered, compare the learning statement code(s) on the Federal Aviation Administration Airmen Computer Test Report to the following learning statement outline. The total number of test items missed may differ from the number of learning statement codes shown on the test report, since you may have missed more than one question in a specific learning statement code.

Learning Statement Codes and Learning Statements for Pilots, Instructors, Flight Engineers, Dispatchers, Navigators, and Pilot Examiners Exams

Code	Learning Statement
PLT001	Calculate a course intercept
PLT002	Calculate aircraft performance - airspeed
PLT003	Calculate aircraft performance - center of gravity
PLT004	Calculate aircraft performance - climb / descent
PLT005	Calculate aircraft performance - density altitude
PLT006	Calculate aircraft performance - glide
PLT007	Calculate aircraft performance - IAS / EPR
PLT008	Calculate aircraft performance - landing
PLT009	Calculate aircraft performance - measured gas temperature (MGT)
PLT010	Calculate aircraft performance - STAB TRIM
PLT011	Calculate aircraft performance - takeoff
PLT012	Calculate aircraft performance - time/speed/distance/course/fuel/wind
PLT013	Calculate crosswind / headwind components
PLT014	Calculate distance / bearing from/to a station
PLT015	Calculate flight performance / planning - range
PLT016	Calculate fuel dump - time / weight / volume
PLT017	Calculate L/D ratio
PLT018	Calculate load factor / stall speed / velocity / angle of attack
PLT019	Calculate pressure altitude
PLT020	Calculate turbulent air penetration
PLT021	Calculate weight and balance
PLT022	Define Aeronautical Decision Making (ADM)
PLT023	Define altitude - absolute / true / indicated / density / pressure
PLT024	Define atmospheric adiabatic process
PLT025	Define Bernoulli`s principle
PLT026	Define ceiling
PLT027	Define coning

Code	Learning Statement
PLT028	Define crewmember
PLT029	Define critical phase of flight
PLT030	Define false lift
PLT031	Define isobars / associated winds
PLT032	Define MACH speed regimes
PLT033	Define MEA / MOCA / MRA
PLT034	Define stopway / clearway
PLT035	Define Vne / Vno
PLT036	Interpret a MACH meter reading
PLT037	Interpret a radar weather report
PLT038	Interpret aircraft Power Schedule Chart
PLT039	Interpret airport landing indicator
PLT040	Interpret airspace classes - charts / diagrams
PLT041	Interpret altimeter - readings / settings
PLT042	Interpret Analysis Heights / Isotachs Chart
PLT043	Interpret Analysis Heights / Temperature Chart
PLT044	Interpret ATC communications / instructions / terminology
PLT045	Interpret Descent Performance Chart
PLT046	Interpret drag ratio from charts
PLT047	Interpret Flight Director - modes / operation / indications
PLT048	Interpret Hovering Ceiling Chart
PLT049	Interpret ILS - charts / RMI / CDI / indications
PLT050	Interpret information on a Brake Energy Limit Chart
PLT051	Interpret information on a Convective Outlook
PLT052	Interpret information on a Departure Procedure Chart
PLT053	Interpret information on a Flight Plan
PLT054	Interpret information on a Glider Performance Graph
PLT055	Interpret information on a High Altitude Chart
PLT056	Interpret information on a Horizontal Situation Indicator (HSI)
PLT057	Interpret information on a Hot Air Balloon Performance Graph
PLT058	Interpret information on a Low Altitude Chart
PLT059	Interpret information on a METAR / SPECI report
PLT060	Interpret information on a Performance Curve Chart
PLT061	Interpret information on a PIREP
PLT062	Interpret information on a Pseudo-Adiabatic Chart
PLT063	Interpret information on a Radar Summary Chart
PLT064	Interpret information on a Sectional Chart
PLT065	Interpret information on a Service Ceiling Engine Inoperative Chart
PLT066	Interpret information on a Severe Weather Outlook Chart
PLT067	Interpret information on a SIGMET
PLT068	Interpret information on a Significant Weather Prognostic Chart
PLT069	Interpret information on a Slush/Standing Water Takeoff chart
PLT070	Interpret information on a Stability Chart
PLT071	Interpret information on a Surface Analysis Chart
PLT072	Interpret information on a Terminal Aerodrome Forecast (TAF)

Code	Learning Statement
PLT073	Interpret information on a Tower Enroute Control (TEC)
PLT074	Interpret information on a Velocity/Load Factor Chart
PLT075	Interpret information on a Weather Depiction Chart
PLT076	Interpret information on a Weather Depiction Chart
PLT077	Interpret information on an Airport Diagram
PLT078	Interpret information on an Airport Facility Directory (AFD)
PLT079	Interpret information on an airways chart
PLT080	Interpret information on an Arrival Chart
PLT081	Interpret information on an Aviation Area Forecast (FA)
PLT082	Interpret information on an Aviation Area Forecast (FA)
PLT083	Interpret information on an Instrument Approach Procedures (IAP)
PLT084	Interpret information on an Observed Winds Aloft Chart
PLT085	Interpret information on Takeoff Obstacle / Field / Climb Limit Charts
PLT086	Interpret readings on a Turn and Slip Indicator
PLT087	Interpret readings on an Aircraft Course and DME Indicator
PLT088	Interpret speed indicator readings
PLT089	Interpret Takeoff Speeds Chart
PLT090	Interpret VOR - charts / indications / CDI / ADF / NAV
PLT091	Interpret VOR / ADF / NDB / CDI / RMI - illustrations / indications / procedures
PLT092	Interpret weight and balance - diagram
PLT093	Recall administration of medical oxygen
PLT094	Recall aerodynamics - airfoil design / pressure distribution
PLT095	Recall aerodynamics - longitudinal axis / lateral axis
PLT096	Recall aeromedical factors - effects of altitude
PLT097	Recall aeromedical factors - effects of carbon monoxide poisoning
PLT098	Recall aeromedical factors - fitness for flight
PLT099	Recall aeromedical factors - scanning procedures
PLT100	Recall aeronautical charts - IFR En Route Low Altitude
PLT101	Recall aeronautical charts - pilotage
PLT102	Recall aeronautical charts - terminal procedures
PLT103	Recall Aeronautical Decision Making (ADM) - hazardous attitudes
PLT104	Recall Aeronautical Decision Making (ADM) - human factors
PLT105	Recall airborne radar/thunderstorm detection equipment - use / limitations
PLT106	Recall aircraft air-cycle machine
PLT107	Recall aircraft alternator / generator system
PLT108	Recall aircraft anti-icing / deicing - methods / fluids
PLT109	Recall aircraft batteries - capacity / charging / types / storage / rating / precautions
PLT110	Recall aircraft brake system
PLT111	Recall aircraft circuitry - series / parallel
PLT112	Recall aircraft controls - proper use / techniques
PLT113	Recall aircraft design - categories / limitation factors
PLT114	Recall aircraft design - construction / function
PLT115	Recall aircraft engine - detonation cause / characteristics
PLT116	Recall aircraft general knowledge / publications / AIM / navigational aids
PLT117	Recall aircraft heated windshields

Code	Learning Statement
PLT118	Recall aircraft instruments - gyroscopic
PLT119	Recall aircraft lighting - anti-collision / landing / navigation
PLT120	Recall aircraft limitations - turbulent air penetration
PLT121	Recall aircraft loading - computations
PLT122	Recall aircraft operations - checklist usage
PLT123	Recall aircraft performance - airspeed
PLT124	Recall aircraft performance - atmospheric effects
PLT125	Recall aircraft performance - climb / descent
PLT126`	Recall aircraft performance - cold weather operations
PLT127	Recall aircraft performance - density altitude
PLT128	Recall aircraft performance - effects of icing
PLT129	Recall aircraft performance - effects of runway slope
PLT130	Recall aircraft performance - fuel
PLT131	Recall aircraft performance - ground effect
PLT132	Recall aircraft performance - instrument markings / airspeed / definitions / indications
PLT133	Recall aircraft performance - normal climb / descent rates
PLT134	Recall aircraft performance - takeoff
PLT135	Recall aircraft pressurization - system / operation
PLT136	Recall aircraft systems - anti-icing / deicing
PLT137	Recall aircraft systems - environmental control
PLT138	Recall aircraft tires - types / characteristics
PLT139	Recall aircraft warning systems - stall / fire / retractable gear / terrain awareness
PLT140	Recall airport operations - LAHSO
PLT141	Recall airport operations - markings / signs / lighting
PLT142	Recall airport operations - noise avoidance routes
PLT143	Recall airport operations - rescue / fire fighting vehicles and types of agents
PLT144	Recall airport operations - runway conditions
PLT145	Recall airport operations - runway lighting
PLT146	Recall airport operations - traffic pattern procedures
PLT147	Recall airport operations - visual glideslope indicators
PLT148	Recall airport operations lighting - MALS / ALSF / RCLS / TDZL
PLT149	Recall airport taxi operations - procedures
PLT150	Recall airport traffic patterns - entry procedures
PLT151	Recall airship - buoyancy
PLT152	Recall airship - flight characteristics / controllability
PLT153	Recall airship - flight operations
PLT154	Recall airship - ground weigh-off / static / trim condition
PLT155	Recall airship - maintaining pressure
PLT156	Recall airship - maximum headway / flight at equilibrium
PLT157	Recall airship - pressure height / dampers / position
PLT158	Recall airship - pressure height / manometers
PLT159	Recall airship - pressure height / super heat / valving gas
PLT160	Recall airship - stability / control / positive superheat
PLT161	Recall airspace classes - limits / requirements / restrictions / airspeeds / equipment
PLT162	Recall airspace requirements - operations

Code	Learning Statement
PLT163	Recall airspace requirements - visibility / cloud clearance
PLT163	Recall airspeed - effects during a turn
PLT164	Recall altimeter - effect of temperature changes
PLT165	Recall altimeter - settings / setting procedures
PLT167	Recall altimeters - characteristics / accuracy
PLT168	Recall angle of attack - characteristics / forces / principles
PLT169	Recall antitorque system - components / functions
PLT170	Recall approach / landing / taxiing techniques
PLT171	Recall ATC - reporting
PLT172	Recall ATC - system / services
PLT173	Recall atmospheric conditions - measurements / pressure / stability
PLT174	Recall autopilot - components / operating principles / characteristics
PLT175	Recall autorotation
PLT176	Recall balance tab - purpose / operation
PLT177	Recall balloon - flight operations
PLT178	Recall balloon - flight operations / gas
PLT179	Recall balloon - ground weigh-off / static equilibrium / load
PLT180	Recall balloon - hot air / lift / false lift / characteristics
PLT181	Recall balloon - hot air / physics
PLT182	Recall balloon - inspecting the fabric
PLT183	Recall balloon flight operations - ascent / descent
PLT184	Recall balloon flight operations - launch / landing
PLT185	Recall basic instrument flying - fundamental skills
PLT186	Recall basic instrument flying - pitch instruments
PLT187	Recall basic instrument flying - turn coordinator / turn and slip indicator
PLT188	Recall cabin atmosphere control
PLT189	Recall carburetor - effects of carburetor heat / heat control
PLT190	Recall carburetor ice - factors affecting / causing
PLT191	Recall carburetors - types / components / operating principles / characteristics
PLT192	Recall clouds - types / formation / resulting weather
PLT193	Recall cockpit voice recorder (CVR) - operating principles / characteristics / testing
PLT194	Recall collision avoidance - scanning techniques
PLR195	Recall collision avoidance - TCAS
PLT196	Recall communications - ATIS broadcasts
PLT197	Recall Coriolis effect
PLT198	Recall course / heading - effects of wind
PLT199	Recall cyclic control pressure - characteristics
PLT200	Recall dead reckoning - calculations / charts
PLT201	Recall departure procedures - ODP / SID
PLT202	Recall DME - characteristics / accuracy / indications / Arc
PLT203	Recall earth`s atmosphere - layers / characteristics / solar energy
PLT204	Recall effective communication - basic elements
PLT205	Recall effects of alcohol on the body
PLT206	Recall effects of temperature - density altitude / icing
PLT207	Recall electrical system - components / operating principles / characteristics

Code	Learning Statement
PLT208	Recall emergency conditions / procedures
PLT209	Recall engine pressure ratio - EPR
PLT210	Recall engine shutdown - normal / abnormal / emergency / precautions
PLT211	Recall evaluation testing characteristics
PLT212	Recall fire extinguishing systems - components / operating principles / characteristics
PLT213	Recall flight characteristics - longitudinal stability / instability
PLT214	Recall flight characteristics - structural / wing design
PLT215	Recall flight instruments - magnetic compass
PLT216	Recall flight instruments - total energy compensators
PLT217	Recall flight maneuvers - quick stop
PLT218	Recall flight operations - common student errors
PLT219	Recall flight operations - maneuvers
PLT220	Recall flight operations - night and high altitude operations
PLT221	Recall flight operations - takeoff / landing maneuvers
PLT222	Recall flight operations - takeoff procedures
PLT223	Recall flight operations multiengine - engine inoperative procedures
PLT224	Recall flight plan - IFR
PLT225	Recall flight plan - requirements
PLT226	Recall fog - types / formation / resulting weather
PLT227	Recall FOI techniques - integrated flight instruction
PLT228	Recall FOI techniques - lesson plans
PLT229	Recall FOI techniques - professionalism
PLT230	Recall FOI techniques - responsibilities
PLT231	Recall FOI techniques / human behavior - anxiety / fear / stress
PLT232	Recall FOI techniques / human behavior - dangerous tendencies
PLT233	Recall FOI techniques / human behavior - defense mechanisms
PLT234	Recall forces acting on aircraft - 3 axis intersect
PLT235	Recall forces acting on aircraft - aerodynamics
PLT236	Recall forces acting on aircraft - airfoil / center of pressure / mean camber line
PLT237	Recall forces acting on aircraft - airspeed / air density / lift / drag
PLT238	Recall forces acting on aircraft - aspect ratio
PLT239	Recall forces acting on aircraft - buoyancy / drag / gravity / thrust
PLT240	Recall forces acting on aircraft - CG / flight characteristics
PLT241	Recall forces acting on aircraft - drag / gravity / thrust / lift
PLT242	Recall forces acting on aircraft - lift / drag / thrust / weight / stall / limitations
PLT243	Recall forces acting on aircraft - propeller / torque
PLT244	Recall forces acting on aircraft - stability / controllability
PLT245	Recall forces acting on aircraft - stalls / spins
PLT246	Recall forces acting on aircraft - steady state climb / flight
PLT247	Recall forces acting on aircraft - thrust / drag / weight / lift
PLT248	Recall forces acting on aircraft - turns
PLT249	Recall fuel - air mixture
PLT250	Recall fuel - types / characteristics / contamination / fueling / defueling / precautions
PLT251	Recall fuel characteristics / contaminants / additives / leak
PLT252	Recall fuel dump system - components / methods

Code	Learning Statement
PLT253	Recall fuel system - components / operating principles / characteristics
PLT254	Recall fuel tank - components / operating principles / characteristics
PLT255	Recall fueling procedures - safety / grounding / calculating volume
PLT256	Recall glider performance - effect of loading
PLT257	Recall glider performance - speed / distance / ballast / lift / drag
PLT258	Recall ground reference maneuvers - ground track diagram
PLT259	Recall ground resonance - conditions to occur
PLT260	Recall gyroplane - aerodynamics / rotor systems
PLT261	Recall hail - characteristics / hazards
PLT262	Recall hazardous material - reports / transportation procedures / labeling
PLT263	Recall hazardous weather - fog / icing / turbulence
PLT264	Recall helicopter approach - settling with power
PLT265	Recall helicopter takeoff / landing - ground resonance action required
PLT266	Recall high lift devices - characteristics / functions
PLT267	Recall hot air balloon - weigh-off procedure
PLT268	Recall hovering - aircraft performance / tendencies
PLT269	Recall human behavior - defense mechanism
PLT270	Recall human behavior - social / self fulfillment / physical
PLT271	Recall human factors (ADM) - judgment
PLT272	Recall human factors - stress management
PLT273	Recall hydraulic systems - components / operating principles / characteristics
PLT274	Recall icing - formation / characteristics
PLT275	Recall ILS - indications / HSI
PLT276	Recall ILS - indications / OBS / CDI
PLT277	Recall ILS - marker beacon / indicator lights / codes
PLT278	Recall indicating systems - airspeed / angle of attack / attitude / heading / manifold pressure / synchro / EGT
PLT279	Recall Inertial Navigation System principles
PLT280	Recall inflight illusions - causes / sources
PLT281	Recall information in an Airport Facility Directory
PLT282	Recall information in the certificate holder`s manual
PLT283	Recall information on a Constant Pressure Analysis Chart
PLT284	Recall information on a Forecast Winds and Temperatures Aloft (FD)
PLT285	Recall information on a Height Velocity Diagram
PLT286	Recall information on a Significant Weather Prognostic Chart
PLT287	Recall information on a Surface Analysis Chart
PLT288	Recall information on a Terminal Aerodrome Forecast (TAF)
PLT289	Recall information on a Weather Depiction Chart
PLT290	Recall information on AIRMETS / SIGMETS
PLT291	Recall information on an Aviation Area Forecast (FA)
PLT292	Recall information on an Instrument Approach Procedures (IAP)
PLT293	Recall information on an Instrument Departure Procedure Chart
PLT294	Recall information on Inflight Aviation Weather Advisories
PLT295	Recall instructor techniques - obstacles / planning / activities / outcome
PLT296	Recall instrument procedures - holding / circling

Code	Learning Statement
PLT297	Recall instrument procedures - unusual attitude / unusual attitude recovery
PLT298	Recall instrument procedures - VFR on top
PLT300	Recall instrument/navigation system checks/inspections - limits / tuning / identifying / logging
PLT301	Recall inversion layer - characteristics
PLT302	Recall jet stream - types / characteristics
PLT303	Recall L/D ratio
PLT304	Recall launch procedures
PLT305	Recall leading edge devices - types / effect / purpose / operation
PLT306	Recall learning process - levels of learning / transfer of learning / incidental learning
PLT307	Recall learning process - memory / fact / recall
PLT308	Recall learning process - principles of learning elements
PLT309	Recall load factor - angle of bank
PLT310	Recall load factor - characteristics
PLT311	Recall load factor - effect of airspeed
PLT312	Recall load factor - maneuvering / stall speed
PLT313	Recall loading - limitations
PLT314	Recall longitudinal axis - aerodynamics / center of gravity / direction of motion
PLT315	Recall Machmeter - principles / functions
PLT316	Recall meteorology - severe weather watch (WW)
PLT317	Recall microburst - characteristics / hazards
PLT318	Recall minimum fuel advisory
PLT319	Recall navigation - celestial
PLT320	Recall navigation - true north / magnetic north
PLT321	Recall navigation - types of landing systems
PLT322	Recall navigation - VOR / NAV system
PLT323	Recall NOTAMS - classes / information / distribution
PLT324	Recall oil system - types / components / functions
PLT325	Recall operations manual - transportation of prisoner
PLT326	Recall oxygen system - components / operating principles / characteristics
PLT327	Recall oxygen system - install / inspect / repair / service / precautions / leaks
PLT328	Recall performance planning - aircraft loading
PLT329	Recall physiological factors - cabin pressure
PLT330	Recall physiological factors - cause / effects of hypoxia
PLT331	Recall physiological factors - effects of scuba diving / smoking
PLT332	Recall physiological factors - hyperventilation
PLT333	Recall physiological factors - night vision
PLT334	Recall physiological factors - spatial disorientation
PLT335	Recall pilotage - calculations
PLT336	Recall pitch control - collective / cyclic
PLT337	Recall pitot-static system - components / operating principles / characteristics
PLT338	Recall pneumatic system - operation
PLT340	Recall positive exchange of flight controls
PLT341	Recall power settling - characteristics
PLT342	Recall powerplant - controlling engine temperature
PLT343	Recall powerplant - operating principles / operational characteristics / inspecting

Code	Learning Statement
PLT344	Recall precipitation - types / characteristics
PLT345	Recall precipitation - pressure altitude
PLT346	Recall primary flight controls - types / purpose / functionality
PLT347	Recall principles of flight - critical engine
PLT348	Recall principles of flight - turns
PLT349	Recall procedures for confined areas
PLT350	Recall propeller operations - constant / variable speed
PLT351	Recall propeller system - types / components / operating principles / characteristics
PLT352	Recall purpose / operation of a stabilizer
PLT353	Recall Radar Summary Chart
PLT354	Recall radio - GPS / RNAV / RAIM
PLT355	Recall radio - HSI
PLT356	Recall radio - ILS / compass locator
PLT357	Recall radio - ILS / LDA
PLT358	Recall radio - LOC / ILS
PLT359	Recall radio - LORAN
PLT360	Recall radio - Microwave Landing System
PLT361	Recall radio - SDF / ILS
PLT362	Recall radio - VHF / Direction Finding
PLT363	Recall radio - VOR / VOT
PLT364	Recall radio system - licence requirements / frequencies
PLT365	Recall reciprocating engine - components / operating principles / characteristics
PLT366	Recall regulations - accident / incident reporting and preserving wreckage
PLT367	Recall regulations - additional equipment/operating requirements large transport aircraft
PLT368	Recall regulations - admission to flight deck
PLT369	Recall regulations - aerobatic flight requirements
PLT370	Recall regulations - Air Traffic Control authorization / clearances
PLT371	Recall regulations - Aircraft Category Class
PLT372	Recall regulations - aircraft inspection / records / expiration
PLT373	Recall regulations - aircraft operating limitations
PLT374	Recall regulations - aircraft owner / operator responsibilities
PLT375	Recall regulations - aircraft return to service
PLT376	Recall regulations - airspace special use / TFRS
PLT377	Recall regulations - airworthiness certificates / requirements / responsibilities
PLT378	Recall regulations - Airworthiness Directives
PLT379	Recall regulations - alternate airport requirements
PLT380	Recall regulations - alternate airport weather minima
PLT381	Recall regulations - altimeter settings
PLT382	Recall regulations - approach minima
PLT383	Recall regulations - basic flight rules
PLT384	Recall regulations - briefing of passengers
PLT385	Recall regulations - cargo in passenger compartment
PLT386	Recall regulations - certificate issuance renewal
PLT387	Recall regulations - change of address
PLT388	Recall regulations - cockpit voice recorder/flight date recorder(s)

Code	Learning Statement
PLT389	Recall regulations - commercial operation requirements / conditions / OpSpecs
PLT390	Recall regulations - communications enroute
PLT391	Recall regulations - communications failure
PLT392	Recall regulations - compliance with local regulations
PLT393	Recall regulations - controlled / restricted airspace - requirements
PLT394	Recall regulations - declaration of an emergency
PLT395	Recall regulations - definitions
PLT396	Recall regulations - departure alternate airport
PLT397	Recall regulations - destination airport visibility
PLT398	Recall regulations - dispatch
PLT399	Recall regulations - display / inspection of licences and certificates
PLT400	Recall regulations - documents to be carried on aircraft during flight
PLT401	Recall regulations - dropping / aerial application / towing restrictions
PLT402	Recall regulations - ELT requirements
PLT403	Recall regulations - emergency deviation from regulations
PLT404	Recall regulations - emergency equipment
PLT405	Recall regulations - equipment / instrument / certificate requirements
PLT406	Recall regulations - equipment failure
PLT407	Recall regulations - experience / training requirements
PLT408	Recall regulations - fire extinguisher requirements
PLT409	Recall regulations - flight / duty time
PLT410	Recall regulations - flight engineer qualifications / privileges / responsibilities
PLT411	Recall regulations - flight instructor limitations / qualifications
PLT412	Recall regulations - flight release
PLT413	Recall regulations - fuel requirements
PLT414	Recall regulations - general right-of-way rules
PLT415	Recall regulations - IFR flying
PLT416	Recall regulations - immediate notification
PLT417	Recall regulations - individual flotation devices
PLT418	Recall regulations - instructor demonstrations / authorizations
PLT419	Recall regulations - instructor requirements / responsibilities
PLT420	Recall regulations - instrument approach procedures
PLT421	Recall regulations - instrument flight rules
PLT422	Recall regulations - intermediate airport authorizations
PLT423	Recall regulations - knowledge and skill test checks
PLT424	Recall regulations - limits on autopilot usage
PLT425	Recall regulations - maintenance reports / records / entries
PLT426	Recall regulations - maintenance requirements
PLT427	Recall regulations - medical certificate requirements / validity
PLT428	Recall regulations - minimum equipment list
PLT429	Recall regulations - minimum flight / navigation instruments
PLT430	Recall regulations - minimum safe / flight altitude
PLT431	Recall regulations - operating near other aircraft
PLT432	Recall regulations - operational control functions
PLT433	Recall regulations - operational flight plan requirements

Code	Learning Statement
PLT434	Recall regulations - operational procedures for a controlled airport
PLT435	Recall regulations - operational procedures for an uncontrolled airport
PLT436	Recall regulations - operations manual
PLT437	Recall regulations - overwater operations
PLT438	Recall regulations - oxygen requirements
PLT439	Recall regulations - persons authorized to perform maintenance
PLT440	Recall regulations - Pilot / Crew duties and responsibilities
PLT441	Recall regulations - pilot briefing
PLT442	Recall regulations - pilot currency requirements
PLT443	Recall regulations - pilot qualifications / privileges / responsibilities
PLT444	Recall regulations - pilot-in-command authority / responsibility
PLT445	Recall regulations - preflight requirements
PLT446	Recall regulations - preventative maintenance
PLT447	Recall regulations - privileges / limitations of medical certificates
PLT448	Recall regulations - privileges / limitations of pilot certificates
PLT449	Recall regulations - proficiency check requirements
PLT450	Recall regulations - qualifications / duty time
PLT451	Recall regulations - ratings issued / experience requirements / limitations
PLT452	Recall regulations - re-dispatch
PLT453	Recall regulations - records retention for domestic / flag air carriers
PLT454	Recall regulations - required aircraft / equipment inspections
PLT455	Recall regulations - requirements of a flight plan release
PLT456	Recall regulations - runway requirements
PLT457	Recall regulations - student pilot endorsements / other endorsements
PLT458	Recall regulations - submission / revision of Policy and Procedure Manuals
PLT459	Recall regulations - takeoff procedures / minimums
PLT460	Recall regulations - training programs
PLT461	Recall regulations - use of aircraft lights
PLT462	Recall regulations - use of microphone / megaphone / interphone
PLT463	Recall regulations - use of narcotics / drugs / intoxicating liquor
PLT464	Recall regulations - use of safety belts / harnesses (crew member)
PLT465	Recall regulations - use of seats / safety belts / harnesses (passenger)
PLT466	Recall regulations - V speeds
PLT467	Recall regulations - visual flight rules and limitations
PLT468	Recall regulations - Visual Meteorological Conditions (VMC)
PLT469	Recall regulations - weather radar
PLT470	Recall rotor system - types / components / operating principles / characteristics
PLT471	Recall rotorcraft transmission - components / operating principles / characteristics
PLT472	Recall rotorcraft vibration - characteristics / sources
PLT473	Recall secondary flight controls - types / purpose / functionality
PLT474	Recall soaring - normal procedures
PLT475	Recall squall lines - formation / characteristics / resulting weather
PLT476	Recall stabilizer - purpose / operation
PLT477	Recall stalls - characteristics / factors / recovery / precautions
PLT478	Recall starter / ignition system - types / components / operating principles / characteristics

Code	Learning Statement
PLT479	Recall starter system - starting procedures
PLT480	Recall static/dynamic stability/instability - characteristics
PLT481	Recall student evaluation - learning process
PLT482	Recall student evaluation - written tests / oral quiz / critiques
PLT483	Recall supercharger - characteristics / operation
PLT484	Recall symbols - chart / navigation
PLT485	Recall taxiing / crosswind / techniques
PLT486	Recall taxiing / takeoff - techniques / procedures
PLT487	Recall teaching methods - demonstration / performance
PLT488	Recall teaching methods - group / guided discussion / lecture
PLT489	Recall teaching methods - known to unknown
PLT490	Recall teaching methods - motivation / student feelings of insecurity
PLT491	Recall teaching methods - organizing material / course of training
PLT492	Recall temperature - effects on weather formations
PLT493	Recall the dynamics of frost / ice / snow formation on an aircraft
PLT494	Recall thermals - types / characteristics / formation / locating / maneuvering / corrective actions
PLT495	Recall thunderstorms - types / characteristics / formation / hazards
PLT496	Recall towrope - strength / safety links / positioning
PLT497	Recall transponder - codes / operations / usage
PLT498	Recall Transportation Security Regulations
PLT499	Recall turbine engines - components / operational characteristics / associated instruments
PLT500	Recall turboprop engines - components / operational characteristics
PLT501	Recall turbulence - types / characteristics / reporting / corrective actions
PLT502	Recall universal signals - hand / light / visual
PLT503	Recall use of narcotics / drugs / intoxicating liquor
PLT504	Recall use of training aids - types / function / purpose
PLT505	Recall use of training aids - usefulness / simplicity / compatibility
PLT506	Recall V speeds - maneuvering / flap extended / gear extended
PLT507	Recall VOR - indications / VOR / VOT / CDI
PLT508	Recall VOR/altimeter/transponder checks - identification / tuning / identifying / logging
PLT509	Recall wake turbulence - characteristics / avoidance techniques
PLT510	Recall weather - causes / formation
PLT511	Recall weather associated with frontal activity / air masses
PLT512	Recall weather conditions - temperature / moisture / dewpoint
PLT513	Recall weather information - TWEB broadcasts
PLT514	Recall weather reporting systems - briefings / forecasts / reports
PLT515	Recall weather services - EFAS / TIBS / WFO / AFSS / HIWAS
PLT516	Recall winds - types / characteristics
PLT517	Recall winds associated with high / low-pressure systems
PLT518	Recall windshear - characteristics / hazards / power management
PLT519	Recall wing spoilers - purpose / operation
PLT520	Calculate density altitude
PLT521	Recall helicopter takeoff/landing - slope operations
PLT522	Recall helicopter - Pinnacle/Ridgeline operations
PLT523	Recall vortex generators - purpose/effects/aerodynamic